STUDIES IN
PALEO-OCEANOGRAPHY

Based on a Symposium
Sponsored by The Society of
Economic Paleontologists and Mineralogists

Edited by
William W. Hay
Rosenstiel School of Marine and Atmospheric Science
University of Miami

Tulsa, Oklahoma, U.S.A.   September 1974

A Publication of

The Society of Economic Paleontologists and Mineralogists

a division of

The American Association of Petroleum Geologists

PREFACE

This volume represents some of the papers presented at the Society of Economic Paleontologists and Mineralogists Research Committee Symposium "Geologic History of the Oceans" at the Annual Meeting on Tuesday, March 30, 1971, in Houston, Texas. The symposium was organized by William W. Hay. The full day session consisted of the following papers:

1. Geologic history of the Oceans: Introduction—*William W. Hay, University of Illinois, Urbana, Illinois,* and *Rosenstiel School of Marine and Atmospheric Science, University of Miami, Miami, Florida.*

2. Distribution of Carbonates in Deep Sea Sediments—*A. T. S. Ramsay, University of East Anglia, Norwich, England.*

3. Physical Chemistry of Carbonates in Oceans—*Robert A. Berner, Yale University, New Haven, Connecticut.*

4. Causes of Temporal Changes in Carbonate Compensation Levels—*Wallace S. Broecker, Lamont-Doherty Geological Observatory, Columbia University, Palisades, New York.*

5. History of Biogenic Silica in the Deep Sea—*James D. Hays, Lamont-Doherty Geological Observatory, Columbia University, Palisades, New York.*

6. Dissolved Silica and its Relation to Deep-Sea Sediments—*G. Ross Heath, Oregon State University, Corvallis, Oregon.*

7. Problems of Chert in the Ocean—*Alfred G. Fischer, Princeton University, Princeton, New Jersey.*

8. Biostratigraphy and History of Circulation of the North Atlantic—*William A. Berggren* and *Charles D. Hollister, Woods Hole Oceanographic Institution, Woods Hole, Massachusetts.*

9. Sources of Sediment in Western Basin of the Atlantic Ocean—*Pierre Biscaye, Lamont-Doherty Geological Observatory, Columbia University, Palisades, New York; E. Julius Dasch, Oregon State University, Corvallis, Oregon; David Krinsley, Sedgwick Museum, Cambridge University, Cambridge, England;* and *Karl K. Turekian, Yale University, New Haven, Connecticut.*

10. History of Circulation in the Pacific Ocean—*Jere H. Lipps, University of California at Davis, Davis, California.*

11. Geologic History of Oceanic Plankton—*Helen Tappan, University of California at Los Angeles, Los Angeles, California;* and *Alfred R. Loeblich, Jr., Chevron Oil Field Research Company, La Habra, California.*

12. Cretaceous-Tertiary Boundary Event—*Thomas R. Worsley, University of Washington, Seattle, Washington.*

13. Chemical History of the Oceans—*Fred T. Mackenzie, Northwestern University, Evanston, Illinois;* and *Robert M. Garrels, Scripps Institution of Oceanography, University of California at San Diego, La Jolla, California.*

14. Evaporites—Clue to Chemistry of Seawater during the Phaneozoic—*H. D. Holland, Princeton University, Princeton, New Jersey.*

15. Early Evolution of Oceans A Weathering Model *G. Michel Lafon, State University of New York at Binghamton, Binghamton, New York;* and *Fred T. Mackenzie, Northwestern University, Evanston, Illinois.*

Manuscripts were received from these authors, and submitted to the S.E.P.M. Publications Committee for approval. The Publications Committee recommended publication of these as a Special Publication, and the Council approved.

In the course of the past year and a half, many developments have taken place in the fields covered by these papers. Virtually all of the manuscripts received were revised and updated by the authors. Several differ markedly from the talk presented at the symposium.

In the course of editing these papers I have very much appreciated the patience and helpfulness of the authors. A great effort has been made on the part of all involved to communicate the results of studies in their area of interest to specialists in other fields, and I wish to express my thanks to the contributors of this volume for their cooperation and assistance.

WILLIAM W. HAY, *Editor*
University of Miami
Miami, Florida

CONTENTS

INTRODUCTION

WILLIAM W. HAY

University of Miami, Miami, Florida

Knowledge of oceanic sediments has been acquired in two ways: 1) directly by sampling and observation, and 2) indirectly through seismic investigations. Until the past decade, direct sampling and observation techniques could only provide information on the surficial materials of the ocean floor. The development of the piston corer (Kullenberg, 1947) has permitted oceanographic vessels to sample the upper 20 meters, and more recently the upper 30 meters, of the ocean floor, but such cores rarely penetrate the Pleistocene and enter older sediments. Until recently, most knowledge of the deeper sedimentary materials in the ocean basins was obtained through seismic reflection studies (Ewing and Ewing, 1970).

Since the early part of the last decade, the development of deep ocean drilling techniques has permitted sampling of the sediments of the oceans to depths in excess of 1,000 meters. Starting with the experimental Moholes drilled off Southern and Baja California (AMSOC Committee, 1961) the recovery of cores taken using oil-field drilling techniques has been increasingly successful. To plan a large scale program of deep sea drilling, several major oceanographic institutions formed an organization known as JOIDES (Joint Oceanographic Institutions Deep Earth Sampling). The original JOIDES members were Woods Hole Oceanographic Institution, Lamont-Doherty Geological Observatory of Columbia University, Rosenstiel School of Marine and Atmospheric Science of the University of Miami, and Scripps Institution of Oceanography of the University of California at San Diego; the Department of Oceanography of the University of Washington, joined subsequently. Scripps Institution of Oceanography submitted the proposal for ocean drilling and manages the program. Known as the Deep Sea Drilling Project, this program has been in effect since 1967, and is expected to continue through the summer of 1975, with the funding being provided by the National Science Foundation. In the early phase of the Deep Sea Drilling Project areas under investigation were limited to the tropical and subtropical regions of the Atlantic and Pacific Oceans. Since 1970, the deep sea drilling vessel *Glomar Challenger* has made excursions into higher latitudes, and will investigate the Southern Ocean during the coming austral summers. During 1971-1972, the *Glomar Challenger* drilled and cored a number of sites in the Indian Ocean, and by the end of the project there will have been reconnaissance drilling in all of the oceans except the Arctic.

Prior to the advent of deep sea drilling, it had been widely assumed that the sediments encountered at depth in the ocean basins would be identical or very similar to the surficial deposits at the site investigated. In the interpretation of seismic reflection profiler records, it was generally assumed that reflecting surfaces represented synchronous horizons. The results of deep sea drilling have shown both these assumptions to be ill-founded.

Recent advances in understanding the complex inter-relations between atmospheric and oceanic circulation, vertical mixing, organic productivity, and dissolution of silica and carbonate in the deep sea permit better understanding of Recent oceanic sedimentation. To explain the complex sedimentary histories encountered at deep sea drilling sites, this model must be considered against the background of sea floor spreading and changing ocean chemistry and circulation patterns.

Sediments come to rest on the ocean floor after having been brought to the site by either of two mechanisms: 1) bottom transport, chiefly turbidity currents, but including also movement by traction from currents, submarine slumping, and creep (see fig. 1); 2) settling through the water column (see fig. 2). Deposits introduced by bottom transport fill basins from the bottom up; sediments which settle through the water column rain down on the underlying topography.

Sediments deposited on the floor of the ocean may also be classified as of continental, volcanic, cosmic, biogenic or authigenic origin. Continental sediment will be used here to refer to material derived through the erosion of large land areas by water, ice or wind, and delivered to the ocean in particulate form. Volcanic sediments are those produced by volcanic activity, chiefly through the introduction of ash into the atmosphere but also through

1

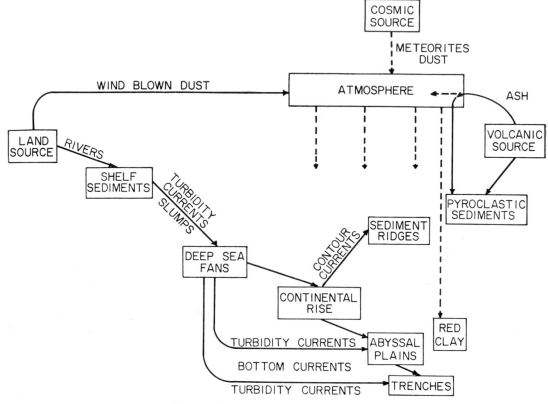

FIG. 1.—Clastic sedimentation in the ocean.

the agency of pyroclastic flows. Cosmic materials include extraterrestrial dust and particles produced by disintegration of meteorites in the atmosphere. Biogenic sediments are produced through fixation of mineral phases by organisms. Authigenic minerals are those that grow in place on the sea floor.

The kind of sediment which accumulates at a particular site is a function of the different kinds of sediment being supplied, and the rate at which each kind is introduced. The topography of the sea floor controls the distribution of bottom transported sediments, but has no influence on the distribution of materials which settle through the water column. Bottom transported sediments are chiefly continental or volcanic in origin, although in local areas with high relief, sediments which have accumulated by settling may be redeposited by bottom transport mechanisms.

The distribution and origin of Recent sediments in the world ocean has been the subject of another Special Publication by the Society of Economic Paleontologists and Mineralogists (Lisitzin, 1972). It is hoped that the present volume will complement Lisitzin's account, and provide insight into the problems encountered in interpretation of the oceans' history from the sedimentary record.

HISTORICAL PERSPECTIVE

Understanding the ocean as a dynamic system requires both study of present-day processes and an appreciation of the historical development of circulation patterns and climate.

Major reorganization of the distribution of continents and oceans has taken place since the beginning of the Mesozoic Era. In the early Mesozoic, the landmasses were together in a giant supercontinent, Pangaea, and there was but a single major ocean basin, the ancestral Pacific. A nearly circumglobal seaway, the Tethys, which has subsequently been destroyed, extended far into the supercontinent. During the Mesozoic, Pangaea broke up, and between the separating landmasses, ocean basins formed. Each of these was at first narrow, elongate, and connected with the world ocean at one end only. Such proto-oceans, like the modern Red Sea and Gulf of California, are especially prone to become chemical sinks where material is removed from the sea water system and buried. As each of these new ocean basins grew, they became interconnected by one or more passages with the shrinking Pacific basin, developing a more open circulation. The global ocean water mass became fractionated into the Pacific, Indian and Atlantic Oceans and their tributary smaller oceans and seas. As this occurred, the Earth's climatic gradient increased, and climatic differentiation of water masses became more effective in isolating the parts of the world ocean. These changes have resulted in the circulation patterns observed today. Because many chemical processes in the ocean now appear to be controlled by kinetics and biological factors, the present system of oceanic sources, reservoirs, and sinks of chemical materials is a product of the evolution of these factors.

One of the primary objectives of the Deep Sea Drilling Project was establishment of a data base for the study of oceanic circulation through time. The reconnaissance drilling

phases have provided a large part of this, but some critical gaps remain that place severe limitations on possible interpretations. To a large extent, these gaps result from a much more restricted preservation of ancient sediments than anticipated, from unexpected differences in geographic location as a result of plate movements, and from drilling problems which are now largely solved.

Initial results and their interpretation suggest that the history of the surface circulation deduced by study of oceanic plankton fossils and of deep circulation revealed by study of benthic fossils will permit estimation of oceanic mass balances and changes.

Understanding of modern oceanic circulation and climate is enhanced by historical perspective. The present circulation scheme is a result of modification of that which existed during the Pleistocene, and is undoubtedly closely related to it. The Pleistocene circulation patterns are currently being studied in detail, using DSDP and other cores. Pleistocene circulation was variable, changing with glaciations and interglacials, but it ultimately rep-

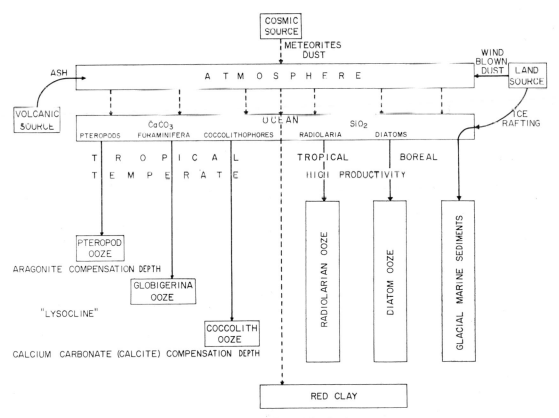

Fig. 2.—Pelagic sedimentation in the ocean.

resents a modification of earlier Neogene circulation patterns. It is thought that Neogene
circulation was similar to that observed today,
although there may have been important differences in the rates of vertical mixing and
in the speed of surficial and deep currents. It
should be possible to determine Neogene current patterns in quantitative or semi-quantitative fashion after analysis of the data obtained by the Deep Sea Drilling Project. A
few additional holes in critical places would
serve to test the accuracy of hypothetical
models of Neogene circulation.

Oceanic circulation in the Paleogene was
certainly dissimilar to that observed at present. The distribution of the continents and
passages between the oceans was sufficiently
different so that the patterns of horizontal and
vertical mixing have changed drastically since
that time. The Indian Ocean was in the process of being formed, Australia was breaking
away from Antarctica, South America and
Antarctica were probably connected, and the
Atlantic and Pacific were connected in the
region of Panama. The circum-Antarctic current system, one of the major features of
modern oceanic circulation, probably did not
exist. The Arctic-Atlantic connection was not in
existence and has formed subsequently.

The situation in the Mesozoic was even more
at variance with that observed today. Climates
were much more equable, the forming Atlantic and Indian Oceans much narrower, and
the great bulk of the ocean volume concentrated in the Pacific. Understanding of circulation and climate in the Mesozoic requires
drilling at more Mesozoic oceanic sites than
can be accomplished during the Deep Sea
Drilling Project, and that the subsequent results be combined with knowledge of sections
exposed on land. There are limits to the extent to which our knowledge of past oceanic
conditions can be extended; the areas of Mesozoic sea floor which have not been subducted
into trenches, and which can be explored, decrease with increasing age.

STUDIES OF PALEO-OCEANOGRAPHY

Although geologists have long been concerned with interpretation of marine conditions in sediments deposited in marginal seas
and in geosynclinal areas, reconstruction of
past conditions in the world ocean have been
largely speculative until recently. The purpose
of this volume is to present a number of observations, ideas, interpretations, and speculations which will be of value in considering
the meaning of the increasing volume of data
from older deep sea deposits.

The next article in this volume, "Implications of some Pre-Quaternary sediment cores
and dredgings," by T. Saito, L. Burckle, and
J. D. Hays, presents an account of the Pre-
Quaternary cores collected by vessels of the
Lamont-Doherty Geological Observatory and
the R. V. *Eltanin* operated by the National
Science Foundation. This account, along with
the list of Pre-Quaternary sediment cores at
other institutions prepared by Funnell (1971)
and the Initial Reports of the Deep Sea Drilling Project provides a list of most of the cores
which are available for study, and which form
the basic reservoir of information concerning
the geologic history of oceans.

The following three papers are concerned
with calcium carbonate compensation in the
ocean. There exists a delicate balance between
input of calcium and carbon dioxide as carbonate and bicarbonate ions into the ocean and
fixation and removal of calcium carbonate by
burial of the tests of planktonic foraminifers,
coccoliths, and shells of pteropods. Because the
proportions of dissolved carbonate, bicarbonate,
carbon dioxide and oxygen in the ocean, rivers,
rainwater, and the atmosphere are intimately
related to biological activity and productivity,
the changes in carbonate compensation which
have occurred reflect general changes in atmospheric and oceanic chemistry. Biological
productivity is, as Broecker (1971) has noted,
related to kinetic processes in the ocean, particularly vertical mixing, which are in turn a
function of the climatic gradient on the earth,
wind direction, and velocity. The first paper
of this group, "Physical chemistry of carbonates in the ocean," by R. A. Berner, outlines
the principles controlling carbonate compensation as it occurs today. The second paper,
"Carbonate dissolution on the western flank of
the East Pacific Rise," by W. S. Broecker and
S. Broecker, describes carbonate compensation
in the eastern Pacific and discusses the mechanisms responsible for it. The third paper, by
A. T. S. Ramsay, "The distribution of calcium carbonate in deep sea sediments presents
an account of the fluctuations in calcium carbonate compensation which have occurred in
the past and attempts to define the magnitude
and rates of change indicated by the sedimentary record.

Silica compensation is also an important process in the oceans. Introduced from a variety
of sources, silica is very effectively removed
from sea water through biological activity,
chiefly by diatoms and radiolarians. Deposits
of siliceous pelagic sediment seem, however, to
be restricted to areas of high organic productivity, and are also related to kinetic processes

in the ocean. The next article in this volume by R. Heath, "Dissolved silica and deep sea sediments," provides a summary of knowledge concerning silica in the ocean.

The Cretaceous-Tertiary boundary event appears to be of particular significance in the history of the ocean. Evidence accumulated to present indicates that the magnitude of the hiatus associated with this event increases from shelf seas into the ocean basins. The event also separates two distinct periods in the chemical history of the ocean, the late Mesozoic when deposition of chalk was widespread and apparently most of the sea floor was above the calcium carbonate compensation depth, and the Cenozoic, during which calcium carbonate has accumulated only in shallow seas and on oceanic rises and ridges. T. R. Worsley's article "The Cretaceous-Tertiary boundary event in the ocean" provides a description of the geological and biological record of the event and discusses some of the hypotheses which have been proposed to explain the event.

The history of the Atlantic Ocean is now known in some detail. Because it is not bounded by trenches, the sedimentary record of its history since the time of its origin is potentially available. W. A. Berggren and C. D. Hollister describe the development of this ocean in "Paleogeography, paleobiogeography, and the history of circulation in the Atlantic Ocean."

The last three articles in this volume are concerned with the long term aspects of the chemical history of the ocean. H. D. Holland,

in "Marine evaporates and the composition of sea water during the Phanerozoic" describes how evaporites can be used to define the limits of fluctuation in the composition of sea water. R. M. Garrels and F. T. Mackenzie in "Chemical history of the oceans deduced from postdepositional changes in sedimentary rocks" indicate processes which have resulted in present chemistry of the oceans. Finally, G. M. Lafon and F. T. Mackenzie in "Early evolution of the oceans—a weathering model" present a model for derivation of ocean chemistry by physical weathering processes.

As the reader will discover, there are a number of differences of opinion between the authors contributing to this volume. Interpretation of the record by paleontologists and sedimentologists does not always agree with what is considered reasonable or possible by the geochemists. The differences between the thermodynamic and kinetic schools of thought among the ocean chemists are also evident. It is hoped that these differences will stimulate further thought and better understanding of the processes involved and of the history of the oceans.

ACKNOWLEDGMENT

This work has been supported by Grant GA-31969X from the Oceanography Section of the National Science Foundation. The author is indebted to Dr. John Southam, Mr. John C. Steinmetz, Mr. James F. Behensky and Mr. Larry Stanker for their assistance.

REFERENCES

AMSOC COMMITTEE, 1961, Experimental drilling in deep water at LaJolla and Guadalupe sites: Washington, D.C., Natl. Acad. Sci., Natl. Research Council, Pub. 914, xiii + 183 p.
BROECKER, W. S., 1971, A kinetic model for the chemical composition of sea water: Quaternary Research, v. 1, p. 188–207.
EWING, J., AND EWING, M., 1970, Seismic reflection, *in* MAXWELL, A. E. (ed.), The sea, v. 4, New concepts of sea floor evolution: New York, Wiley-Interscience, p. 1–51.
FUNNELL, B. M., 1971, The occurrence of pre-Quaternary microfossils in the oceans, *in* FUNNELL, B. M., AND RIEDEL, W. R. (eds.), The micropalaeontology of oceans: Cambridge Univ. Press, x + 828 p.
KULLENBERG, B., 1947, The piston core sampler: Svenska Hydrog.-biol. Komm. Skr. (ser. 3, Hydrog.) 1, no. 2, p. 1–46.
LISITZIN, A. P., 1972, Sedimentation in the world ocean with emphasis on the nature, distribution and behavior of marine suspensions: Soc. Econ. Paleontologists and Mineralogists Special Pub. 17, xiii + 218 p.

IMPLICATIONS OF SOME PRE-QUATERNARY SEDIMENT CORES AND DREDGINGS

TSUNEMASA SAITO, LLOYD H. BURCKLE[1] AND JAMES D. HAYS
Lamont-Doherty Geological Observatory, Palisades, New York;[1] and
Hunter College of C.U.N.Y., New York, New York

ABSTRACT

The Lamont-Doherty deep-sea sediment core library contains over 900 deep-sea sediment cores and dredgings containing pre-Quaternary microfossils.

The oldest outcropping or near-outcropping sediments in the collection are Early Cretaceous and are from the Northwestern Atlantic Ocean. Late Cretaceous sediments have been cored in widely scattered localities throughout the world's oceans but principally from the ocean margins. Paleocene and Oligocene sediment cores are rare but have been recovered from the three major oceans. More than 90 cores containing Eocene sediments have been recovered and are broadly distributed throughout the ocean. Three hundred and thirty Miocene cores have been obtained and several contain complete or nearly complete sequences back to the late Miocene. Pliocene is the most common pre-Quaternary sediment in the collection. The majority of these contain biogenic silica (Radiolaria and diatoms) and are commonly found in areas of low sedimentation rate where a complete Quaternary section is less than ten meters thick. Most pre-Quaternary cores have been recovered from submarine topographic highs such as plateaus marginal to continents, flanks of the mid-ocean ridge system, aseismic ridges and seamounts. Notable exceptions to this are two areas of broadly outcropping sediments, one of Middle and Late Cretaceous age northeast of the Bahama Islands and a second of Eocene to Pliocene age in the Eastern Equatorial Pacific.

Cores recovered from plateaus marginal to continents reflect varying geologic histories. For example, features such as the Blake Plateau, East Falkland Plateau, and Walvis Ridge show fossil evidence for having been considerably shallower than at present. Features such as the Agulhas Plateau and the Naturaliste Plateau, on the other hand, display little or no evidence of vertical movement. In general, cores from the flanks of the mid-ocean ridge system show increasing age with greater distance from the axis, reflecting the lateral movement of the sea floor away from the ridge axis as suggested by sea floor spreading theory.

INTRODUCTION

Since 1947, under the leadership of M. Ewing, research vessels of the Lamont-Doherty Geological Observatory of Columbia University have collected more than 7,000 deep-sea sediment cores during some 40 cruises in the world's ocean. This collection, housed at Lamont-Doherty's Core Laboratory, also includes dredge hauls and cores raised by other ships.

Micropaleontological examination of these cores and dredges reveals that over 900 cores and dredgings contain pre-Quaternary microfossils.

The object of this paper is to catalogue those cores containing pre-Quaternary sediment and briefly discuss their distribution pattern in order to shed light on the occurrence of pre-Quaternary sediments at or near the sea floor. Only a small proportion of these pre-Quaternary samples have been dealt with elsewhere in the literature, and this is the first comprehensive list of pre-Quaternary sediment samples in the Lamont-Doherty collection.

The collection of pre-Quaternary deep-sea sediments has not grown at a steady pace. In fact, up until about 1964, less than 150 cores in the Lamont-Doherty Core Library contained pre-Quaternary microfossils (published in part by Ericson and others, 1961). Since then, however, the rate of acquisition of pre-Quaternary materials has climbed steeply largely due to two factors. First was the development and deployment of the continuous seismic reflection profiler in the 1950's (Ewing and others, 1960) and its improvement by use of a pneumatic sound source since 1960 (Ewing and Zaunere, 1964). With the aid of this profiler, many outcrops or near outcrops of deeper layers of sediment were located on the ocean floor and sediments as old as early Cretaceous were successfully cored (Ewing and others, 1966; Saito and Burckle, 1966; Burckle and others, 1967; Windisch and others, 1968). The second factor was an increasing demand for long piston cores suitable for paleomagnetic and paleoclimatic studies. During recent cruises of the Lamont-Doherty vessels, piston cores longer than 20 meters are no longer exceptional; these "longer" cores frequently penetrate through the Quaternary and reach layers as old as Miocene (Hays and Opdyke, 1965; Foster and Opdyke, 1970; Opdyke and others, 1970).

BIOSTRATIGRAPHY

The surge of interest in oceanic micropaleontology in recent years has resulted in the delineation and application of planktonic microfloral and -faunal successions to Cretaceous and Tertiary deep-sea sequences. A strong impetus was given to oceanic micropaleontology with the discovery in deep-sea sediments of the record of paleomagnetic reversals. This made it possible for micropaleontologists to compare ranges of microfossils to true time surfaces. General principles of oceanic micropaleontology and reviews of progress during the past decade are given in Saito and Bé (1967), Funnell and Riedel (1971) and the Initial Reports of the Deep-Sea Drilling Project.

Age determinations of pre-Quaternary sediments in this paper are largely based on planktonic foraminifers for calcareous sediments and Radiolaria and diatoms for non-calcareous siliceous oozes. The correlation between dates based on foraminifers and those on Radiolaria and diatoms have been attempted wherever these three microfossil groups occur together; in general, good agreement has been observed.

Planktonic foraminiferal criteria used in this paper to relate deep-sea sediments to Cretaceous and Cenozoic chronostratigraphy are summarized in fig. 1. Age determinations of most of the cores barren of foraminifers were carried out by using diatoms and Radiolaria. The Systems and Series determinations in this paper based on Radiolaria largely use the criteria provided by Hays and Opdyke (1967), Riedel and Sanfilippo (1970) and Hays (1970).

Those cores which contained diatoms were dated by reference to Kanaya (1957) for the Eocene, Hanna (1932) for the Oligocene and Early Miocene and Burckle (1972) for the Middle Miocene to Pliocene. No adequate diatom criteria have been developed for defining the Eocene/Oligocene and Oligocene/Miocene boundaries. However, the Miocene/Pliocene boundary may be defined by the last appearance of *Nitzschia miocenica* Burckle and the joint occurrence of *Thalassiosira convexa* Muchina and *Th. usatschevii* Sheshukova-Poryetzkaya prior to the first appearance of *Nitzschia jouseae* Burckle. The Pliocene/Pleistocene boundary is defined by the last appearance of *Rhizosolenia praebergonii* Muchina and the first evolutionary appearance of *Pseudoeunotia doliolus* (Wallich) Grunow.

DISTRIBUTION OF PRE-QUATERNARY SEDIMENTS

The nature of pre-Quaternary outcropping sediment varies from ocean to ocean. In the Pacific the generally slower accumulation rates allow piston cores to penetrate pre-Quaternary fossiliferous sediments in many localities. Fig. 2 shows large numbers of cores reaching Pliocene sediments in the Equatorial Pacific, the North Pacific and in the Bellingshausen Basin in the South Pacific. This large areal extent of Pliocene sediments within reach of the piston corer indicates that over broad areas of the Pacific (probably at least two-thirds of the total area of this ocean) Quaternary sediments are less than 10 meters thick. This suggests that over much of the Pacific the accumulation rates are less than ½ cm per thousand years for the Pleistocene. The large areas of nonfossiliferous sediments below the stable central water masses of the North and South Pacific have even slower accumulation rates (Opdyke and Foster, 1970; Ku, Broecker and Opdyke, 1968). The reasons for the slow Pacific accumulation rates compared to other oceans are given in Revelle and others (1955) and point to the lack of terrigenous input and not to reduced productivity in the Pacific. The equatorial region of the Pacific is unique in that pre-Pliocene sediments (Eocene, Oligocene and Miocene) outcrop across a broad area north of the Equator. These outcrops are not associated with local topography but represent a broad area where these older sediments come near the water-sediment interface. This is the largest area in the world of this type and is probably a result of both the low accumulation rates in the Pacific and the tectonic motion of the Pacific floor.

The Atlantic by contrast has accumulation rates generally two to four times those of the Pacific. Consequently, few cores reach pre-Quaternary sediments without passing through hiatuses. The result is that most of the Tertiary sediments collected from the Atlantic are located on the tops or flanks of local topographic elevations where the effects of winnowing and/or slumping of surficial sediments have exposed or nearly exposed Tertiary sediments. Thus concentrations of pre-Quaternary cores are found on the Walvis Ridge, Rio Grande Rise, Falkland Plateau, Blake Plateau, etc. (figs. 3 and 4). An exception to this is the Horizon A outcrop area east of the Bahamas where upper Mesozoic and lower Tertiary sediments come near the level ocean floor at abyssal depths. Coverage of the Indian Ocean is much less complete than the Pacific or Atlan-

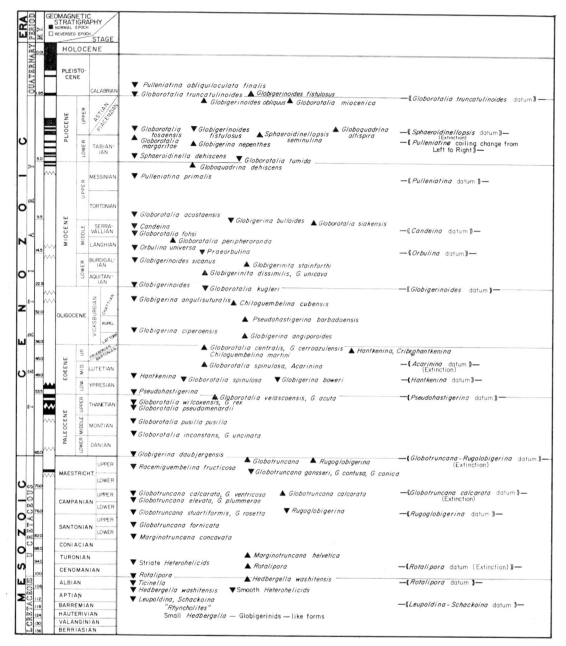

FIG. 1.—Summary of Cretaceous and Cenozoic stratigraphy with important foraminiferal datum levels. Paleomagnetic reversals are plotted wherever they are established. Inverted triangles indicate evolutionary first appearances and upright triangles indicate extinctions.

tic but the pattern of exposed Tertiary sediments seems closer to that of the Atlantic than to the Pacific pattern (fig. 5).

PACIFIC OCEAN

In the Pacific there are three areas where large numbers of cores penetrate Tertiary sediments: the North Pacific, Eastern Equatorial Pacific and Antarctic. This clustering is partly due to coring density (this is particularly true of the Bellingshausen Basin that has been intensively sampled by U.S.N.S. *Eltanin*), and to the presence of microfossils, mainly siliceous, that can be used for age determination. Surely large numbers of cores from fossil-barren red clay areas of the central North and South Pacific also penetrate Tertiary sediments. Pre-Quaternary sediments in other areas of the Pacific occur mainly on steep slopes.

North Pacific.—North of about 40° North the counterclockwise gyral circulation induces relatively high productivity and the sediments underlying this sub-Arctic North Pacific water mass contain large quantities of diatoms and Radiolaria. To the south the clockwise rotating circulation of the Central Pacific gyre is much less productive and the sediments below it are largely barren of fossil remains.

The paleomagnetic stratigraphy of more than 100 cores from the North Pacific north of latitude 20°N have been determined by Opdyke and Foster (1970) and the paleontological ages of many of these have been determined on the basis of Radiolaria (Hays, 1970) and diatoms (Donahue, 1970).

South of the Aleutians, between 40°N and 45°N, the sedimentation rates are slow enough so that a number of 10 meter cores penetrate to Pliocene sediments. To the north, west and east of this area the sedimentation rates increase so that the Pleistocene section is considerably greater than 10 meters thick. The few pre-Pliocene cores from the far North Pacific are all taken on topographic highs and contain hiatuses.

Eastern Equatorial Pacific.—An extensive seismic profiling study of the North Pacific Ocean by Ewing and others (1968) indicates that a continuous belt of thick sediment underlies the equatorial region of the Pacific. Except in its central zone where sediment is relatively thin (170°E to 170°W), the crest of this belt lies a few degrees to the north of the Equator in the Eastern Pacific and to the south in the Western Pacific. Highly stratified sediments characterize both the eastern and the western part of this belt; whereas sediments of the central zone are acoustically transparent, represented by lutites containing very little biogenous material (Ewing and others, 1968; *e.g.* cores RC10-118 through RC10-122). The upper layers of the highly stratified section thin northward from the crest while the deeper layers appear to be continuous from south to north, emerging at the ocean floor north of the Clipperton Fracture Zone.

A similar thinning of layers has been demonstrated in some areas on the southern flank of the thick sediment belt west of the East Pacific Rise (Ewing and others, 1968). This pattern of outcropping deeper sedimentary layers results in easy access to pre-Quaternary sediments by the piston corer along the northern border of this sediment belt.

This widespread occurrence of outcropping or near outcropping pre-Quaternary sediments on a relatively level, deep-ocean floor is unique. The pattern of core ages clearly shows two trends: first, increasing age of sediments cored from the Equator northward and less distinctly from the Equator southward; second, increasing age of oldest sediments cored with increasing distance from the axis of the East Pacific Rise. The second trend has been discussed by Burckle and others (1967) and Riedel (1967) and has been shown to support the theory of ocean-floor spreading (Hess, 1962; Dietz, 1961).

The sediment age given in this report is that of sediment at the bottom of the core, but frequently these cores have a similar age at the top. In the Equatorial Pacific, this is particularly true of cores penetrating Oligocene and Eocene sediments. Cores penetrating Miocene sediments may have a short interval of late Pleistocene overlying Miocene or an unfossiliferous section overlying fossiliferous Miocene sediments. Cores penetrating Quaternary and Pliocene sediments occur together along the Equator and contain complete or nearly complete stratigraphic sequences. In this region, the Middle and Upper Miocene and Eocene sediments are predominantly siliceous, while Lower Miocene and Oligocene cores contain abundant calcium carbonate.

The near outcropping of Miocene and older sediments north of the Clipperton Fracture Zone (trending gently southwestward from 11°N latitude at 105°W longitude to 3°N latitude at 148°W longitude) suggests that some bottom process has removed much or all of the younger sediment or that conditions have changed significantly, resulting in very little sediment accumulation since Miocene time.

The mechanisms responsible for such a long period of non-accumulation of sediment on a vast area of the sea floor are not yet understood. The most plausible interpretation is that since Miocene time there has been a reduction in the productivity of the surface waters overlying the outcropping areas of the pre-Quaternary and that the amount of pelagic sediment may have been limited by transportation away from this region by bottom waters. The submerged mid-American land bridge during the pre-Pliocene (Lloyd, 1963) might have produced the higher productivity by stimulating the circulation of the eastern Pacific water via the injection of Atlantic water through this

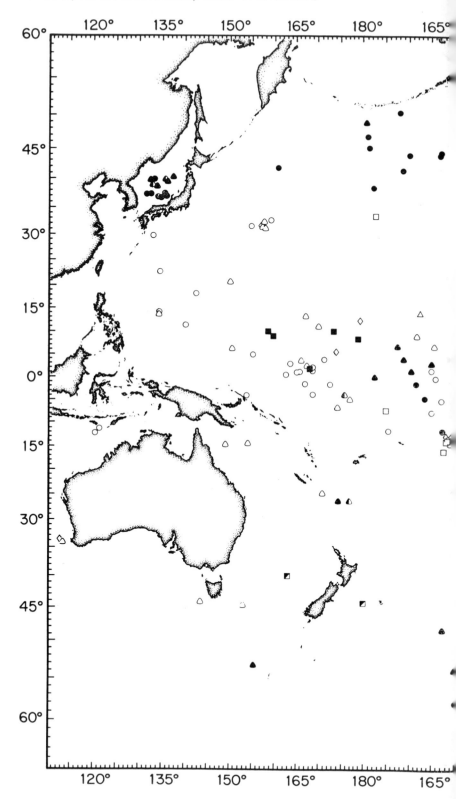

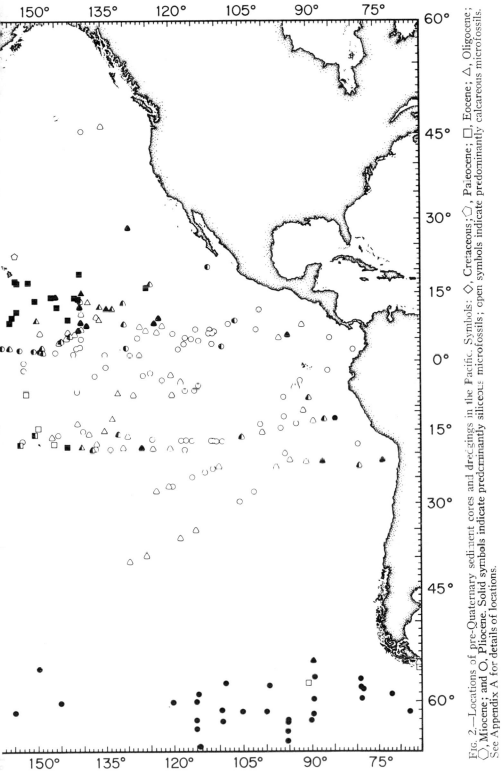

FIG. 2.—Locations of pre-Quaternary sediment cores and dredgings in the Pacific. Symbols: ◇, Cretaceous; ◻, Paleocene; ◻, Eocene; △, Oligocene; ⬠, Miocene; and ◯, Pliocene. Solid symbols indicate predominantly siliceous microfossils; open symbols indicate predominantly calcareous microfossils. See Appendix A for details of locations.

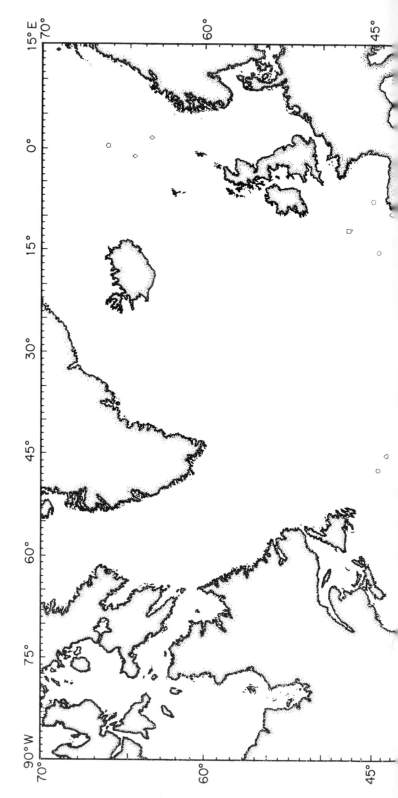

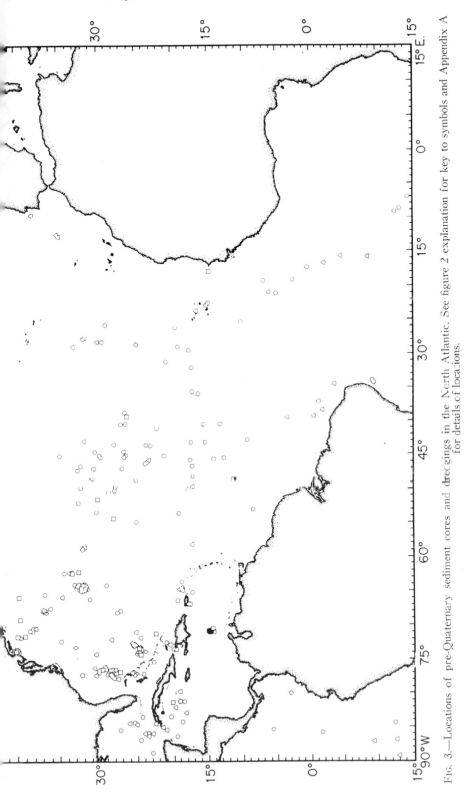

Fig. 3.—Locations of pre-Quaternary sediment cores and dredgings in the North Atlantic. See figure 2 explanation for key to symbols and Appendix A for details of locations.

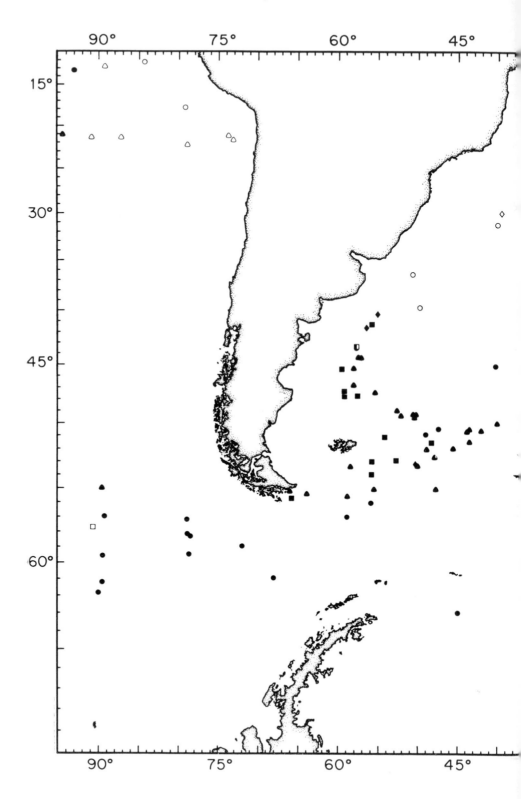

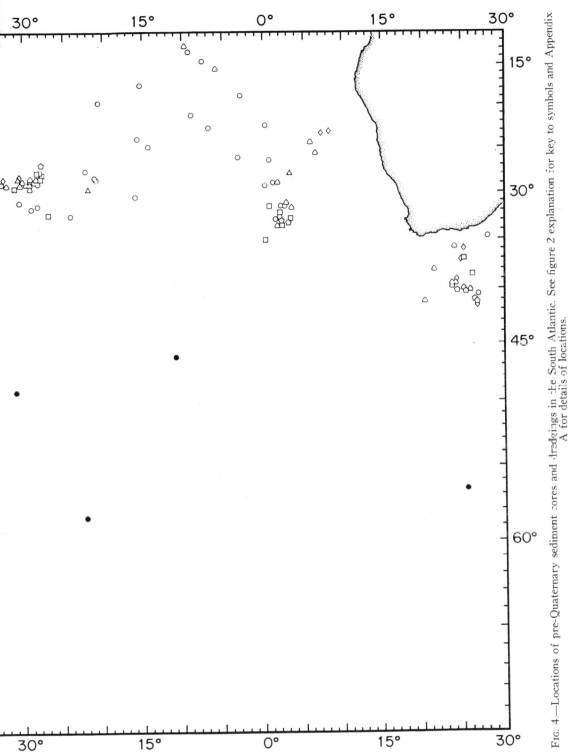

FIG. 4.—Locations of pre-Quaternary sediment cores and dredgings in the South Atlantic. See figure 2 explanation for key to symbols and Appendix A for details of locations.

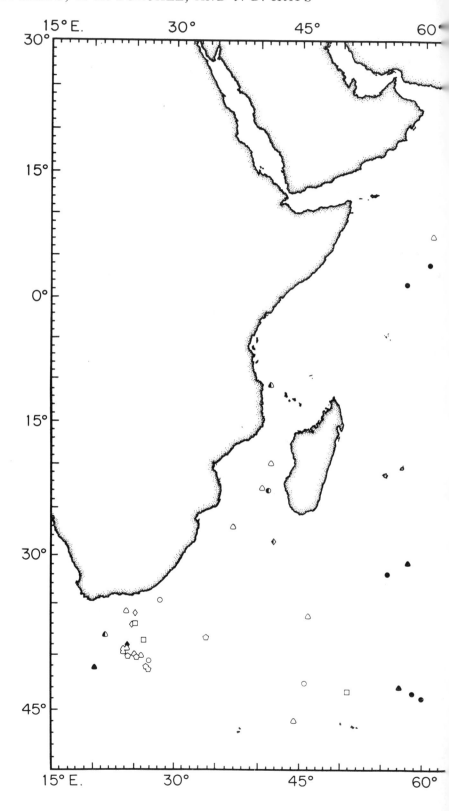

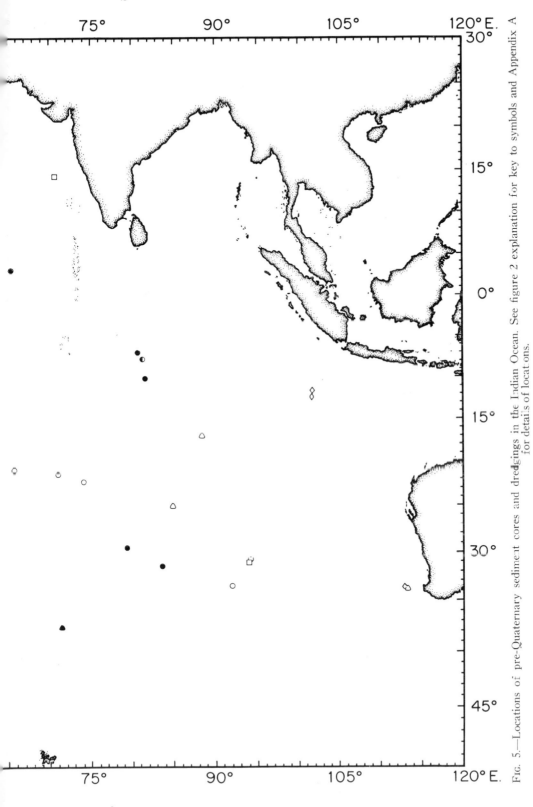

FIG. 5.—Locations of pre-Quaternary sediment cores and dredgings in the Indian Ocean. See figure 2 explanation for key to symbols and Appendix A for details of locations.

channel. No radiolarian oozes are known in recent sediments of the Equatorial Atlantic or Caribbean. Eocene radiolarian oozes, however, have been recovered from the Equatorial Atlantic (RC8-2), from the western Atlantic (Saito and others, 1966), Sierra Leone Rise, eastern Atlantic and along the coast of Senegal, West Africa (Maxwell and others, 1970), Caribbean (Ewing and others, 1967; Bader and others, 1970) Barbados (Beckman, 1954) and the Gulf of Mexico (Worzel and others, 1970). This suggests an Eocene belt of high productivity extending from the Equatorial Atlantic through the Caribbean and Gulf of Mexico into the Pacific.

An alternative explanation is that rates of sediment accumulation vary with time depending on the position of the sediment-collecting ocean floor with respect to the equator. Today accumulation rates are highest under the equator and decrease both to the north and south (Hays and others, 1969). The decreasing accumulation rate or non-accumulation of post-Middle Miocene sediment over a vast area between 3° and 10°N in the eastern Equatorial Pacific could as well be explained by a northwestward motion of this portion of the Pacific floor due to sea floor spreading since Middle Miocene thereby moving the ocean floor from underneath a zone of high productivity to one of low productivity. The relatively uniform occurrence of pre-Middle Miocene sediments in this area suggest that the motion of the ocean floor was parallel to the sediment accumulation-rate isopleths during this time or nearly due west.

Bellingshausen Basin.—The Bellingshausen Basin of the Antarctic is one of the most intensively cored regions in the world. The accumulation rates in this basin seem to be slower than in other areas around the Antarctic. Consequently, a number of cores penetrate through complete or nearly complete Quaternary sequences into Pliocene sediments and one penetrates through a complete or nearly complete Quaternary and Pliocene sequence into Miocene sediments (E13-17). The few remaining cores that reach sediments older than Pliocene contain hiatuses. In general, sedimentation rates are highest near Antarctica and beneath the Antarctic polar front.

ATLANTIC OCEAN

Outcrops of pre-Quaternary sediment in the Atlantic and its adjoining seas generally occur on steep scarps and slopes of submarine topographic elevations such as plateaus marginal to continents, flanks of the Mid-Atlantic Ridge, aseismic ridges and seamounts. One notable

exception to this is the area east of the Bahamas where exposures of sediment as old as mid-Cretaceous were found on relatively level ocean floor at great depths (Ewing and others, 1966; Saito and Burckle, 1966; Windisch and others, 1968).

In general, those cores raised from the flanks of the mid-Atlantic Ridge show increasing age with greater distance from the ridge axis. However, this pattern is less clearly defined in the Atlantic than in the Equatorial Pacific.

Sediment cores recovered from plateaus marginal to continents reflect varying histories. For example, features such as the Blake Plateau, Rio Grande Rise, Walvis Ridge and East Falkland Plateau all show fossil evidence for having been considerably shallower in the geologic past than at present (Ewing and others, 1966; Heezen and Sheridan, 1966; Sheridan and others, 1969; Maxwell and others, 1970). On the other hand, features such as the Naturaliste Plateau, in the Indian Ocean, display little or no evidence of vertical movement (Burckle and others, 1967).

Blake Plateau.—The Blake Plateau is a broad, flat area with an average depth of 850 meters; it constitutes an intermediate topographic level between the continental shelf and the deep ocean basin to the east. The Plateau is bound on the east by the Blake Escarpment which separates the 1000 meter level of the Plateau from the 5000 meter depth of the Blake-Bahama Basin. Near the base of the Escarpment, Aptian to Neocomian shallow water algal calcarenites were found to crop out (Sheridan and others, 1969). Numerous Cretaceous and Tertiary sediments cored along the Escarpment together with seismic profiling studies indicate that rocks of similar age on the coastal plain continue seaward beneath the Blake Plateau, emerging along the Escarpment (Bunce and others, 1965; Heezen, 1968).

Walvis Ridge.—Walvis Ridge is a prominent, aseismic linear feature in the South Atlantic Ocean, extending southwestward from Walvis Bay, Africa. It is a single linear feature near the African coast, but about halfway between Walvis Bay and the mid-Atlantic Ridge (about 2°E longitude) it diverges into several parallel chains of topographic highs. Summits of most of these elevations are rather flat and have depths between 1000 and 1800 meters.

Throughout most of the ridge, Miocene and Pliocene sediments are found on the crest overlain by a blanket of a few meters of coarse-grained Pleistocene sediments often containing reworked Cretaceous and Tertiary faunas. The very coarse nature of these Quaternary sediments indicates that bottom currents are operating to remove most of the younger sediments.

Two Maestrichtian (Upper Cretaceous) cores have been reported (Saito and others, 1966; Ewing and others, 1966; Todd, 1970) from a steep scarp on the nearshore portion of the ridge. In fourteen Tertiary sediment cores recovered from the region where the main ridge divides, the oldest material taken from the ridge top is Early Eocene, but Late Paleocene to Middle Eocene sediments have been recovered from the flanks. One Middle Eocene core (V22-143) raised from the southeastern flank consists of a pebbly coarse-grained sandstone with abundant littoral larger foraminifers. The remarkable flatness and concurrent elevations of the basement topography in this portion of the ridge and the presence of shallow water Paleocene and Eocene faunas can be interpreted in the following way: 1) the ridge existed in Paleocene time probably as an island chain; 2) emergence and truncation occurred prior to Middle Eocene time and 3) moderate subsidence to present depths followed (Ewing and others, 1966).

Rio Grande Rise.—The Rio Grande Rise is a large uplifted segment of the southwestern Atlantic floor, the surface of which slopes gently southward. On the north, it is bound by a steep scarp rising more than 1800 meters from the adjoining floor of the Brazil Basin. Seismic profiler studies have shown that the Rio Grande Rise is covered by more than 500 meters of stratified sediment on the north and thickens toward the south (LePichon and others, 1966). It is along this faulted northern scarp, where deeper layers of stratified sediment crop out that coring and dredging have recovered latest Cretaceous and Tertiary sequences.

Drilling on the northeastern edge of the Rise has revealed that Campanian or older coquina, indicative of shallower, higher energy environments, underlies the bathyal Maestrichtian sediments (Maxwell and others, 1970).

Falkland Plateau and southern Argentine continental slope.—The Falkland Plateau is similar to other marginal plateaus in that Cretaceous and Tertiary sediments are present at or near the surface. These outcrops are probably due to bottom currents which both erode older sediments and inhibit recent deposition. Of some 100 cores retrieved from the Falkland Plateau and the southern Argentine continental slope, more than 40 penetrate pre-Pleistocene sediments. Ages range from Late Cretaceous (probably Maestrichtian) to latest Pliocene and sediment type ranges from manganese clay to pure siliceous ooze. The biogenic components are predominantly Radiolaria and diatoms, although coccolith ooze is noted in one Eocene (RC12-242) and one Middle Miocene (V14-47) core. Some foraminifers are present in older Tertiary sediments along the Argentine continental slope. Cretaceous and Eocene sediment cores are largely restricted to the Argentine continental slope and the west end of the Falkland Plateau. The Cretaceous sediments are largely detrital with a small biogenic component (chiefly Radiolaria). Eocene cores contain little non-biogenic detritus, diatoms and Radiolaria being the major component in most cores. Miocene and Pliocene cores predominate in the central and eastern side of the plateau. Two distinct facies are evident: Miocene cores in the central part of the Plateau exhibit a manganese clay facies with minor biogenic components but cores taken from the eastern side of the Plateau are largely pelagic in character.

Preliminary conclusions based upon a study of the diatoms suggest gradual subsidence of this area since Eocene times. Periods of high productivity and resultant high sedimentation rates are noted for the Eocene and the Miocene-Pliocene.

INDIAN OCEAN

Cores of pre-Quaternary sediments have been taken only on the Agulhas Plateau. This feature is a broad, asymmetrical anticlinal structure with a highly dissected top. It is bound on the east and west by steep scarps interpreted as fault scarps (Heezen and Tharp, 1966). Although the sediment thickness over the Plateau, recorded by a seismic profiler, is on the order of a few hundred meters, coring has shown that Tertiary and even Upper Cretaceous sediments are within reach of the piston corer over a large part of the Plateau.

Cretaceous and Tertiary sediments are fine-grained coccolith-foraminiferal oozes containing no more than a few percent benthonic foraminifers, suggesting a deep-water depositional environment. Pleistocene and Recent sediments consist mainly of foraminiferal sand, the thickness of which nowhere exceeds a few meters. A marked contrast in grain size between pre-Quaternary and Recent-Pleistocene sediments suggests that scouring by strong currents occurred sometime around the end of the Tertiary. Current ripples shown in numerous underwater photographs taken on the Plateau are additional evidence of this.

ACKNOWLEDGMENTS

We express our sincere appreciation to David B. Ericson who conducted the earlier phase of pre-Quaternary sediment core study at the Lamont-Doherty Geological Observatory and also was the first curator of the Core Library.

We are also grateful to Doctors Neil D. Opdyke, Andrew McIntyre, and Dragoslav Ninkovich who critically reviewed the manuscript and made numerous helpful suggestions. Thanks are also extended to Linda Murphy for typing and preparing the catalogue and to Harry Breger and David Johnson for drafting.

We are particularly grateful to Dr. Maurice Ewing, Director of the Lamont-Doherty Geological Observatory, who organized the cruises which obtained the majority of sediment samples catalogued in this article. We are indebted to the crews of the R/V CONRAD and R/V VEMA and Mr. Roy R. Capo for collecting and curating the cores.

Collection of cores and laboratory work have been supported for the last five years through grants GA 558, GA 1193, GA10635, GA19690, GA 29460, GA 4499, GA 21174 of the National Science Foundation and grant N-00014-67-A-0108-0004 of the Office of Naval Research.

This paper is Contribution Number 2076 of the Lamont-Doherty Geological Observatory.

REFERENCES

BADER, R. G., AND OTHERS, 1970, Initial reports of the Deep Sea Drilling Project: Washington, D.C., U.S. Govt. Printing Office, v. 4, xxi + 753 pp.

BECKMAN, J. P., 1954, Foraminiferen der Oceanic Formation, Barbados: Ecologae Geol. Helvetiae, v. 46, p. 301–407.

BUNCE, E. T., EMERY, K. O., GERARD, R. D., KNOTT, S. T., LIDZ, L., SAITO, T. AND SCHLEE, J., 1965, Ocean drilling on the continental margin: Science, v. 150, p. 709–716.

BURCKLE, L. H., 1972, Late Cenozoic planktonic diatom zones from the eastern equatorial Pacific: Symposium on Fossil and Recent Marine Diatoms, Nova Hedwegia, v. 39, p. 217–246.

———, EWING, J., SAITO, T. AND LEYDEN, R., 1967, Tertiary sediment from the East Pacific Rise: Science, v. 157, p. 537–540.

DIETZ, R. S., 1961, Continent and ocean basin evolution by spreading of the sea floor: Nature, v. 190, p. 854–857.

DONAHUE, J. G., 1970, Diatoms as indicators of Pleistocene climatic fluctuations in high latitudes of the Pacific Ocean (Ph.D. dissertation): New York, Columbia Univ., 210 p.

ERICSON, D. B., EWING, M., WOLLIN, G. AND HEEZEN, B. C., 1961, Atlantic deep-sea sediment cores: Geol. Soc. America Bull., v. 72, p. 193–286.

EWING, J., EWING, M., AITKEN, T. AND LUDWIG, W., 1968, North Pacific sediment layers measured by seismic profiling, in KNOPOFF, L., DRAKE, C., AND HART, P. (eds.), The crust and upper mantle of the Pacific area: Am. Geophys. Union Mon. 12, p. 147–173.

———, LUSKIN, B., ROBERTS, A., AND HIRSHMAN, J., 1960, Subbottom reflection measurements on the continental shelf, Bermuda Banks, West Indes Arc, and in the west Atlantic basin: Jour. Geophys. Research, v. 65, p. 2849–2859.

———, AND ZAUNERE, R., 1964, Seismic profiling with a pneumatic sound source: ibid., v. 69, p. 4913–4915.

EWING, M., SAITO, T., EWING, J. AND BURCKLE, L. H., 1966, Lower Cretaceous sediments from the northwest Pacific: Science, v. 152, p. 751–755.

———, ———, AND LEPICHON, X., 1967, Reply to "Comments on mantle convection and mid-ocean ridges" by Peter R. Vogt and Ned A. Ostenso: Jour. Geophys. Research, v. 72, p. 2085.

FOSTER, J., AND OPDYKE, N. D., 1970, Upper Miocene to Recent magnetic stratigraphy in deep-sea sediments: ibid., v. 75, p. 4465–4473.

FUNNELL, B. M., AND RIEDEL, W. R., 1971, The micropaleontology of oceans: Cambridge Univ. Press, 828 p.

HANNA, G. D., 1932, The diatoms of Sharktooth Hill, Kern County, California: Calif. Acad. Sci. Proc., ser. 4, v. 20, p. 161–263.

HAYS, J. D., 1970, The stratigraphy and evolutionary trends of Radiolaria in North Pacific deep-sea sediments, in HAYS, J. D. (ed.), Geological investigations of the North Pacific: Geol. Soc. America Mem. 126, p. 185–218.

———, AND OPDYKE, N. D., 1967, Antarctic Radiolaria, magnetic reversals and climatic change: Science, v. 158, p. 1001–1011.

———, SAITO, T., OPDYKE, N. D. AND BURCKLE, L. H., 1969, Pliocene/Pleistocene sediments of the equatorial Pacific: their paleomagnetic, biostratigraphic and climatic record: Geol. Soc. America Bull., v. 80, p. 1481–1514.

HEEZEN, B. C., 1968, The Atlantic continental margin: Univ. Missouri at Rolla Jour., no. 1, p. 5–25.

———, AND SHERIDAN, E., 1966, Lower Cretaceous rocks (Neocomian-Albian) dredged from Blake Escarpment: Science, v. 154, p. 1644–1647.

HEEZEN, B. C., AND THARP, M., 1966. Physiography of the Indian Ocean: Philos. Trans. Roy. Soc. London, ser. A, v. 259, p. 137–149.

HESS, H. H., 1962, History of ocean basins, in ENGEL, A. E. J., JAMES, H. C., AND LEONARD, B. C. (eds.), Petrologic studies, A volume to honor A. F. Buddington: Geol. Soc. America, p. 599–620.

KANAYA, T., 1957, Eocene diatom assemblages from the Kellog and "Sidney" shales, Mt. Diablo area, California: Tohoku Univ. Sci. Rept., ser. 2 (Geology), v. 28, p. 27–124.

Ku, T. L., Broecker, W. S. and Opdyke, N. D., 1968, Comparison of sedimentation rates measured by paleomagnetic and the ionium methods of age determination: Earth and Planet. Sci. Letters, v. 4, p. 1–16.

LePichon, X., Saito, T. and Ewing, J., 1968, Mesozoic and Cenozoic sediments from the Rio Grande Rise: Geol. Soc. America Special Paper, 101, p. 121.

Lloyd, J. J., 1963, Tectonic history of the South-Central American orogen, in Childs, O. E. (ed.), The backbone of the Americas—tectonic history from pole to pole, a symposium: Am. Assoc. Petroleum Geologists Mem. 2, p. 88–100.

Maxwell, A. E., and others, 1970, Initial reports of the Deep Sea Drilling Project: Washington, D.C., U.S. Govt. Printing Office, v. 3, xx + 806 p.

Opdyke, N. D., and Foster, J. H., 1970, The paleomagnetism of cores from the North Pacific, in Hays, J. D. (ed.), Geological investigations of the North Pacific: Geol. Soc. America, Mem. 126, p. 83–119.

———, Burckle, L. H., Hays, J. D. and Saito, T., 1970, Extension of the magnetic stratigraphy to the middle Miocene: ibid., Abs. with programs, v. 2, p. 642.

Revelle, R. R., Bramlette, M. N., Arrhenius, G. and Goldberg, E. D., 1955, Pelagic sediments of the Pacific, in Poldervaart, A. (ed.), Crust of the earth: ibid., Special Paper 62, 221–236.

Riedel, W. R., 1967, Radiolarian evidence consistent with spreading of the Pacific floor: Science, v. 157, p. 540–542.

———, and Sanfilippo, A., 1970, Radiolaria, Leg 4, Deep Sea Drilling Project, in Bader, R. G., and others, 1970, Initial reports of the Deep Sea Drilling Project: Washington, D.C., U.S. Govt. Printing Office, v. 4, p. 503–575.

Saito, T. and Bé, A., 1967, Paleontology of deep-sea deposits, in Runcorn, S. K. (ed.), Internat. dictionary geophysics: London, Pergamon Press, Ltd., v. 2, p. 1143–1153.

———, and Burckle, L. H., 1966, Lithology and paleontology of the reflective layer Horizon A: Science, v. 154, p. 1173.

———, Ewing, M. and Burckle, L. H., 1966, Tertiary sediment from the Mid-Atlantic Ridge: ibid., v. 151, p. 1075–1079.

Sheridan, R. E., Smith, J. D., and Gardner, J., 1969, Rock dredges from Blake Escarpment near Great Abaco Canyon: Am. Assoc. Petroleum Geologists Bull., v. 53, p. 2551–2558.

Todd, R., 1970, Maestrichtian (Late Cretaceous) foraminifera: Revista Española Micropaleontologia, v. 2, p. 131–154.

Windisch, C. C., Leyden, R. J., Worzel, J. L., Saito, T., and Ewing, J., 1968, Investigation of Horizon Beta: Science, v. 162, p. 1473–1479.

Worzel, J. L., and others, 1970, Deep-Sea Drilling Project: Leg 10: Geotimes, v. 15, no. 6, p. 11–13

APPENDIX A

List of pre-Quaternary sediment cores and dredgings arranged according to age. Letter symbols indicate ship followed by cruise number and core number. Dredges are preceded by the letter symbol RD for Rock Dredge and BBD for Blake Bottom Dredge. Key to ship letter symbols as follows:

A =	Atlantis
A3 =	Atlantic Seal
C =	Caryn
D =	"Balanus" cruise (1947)
E =	Eltanin
E8 =	Eastward
G =	Goldberger
KM =	Kevin Moran
R =	Rehoboth
RC =	Robert Conrad
SP =	San Pablo
V =	Vema

The letter symbols "C," "S" and "C/S" in the far right column indicate whether the major fossil element is calcareous (C), siliceous (S) or mixed (C/S). The Eltanin cores are stored at the Florida State Universiy, Tallahassee, Florida. All others are in Lamont-Doherty Collections. See figures 2–5 for map locations of the cores and dredgings.

(Tables 1–6 follow)

TABLE 1.—CRETACEOUS CORES

Core number	Position				Depth in meters	Remarks	
	Latitude		Longitude				
A158-2	36°42'	N	67°58'	W	3260	Maestrichtian	C
A158-4	36°41.5'	N	67°59'	W	3940	Upper Cretaceous	C
A164-10	36°43'	N	67°56'	W	4654	Upper Cretaceous	C
A167-8	33°13'	N	73°39.5'	W	4803	Upper Cretaceous	C
A167-25	28°52'	N	76°47'	W	1747	Cenomanian	C
A167-51	25°23.5'	N	77°24'	W	3383	Upper Cretaceous	C
RC8-56	33°40'	S	112°40'	E	3063	Upper Cretaceous	C
C10-2	33°39'	N	62°26'	W	2370	Maestrichtian	C
C10-5	33°37'	N	62°29'	W	2670	Maestrichtian	C
G7	40°18'38"	N	73°57'47"	W	13	Maestrichtian-Campanian	C
G13	40°14'59"	N	73°58'58"	W	13	Maestrichtian-Campanian	C
G31	40°17'55"	N	73°58'15"	W	13	Maestrichtian-Campanian	C
RC5-12	26°35'	N	56°29'	W	5104	Campanian	C
RC8-56	33°40'	S	112°40'	E	3063	Turonian	C
RC9-151	30°46'	S	114°23.3'	E	2543	Maestrichtian	C
RC10-267	24°03.3'	N	94°22.8'	W	3749		C
RC10-281	24°53.5'	N	73°52'	W	5340	Cenomanian	C
RC10-282	24°54.2'	N	73°51.5'	W	5302	Cenomanian	C
RC10-283	24°54.6'	N	73°51.3'	W	5305	Cenomanian	C
RC10-284	24°55.7'	N	73°51'	W	5314	Aptian-Albian	C
V12-47	47°53.8'	S	59°21.5'	W	935	Maestrichtian	C
V12-65	22°58.6'	S	08°06.5'	E	4118	Maestrichtian	C
V14-80	28°34'	S	41°58'	E	4603	Cenomanian, Rework	C
V16-56	41°21'	S	26°38'	E	2961	Cenomanian	C
V17-144	40°34'	S	55°10'	W	2503		S
V18-105	53°23'	S	50°31'	W	534	Reworked	S
V18-129	41°42'	S	56°35'	W	2039		S
V18-263	12°05'	S	160°55'	W	3630	Reworked	S
V18-266	12°16.5'	S	161°03'	W	2893	Reworked	S
V18-267	12°16.5'	S	161°03'	W	2760*	Reworked	S
V18-270	12°14.5'	S	160°57'	W	3157*	Reworked	S
V19-154	11°41'	S	101°40'	E	4964	Reworked	C
V19-155	12°24'	S	101°32'	E	4731	Reworked	C
V19-253	23°28'	S	07°07'	E	4197		C
V21-143	31°51'	N	157°20'	E	3592	Albian	C
V21-229	23°40'	N	73°51'	W	4944		C
V21-236	25°15'	N	72°47'	W	5471	Maestrichtian	C
V21-237	25°16'	N	72°47'	W	5466	Maestrichtian	C
V21-238	25°14'	N	72°48'	W	5475	Maestrichtian	C
V21-239	25°12'	N	72°51'	W	5468	Maestrichtian	C
V21-241	25°15'	N	72°40'	W	5468	Maestrichtian	C
V22-8	24°52'	N	74°01'	W	5508	Cenomanian	C
V22-12	24°45'	N	73°10'	W	5130	Maestrichtian	C
V22-16	24°44'	N	73°38'	W	5383	Maestrichtian	C
V22-64	28°34'	S	30°34'	W	2273	Maestrichtian	C
V22-124	40°02'	S	25°18'	E	2624	Senonian	C
V22-134	39°05'	S	24°09'	E	4517	Turonian	C
V23-71	69°15.7'	N	14°23.9'	E	1011	Reworked	C
V23-75	64°48'	N	01°19'	W	2930	Upper Cret	C
V23-76	63°39'	N	01°22'	E	1734	Reworked	C
V24-13	24°44'	N	73°41'	W	5323	Barremian-Hauterivian	C
V24-15	24°44'	N	73°45'	W	5305	Cenomanian (Oligo.)	C
V24-101	13°10'	N	178°53'	E	3336*	Barremian	C
V24-103	06°34'	N	173°30'	E	4991	Upper Cretaceous	C
V24-213	36°59'	S	25°07'	E	3777	Maestrichtian	C
V24-215	37°07'	S	24°46'	E	3691	Mixed	C
V24-251	30°08'	S	39°28'	W	4111	Cretaceous?	C
V26-3	32°25.7'	N	58°58.1'	W	3453		C
V26-62	28°26.9'	S	30°28.4'	W	3799	Campanian	C

* Approximate

TABLE 2.—PALEOCENE CORES

Core number	Position				Depth in meters	Remarks	
	Latitude		Longitude				
A158-3	36°42.5'	N	67°58.5'	W	3790		C
AS1-9	66°21'	N	00°18'	E	3018		C
E8-67-11	32°10.5'	N	58°58'	W	3007		C
RC9-5	32°20.2'	N	77°37.4'	W	4424		C
RC11-144	29°42'	S	112°40.5'	E	4813	Paleocene?	C
RC12-76	23°11.7'	N	154°27.2'	W	1506		C
RC12-199	07°35'	N	178°25'	E	5565*	Paleocene-Eocene	C
V8-18	19°11'	N	81°21'	W	1984		C
V16-55	40°14'	S	25°15'	E	2772		C
V18-187	38°20'	S	33°55'	E	3680		C
V19-94	04°06'	S	176°28'	E	5298	Reworked	S
V22-126	41°10'	S	26°30'	E	2791		C
V22-127	41°18'	S	26°43'	E	2932		C
V22-132	40°13'	S	24°10'	E	3898		C
V22-133	39°39'	S	24°47'	E	3065		C
V22-140	33°37'	S	02°21'	E	4433		C
V22-145	32°22'	S	02°09'	E	2056		C
V24-243	31°02'	S	35°43'	W	1020		C
V26-65	26°42.3'	S	27°51.9'	W	4371		C
V26-81	23°45.9'	S	34°22.4'	W	4387		C
V27-130	45°03.9'	N	07°59.1'	W	4526	Upper Paleocene	C
V27-133	45°05.4'	N	07°56.9'	W	4682		C

* Approximate

TABLE 3. EOCENE CORES

Core number	Position				Depth in meters	Remarks	
	Latitude		Longitude				
A150-1	32°42'	N	62°30'	W	1597		C
A162-1	39°12'	N	71°48'	W	2167		C
A167-21	29°49'	N	76°35'	W	1454		C
C10-1	33°39.7'	N	62°29.8'	W	1480		C
C22-5	32°17'	N	64°38.5'	W	1097	Eocene-Oligocene	C
C22-6	32°16'	N	64°34.75'	W	1509	Eocene-Oligocene	S
E6-8	53°01'	S	55°47.5'	W	1992		S
E6-9	53°59.5'	S	55°58'	W	1800		S
E13-4	57°46'	S	90°47'	W	4812		C
G28	40°14'31"	N	73°59'12"	W	9		C
KM1-55	14°57.2'	N	17°16.8'	W	693		C
D-20	39°50'	N	70°50'	W	1000		C/S
RC8-2	11°12'	N	48°05'	W	4625		C/S
RC8-35	38°30'	S	26°05'	E	2922		C
RC8-41	43°38'	S	51°16'	E	2897		C
RC8-109	14°38'	N	70°50'	W	3760		C
RC9-55	14°41'	N	70°53.5'	W	3609		C/S
RC9-56	14°38.2'	N	70°52.8'	W	3404		C/S
RC9-57	14°33.8'	N	70°47.6'	W	3660		C/S
RC9-58	14°33.4'	N	70°48.6'	W	3548		C/S
RC9-59	14°37.3'	N	70°50.3'	W	3689		C/S
RC9-107	44°13.1'	S	179°34.4'	E	902		C/S
RC9-122	25°08.5'	S	177°46'	E	4330		C/S
RC9-129	39°31.2'	S	163°07.5'	E	2836		C/S
RC10-27	22°27.2'	N	71°36.1'	W	5192		C
RC10-33	20°16'	N	81°29'	W	2875		C
RC10-103	10°02'	N	143°37.8'	W	5253		S
RC10-279	24°30.8'	N	74°26'	W	4984		C
RC11-RD4	31°17'	S	94°16'	E	2668–1492		C
RC11-25	28°33.4'	S	30°03'	W	1842		C
RC11-199	19°28.8'	N	140°01.5'	W	5574		S
RC11-203	11°01'	N	139°58'	W	4877		S
RC11-247	24°43.2'	N	73°47'	W	5316		S

(Table 3—Continued on next page)

TABLE 3—(*Continued*)

Core number	Position Latitude		Longitude		Depth in meters	Remarks	
RC12-50	16°35′	N	125°35′	W	4369		S
RC12-93	13°42.7′	S	161°41.9′	W	3296	Middle Eocene	C
RC12-94	15°25′	S	162°45′	W	5480		S
RC12-199	07°35′	N	178°25′	E	5565	Paleocene-Eocene	S
RC12-203	07°07.5′	S	175°36.3′	W	5932		C
RC12-237	47°45.7′	S	57°38.5′	W	3652		S
RC12-342	43°28′	S	57°39.5′	W	3638		C
RC13-68	07°12′	S	152°10′	W	4043	Lower middle Eocene	C
RC13-74	17°55.6′	S	146°14.6′	W	3959	Middle Eocene	C
RC13-75	18°30.5′	S	143°18.2′	W	4319	Uppermost Eocene	C
V10-96	27°52′	N	54°38′	W	4839		C
V12-4	24°16.9′	N	53°04.1′	W	5009		C
V12-40	45°27.9′	S	59°40.1′	W	1044		S
V12-46	47°28.7′	S	59°20.6′	W	1167		S
V15-195	27°08.5′	N	77°21′	W	1812		C
V16-209	30°00′	N	51°52′	W	4673		C
V17-107	51°08′	S	54°22′	W	1525		S
V18-BBD6	17°47.5′	S	154°03.5′	W	1492–1679		C
V18-RD29	55°28.5′	S	65°56.5′	W	1966–1719		C
V18-RD32	14°18′	S	149°32′	W	1937–2087		C
V18-RD33	14°20.5′	S	149°37.5′	W	2536–2657		C
V18-RD37	39°40′	N	65°55′	W	2496–2166		C
V18-104	53°01′	S	52°52′	W	2880		S
V18-112	51°40′	S	48°29′	W	2429		S
V18-130	41°30′	S	56°37′	W	1415		S
V18-192	31°12′	S	48°05′	E	4396	Pliocene with Eocene	C
V18-295	15°39.5′	S	150°08′	W	4215		C
V19-81	15°13′	S	164°29′	W	5700	Eocene and Miocene mixed	C
V19-97	00°06′	N	170°46′	E	4552	Upper Miocene with reworked Eocene	C/S
V19-103	09°44′	N	158°13′	E	5302		S
V19-104	10°42′	N	158°13′	E	5636		S
V20-42	14°06′	N	140°17′	W	4916		S
V20-43	14°28′	N	141°08′	W	4881		S
V20-45	15°28′	N	143°49′	W	5385		S
V20-49	14°29′	N	146°19′	W	6002		S
V20-54	17°10′	N	152°15′	W	5267		S
V20-57	17°21′	N	153°52′	W	5106		S
V20-58	17°52′	N	154°15′	W	5051		S
V20-103	33°59′	N	177°50′	W	3442		C
V20-220	28°36′	S	29°01′	W	3601		C
V21-191	13°44′	N	150°00′	W	5218		S
V21-193	12°19′	N	145°08′	W	5519		S
V22-50	28°32′	S	29°00′	W	3566		C
V21-51	28°32′	S	29°00′	W	933**		C
V22-52	28°32′	S	29°00′	W	4361		C
V22-54	28°30′	S	28°58′	W	3781		C
V22-148	32°19.5′	S	02°09.5′	E	2047		C
V22-149	31°26′	S	00°50′	E	4012		C
V22-214	26°00.5′	N	39°31′	W	4147*		C
V24-66	09°18′	N	155°31′	W	5234		S
V24-67	10°13′	N	155°01′	W	5302		S
V24-68	11°46′	N	154°02′	W	5209		S
V24-79	09°17′	N	178°37′	E	5704		S
V24-80	10°53′	N	173°00′	E	5374		S
V24-99	18°32′	N	17 °30′	W	1604	Eocene and Oligocene mixed	C
V24-106	02°43′	N	167°46′	E	4508		C/S
V24-214	37°03′	S	24°57′	E	3290		C
V24-222A	32°59′	S	03°02′	W	1587		C
V24-225	34°54′	S	04°57′	W	1790		C
V24-237	32°12′	S	26°44′	W	4193		C
V27-134	48°00.1′	N	12°06.3′	W	3350	Upper Eocene	C

* Approximate
** Counter depth at time messenger sent

TABLE 4.—OLIGOCENE CORES

Core number	Position Latitude		Longitude		Depth in meters	Remarks	
A156-2	29°12.5′	N	76°49′	W	2140		C
A146-25	32°13′	N	64°31′	W	2955		C
A167-22	29°49.8′	N	76°28.5′	W	2204	Oligocene?	C
C10-4	32°19.4′	N	64°35.6′	W	1550		C
C10-11	32°14.5′	N	64°32.3′	W	2280		C
C22-5	32°17′	N	64°38.5′	W	1097	Oligocene-Eocene	C
C22-6	32°16′	N	64°38.75′	W	1509	Oligocene-Eocene	C
C25-5	32°43.3′	N	64°34.5′	W	1710	Pliocene-Miocene-Oligocene?	C
C25-6	33°47′	N	62°39′	W	2360	Miocene-Oligocene	C
E8-67-13	32°13′	N	58°58′	W	1390		C
E20-16	51°31′	S	102°27′	W	4217	Oligocene-Miocene	C
RC10-133	15°22′	S	151°31.5′	E	2717		C
RC11-200	14°52′	N	140°02′	W	4828		C
RC11-221	12°19′	S	136°57′	W	4103		C
RC12-54	12°12.5′	N	132°33′	W	5028	Uppermost Oligocene	C
RC12-55	11°55.5′	N	133°02′	W	4916	Uppermost Oligocene	C
RC12-58	09°50′	N	136°23′	W	4823		C
RC12-69	09°13.2	N	149°49′	W	5073	Upper Oligocene	C
RC12-89	07°44′	S	162°23′	W	4266		C
RC12-200	01°27.5′	N	174°52′	E	4691		C
RC12-201	01°16.5′	S	176°11.5′	E	5029		C
RC12-296	37°04′	S	07°12.2′	W	2681		C
RC12-297	36°09.4′	S	06°43′	W	3528		C
RC13-53	13°57.3′	N	166°59.8′	W	5442	Upper Oligocene	C
RC13-76	18°43.4′	S	140°16.6′	W	4180		C
V5-14	32°19.5′	N	64°27.3′	W	2365		C
V9-29	03°47.5′	N	34°37′	W	4675	Oligocene-Miocene	C
V16-33	15°20′	S	19°43′	W	4360		C
V18-307	06°32.5′	S	131°57′	W	4711		C
V18-310	04°25.5′	S	129°02′	W	4782		C
V18-316	01°03′	N	120°46′	W	4429		C
V20-37	11°58′	N	134°09′	W	4887		C
V20-38	12°18′	N	135°25′	W	4885		C
V20-39	12°17′	N	135°27′	W	4846		C
V20-40	13°19′	N	138°09′	W	4691		C
V20-220	28°36′	S	29°01′	W	3601		C
V21-51	12°02′	S	133°15′	W	3718		C
V21-52	14°53′	S	135°03′	W	4431		C
V22-57	28°31′	S	29°08′	W	3299		C
V22-129	40°19′	S	26°21′	E	2345		C
V22-187	04°26′	N	20°48′	W	3394		C
V24-15	24°44′	N	73°45′	W	5305	Cretaceous-Oligocene	C
V24-99	18°32′	N	179°30′	W	1604	Eocene-Oligocene mixed	C
V26-19	26°16.5′	N	40°12.3′	W	4548		C
V26-59	28°34.2′	S	30°32.7′	W	2338	Middle Oligocene	C
V26-66	29°27′	S	21°50.6′	W	4510	Eocene-Oligocene	C
V27-RD23	27°52.2′	S	03°13.5′	E	1675–1727	Uppermost Oligocene	C

TABLE 5. MIOCENE CORES

Core number	Position				Depth in meters	Remarks	
	Latitude		Longitude				
A150-RD8	31°49′	N	43°25′	W	3700		C
A153-CC163	14°42′	N	49°33′	W	4000	Miocene, Pliocene or Neogene	C
A164-4	38°12.5′	N	70°51′	W	3330	Probably Miocene	C
A164-8	37°56′	N	70°44′	W	3823	Late Miocene to possibly early Pleistocene (Pliocene)	C
A164-10	36°43′	N	67°56′	W	3548		C
A164-25	32°13′	N	64°31′	W	2953–2955		C
A614-26	32°01′	N	64°58′	W	2706		C
A164-30	30°04′	N	76°57′	W	4630	Middle Miocene	C
A167-29	28°26.5′	N	76°40′	W	1728	Miocene-Pliocene	C
A167-41	25°39′	N	76°56′	W	3109	Miocene-Pliocene	C
A167-43	25°27′	N	77°03.5′	W	2578	Miocene-Pliocene	C
A167-44	25°39.5′	N	77°21′	W	2487	Miocene-Pliocene	C
A172-13	19°24′	N	65°07′	W	6401	Neogene probably Miocene	C
A179-7	19°	N	73°50′	W	3003		C
A180-22	31°47′	N	27°57′	W	2440		C
A180-25	30°15′	N	28°30′	W	1280		C
A180-35	28°56.5′	N	25°45′	W	5029	Pliocene-Miocene	C
A180-99	16°14′	S	36°21′	W	4206		C
A185-6	20°31′	N	73°00′	W	3419		C
A185-16	19°25.5′	N	79°48.5′	W	3060		C
A185-19	19°51′	N	82°00′	W	2210		C
A185-23	21°32′	N	85°04.5′	W	2248		C
A185-25	23°11′	N	86°15′	W	1691		C
C10-4	33°40.9′	N	62°30′	W	1550		C
C10-10	32°19.4′	N	64°35.6′	W	1005		C
C22-2	32°11.5′	N	64°45′	W	1939		C
C25-5	32°43.3′	N	64°34.5′	W	1710	Pliocene-Miocene-Oligocene	C
C25-6	33°47′	N	62°39′	W	2360	Miocene-Oligocene	C
E6-10	55°06′	S	55°35′	W	1210		C
E7-3	44°03′	S	44°40′	W	1910		S
E7-18	53°00.4′	S	48°53′	W	3157		S
E9-2	50°37′	S	43°46′	W	1277		S
E9-3	50°35.5′	S	43°42.5′	W	1267		S
E9-4	49°50′	S	39°56′	W	3076		S
E13-1	55°04.1′	S	89°44.7′	W	4735		S
E13-17	65°41′	S	124°06.3′	W	4827	Pliocene-Miocene	S
E14-3	53°53.7′	S	159°58.8′	W	4375		S
E14-8	59°40′	S	160°17.4′	W	3943	Pliocene-Miocene	S
E16-4	55°36′	S	160°12′	E	4232		S
E20-2	49°00′	S	144°50′	W	4631		C
E20-15	51°57′	S	99°43′	W	4322		C
E20-16	51°31′	S	102°27′	W	4216	Oligocene-Miocene	C
E21-2	32°59′	S	87°57.5′	W	3738		C
E22-10	50°59′	S	46°06′	W	2127		C
E23-19	75°36′	S	115°09′	W	4086		C
G15	40°11′53″	N	73°59′55″	W	11		C
G16	40°10′56″	N	74°00′56″	W	13		C
G17	40°09′57″	N	74°00′34″	W	11		C
G18	40°08′48″	N	74°00′56″	W	11		C
G19	40°07′52″	N	74°01′15″	W	11		C
G20	40°06′47″	N	74°01′47″	W	11		C
KM1-33	31°45′	N	28°00′	W	2525	Upper Miocene (rework)	C
R5-50	34°58.5′	N	13°11′	W	1940	Pliocene-Miocene	C
RC1-5	27°50′	N	76°40′	W	1403	Burdigalian	C
RC4-7	29°47′	N	76°40′	W	1269		C
RC7-5	28°22.5′	N	72°22′	W	4416		C
RC7-28	14°36′	N	70°56′	W	3535		C
RC8-69	53°29′	S	155°37′	E	4303		C
RC8-80	48°18′	S	162°54′	W	4997		C
RC8-81	47°57′	S	159°03′	W	5130		C
RC8-86	40°33′	S	129°23′	W	4852	Lower Miocene	C
RC8-87	39°28′	S	125°30′	W	4583	Lower Miocene	C
RC8-89	36°23′	S	118°06′	W	3900	Upper Miocene	C
RC8-90	34°52′	S	114°48′	W	3396	Upper Miocene	C
RC10-93	07°17.5′	N	125°20.4′	W	4610?	Lower Miocene	C/S

TABLE 5—(*Continued*)

Core number	Position				Depth in meters	Remarks	
	Latitude		Longitude				
RC10-101	06°46′	N	142°34.5′	W	5201		C/S
RC10-104	04°52.4′	N	144°11.7′	W	5011		C/S
RC10-116	08°42′	S	164°20′	W	4916	Miocene-Pliocene	C
RC10-120	02°02.5′	N	169°51′	W	5365		S
RC10-121	04°54′	N	171°25′	W	5411		S
RC10-122	07°31′	N	172°50′	W	5865	Miocene?	S
RC10-124	01°59′	N	177°55′	W	5349		S
RC10-128	06°07′	S	173°38′	E	5561		C/S
RC10-149	06°46′	N	150°23′	E	4451	M. Miocene	C
RC10-163	32°43′	N	157°30′	E	3550		C
RC10-164	31°43.5′	N	157°30′	E	3766		C
RC10-166	31°49.5′	N	157°20′	E	3729		C
RC10-234	28°38′	N	129°06′	W	4281		C
RC10-248	08°27′	N	91°33′	W	3493		S
RC10-270	25°11′	N	84°44.7′	W	2816		C
RC10-271	24°39.3′	N	74°33.1′	W	5000		C
RC10-278	24°23.5′	N	73°55′	W	5325		C
RC10-280	24°42′	N	73°38.3′	W	5334		C
RC11-27	28°30.8′	S	30°04.4′	W	2704		C
RC11-30	28°21′	S	31°04′	W	2479		C
RC11-31	28°21′	S	31°04′	W	2481		C
RC11-88	41°11′	S	20°08′	E	5125		S
RC11-103	43°02′	S	57°21′	E	4673	Miocene	S
RC11-105	38°47′	S	58°50′	E	5256	Miocene-Pliocene	S
RC11-118	16°40′	S	148°11′	W	3935	Lower Miocene	C
RC8-95	22°38′	S	97°11′	W	3826	Upper Miocene	C
RC8-99	10°37′	S	91°19′	W	3819	Upper Miocene?	C
RC8-100	07°42′	S	90°02′	W	4140	Upper Miocene?	C
RC8-117	19°10′	N	65°13′	W	5629		C
RC8-118	19°11.5′	N	65°14′	W	5620		C
RC8-146	33°52.8′	N	62°11.7′	W	2670		C
RC9-7	29°58.3′	N	76°41′	W	1263	Lower Miocene	C/S
RC9-8	30°05′	N	76°42.7′	W	2538		C
RC9-83	21°20.3′	S	73°54.5′	W	4332		C
RC9-84	21°50′	S	73°08.1′	W	1618		C
RC9-90	21°47′	S	87°12.8′	W	4169–4217	Lower Miocene	C
RC9-91	21°26.3′	S	90°58.4′	W	4094	Upper Miocene	C
RC9-92	21°08.6′	S	94°29.7′	W	4122	Middle Miocene	C
RC9-95	22°18.1′	S	109°43.3′	W	3660	Upper Miocene	C
RC9-103	26°32.4′	S	120°34.4′	W	3488	Upper Miocene	C
RC9-104	27°25.6′	S	123°25.7′	W	3632	Upper Miocene	C
RC9-132	44°46.7′	S	152°48.4′	E	4709		C
RC9-134	44°04.9′	S	143°47.3′	E	4570		C
RC9-220	43°32.1′	N	10°24.1′	W	4071–4530		C
RC10-2	34°26′	N	66°05.5′	W	5231		C
RC10-58	06°08.3′	N	94°46.6′	W	3660	Middle lower Miocene	C
RC10-59	05°33.7′	N	96°19.2′	W	3662		C
RC10-92	09°54.7′	N	122°38′	W	4583	Upper Miocene	C/S
RC11-137	33°47′	S	112°46′	E	3043		C
RC11-139	33°48′	S	112°59′	E	3157		C
RC11-158	20°55′	N	149°54.5′	E	3177		C
RC11-201	13°49′	N	140°05′	W	4865	Lower Miocene	C
RC11-202	12°32′	N	140°05′	W	4996		S
RC11-203	11°01′	N	139°58′	W	4877		S
RC11-205	10°29′	N	139°53′	W	4797	Lower Miocene	C
C11-206	08°47′	N	139°58′	W	5086		S
RC11-207	07°24.5′	N	139°56′	W	5081	Lower Miocene	C/S
RC11-223	07°01′	S	128°25′	W	4574		C
RC11-225	02°29′	S	120°03′	W	4316	Upper Miocene	C/S
RC11-226	04°00.4′	S	117°54′	W	3983		C
RC11-245	24°43.5′	N	73°45.7′	W	5310		C
RC11-249	28°15′	N	77°29′	W	1073		C
RC11-250	28°08.8′	N	77°43.2′	W	1027		C
RC11-251	28°13.5′	N	77°34.8′	W	1051		C
RC11-252	28°20′	N	77°28′	W	1069		C
RC12-2	30°22′	N	77°21′	W	934	Upper Miocene	C
RC12-49	17°09′	N	124°36′	W	4321		C/S
RC12-53	13°23′	N	130°42′	W	5108	Lower Miocene	C/S

TABLE 5—(*Continued*)

Core number	Position				Depth in meters	Remarks	
	Latitude		Longitude				
RC12-57	11°02′	N	134°32′	W	4867	Lower Miocene	C/S
RC12-60	08°21′	N	138°47′	W	4956		C/S
RC12-61	07°20.5′	N	140°28.8′	W	5189		C/S
RC12-62	06°44′	N	141°22.5′	W	5073		C/S
RC12-63	05°58′	N	142°39′	W	4949 ± 10*	Upper Miocene	C/S
RC12-64	05°42′	N	143°10′	W	4857		C/S
RC12-65	04°39′	N	144°58′	W	4868		C/S
RC12-66	02°36.6′	N	148°12.8′	W	4755	Lower Miocene	C/S
RC12-67	03°13.5′	N	148°28.5′	W	4777*		C/S
RC12-68	06°33′	N	148°58.6′	W	4508		C/S
RC12-81	07°31.2′	N	164°59.7′	W	4982		C/S
RC12-104	26°03.8′	S	176°42.2′	E	4330		C/S
RC12-106	26°00.5′	S	174°01.3′	E	4669		C/S
RC12-110A	26°00′	S	154°54′	E	1942*		C/S
RC12-114	24°46′	S	170°26.2′	E	3997*	Lower Miocene	C/S
RC12-195	09°41′	N	168°42′	W	5222		C/S
RC12306	26°56′	S	37°00′	E	2501	Middle Miocene	C
RC12-308	22°24′	S	40°27′	E	2361	Miocene?	C
RC12-317	10°21′	S	41°34′	E	1926	Upper Miocene	C
RC12-381	38°55′	N	133°48′	E	1437	Upper Miocene	S
RC12-383	39°42.7′	N	133°07′	E	2113	Lower Miocene	S
RC12-390	39°42′	N	136°01.5′	E	1103	Upper Miocene	S
RC12-398	40°30.5′	N	137°31.2′	E	2664		S
RC13-79	18°58′	S	131°00.5′	W	4241	Lower Miocene	C
RC13-80	18°59′	S	126°56′	W	4032	Lower middle Miocene	C
RC13-81	19°01.1′	S	124°13.5′	W	3751	Lower middle Miocene	C
RC13-82	18°58.3′	S	120°41.3′	W	3555	Upper Miocene	C
V3-2	18°49′	N	67°09.5′	W	1869		C
V3-3	18°51′	N	67°07′	W	2661		C
V3-21	26°05′	N	84°52′	W	1616		C
V3-29	24°10′	N	86°11′	W	1939	Upper Miocene	C
V3-137	23°29′	N	86°18′	W	1891		C
V3-151	27°57.8	N	77°23.5′	W	1161		C
V3-152	28°10′	N	77°37′	W	1033		C
V3-153	28°24′	N	77°56.6′	W	994		C
V4-15	35°11′	N	15°20.5′	W	2439	Miocene-Pliocene	C
V4-19	35°14′	N	15°12′	W	3006	Miocene-Pliocene	C
V4-20	35°07.5′	N	13°04′	W	1770	Miocene?	C
V4-27	35°03′	N	12°57.5	W	1318		C
V4-41	38°12′	N	09°45′	W	None		C
V4-53	33°05′	N	29°18.5′	W	2534		C
V5-2	32°29′	N	65°00′	W	2631	Pliocene or Miocene	C
V5-9	32°13.4′	N	64°42.3′	W	1701	Miocene?	C
V5-12	32°14.7′	N	64°38.2′	W	1926		C
V5-13	32°15.8′	N	64°38.7′	W	1408		C
V5-24	32°32.7′	N	64°51′	W	1456	Neogene probably Miocene	C
V5-25	32°32.8′	N	64°50.9′	W	1370	Miocene?	C
V5-26	32°25.7′	N	64°27.7′	W	1653		C
V5-36	32°12.8′	N	64°45.5′	W	1426	Neogene, probably Miocene	C
V5-42	32°09.6′	N	64°41′	W	2650	Miocene?	
V5-43	32°16.6′	N	64°41′	W	949	Miocene?	
V6-14	27°30′	N	78°08′	W	1093		C
V9-2	01°45.9′	S	35°38.7′	W	3115	Upper Miocene	C
V9-6	03°50.9′	S	34°41.1′	W	1139		C
V9-18	08°58.8′	S	15°54.8′	W	4005?	Upper Miocene	C
V9-29	03°47.5′	N	34°37′	W	4675?	Oligocene-Miocene	C
V12-19	29°51.7′	S	36°48.4′	W	2321		C
V12-42	45°26.8′	S	58°08.2′	W	3266		S
V12-48	46°47.2′	S	58°12.1′	W	2763		S
V14-44	53°28.5	S	58°31′	W	2140**		S
V14-47	50°46.5′	S	42°09′	W	1690**		C
V15-44A	09°31′	S	87°22′	W	4276	Lower Miocene	C
V15-96	53°15.6′	S	68°09.9′	W	11		S
V15-125	55°18.2′	S	64°08.6′	W	3263		S
V15-136	52°10.8′	S	49°04.9′	W	2514		S
V15-203	29°10′	N	76°24.5′	W	4993	Neogene, probably Miocene	C

TABLE 5—(*Continued*)

Core number	Position				Depth in meters	Remarks	
	Latitude		Longitude				
V15-204	29°07'	N	76°47'	W	2820		C
V16-64	46°01'	S	44°22'	E	2202		C/S
V16-95	28°01'	S	95°11'	E	4071	Probably Pliocene-Miocene	C
V16-117	53°24'	S	153°59'	E	3992		S
V16-206	23°20'	N	46°29'	W	3733		C
V17-33	18°22'	N	84°00'	W	4308		C
V17-46	22°21'	S	78°56'	W	4627		C
V18-8	18°37.5'	N	63°54.5'	W	2935	Miocene-Pliocene?	C
V18-RD9	55°28.5'	S	65°56.5'	W	1966–1719		S
V18-RD14	44°21'	S	57°21'	W	4605–4298		S
V18-RD32	14°18'	S	149°32'	W	1937–2087		C
V18-97	55°42.5'	S	59°06'	W	3892		S
V18-106	53°27'	S	50°24'	W	2638		S
V18-107	52°53.5'	S	48°08'	W	2926		S
V18-109	52°12'	S	45°41.5'	W	3232		S
V18-114	49°35'	S	50°34'	W	2576		S
V18-115	49°26'	S	50°42'	W	3493		S
V18-116	49°26'	S	50°28'	W	2367		S
V18-117	49°30'	S	52°15'	W	2559		S
V18-118	49°05"	S	52°54'	W	5319		S
V18-121	47°37'	S	55°29'	W	5236		S
V18-128	44°21'	S	57°21'	W	4333		S
V18-203	22°23'	S	74°22'	E	4014		C
V18-206	25°28.5'	S	85°09'	E	4549		C
V18-266	12°16.5'	S	161°03'	W	2893		C
V18-270	12°14.5'	S	160°57'	W	3157*		C
V18-302	13°18'	S	141°03'	W	4133		C
V18-318	01°03'	N	120°46'	W	4439	Middle Miocene	C/S
V18-360	21°01'	N	85°35'	W	4182		C
V18-370	34°27'	N	65°17'	W	4867	Miocene-Pliocene	C
V19-38	12°30'	S	86°39'	W	4276	Middle Miocene	C
V19-39	12°43'	S	89°08'	W	4173	Upper Miocene	C
V19-42	15°10'	S	100°21'	W	3594	Upper Miocene	C
V19-43	16°21'	S	104°48'	W	4157	Upper Miocene	C
V19-67	16°10'	S	129°52'	W	3952	Upper Miocene	C
V19-68	15°37'	S	131°58'	W	4199	Upper Miocene	C
V19-70	15°39'	S	138°35'	W	3939		C
V19-75	16°19'	S	146°24'	W	1341	Lower Miocene	C
V19-81	15°13'	S	164°29'	W	5700	Eocene-Miocene mixed	C
V19-94	04°06'	S	176°28'	E	5298		S
V19-95	03°12'	S	175°10'	E	5127		C
V19-97	00°06'	N	170°46'	E	4552	Upper Miocene with reworked Eocene	C
V19-99	03°07'	N	167°02'	E	4413		C/S
V19-100	04°31'	N	165°31'	E	4599		S
V19-182	08°16'	N	64°05'	E	4173	Upper Miocene	C
V19-184	07°26'	N	61°04'	E	3471	Upper Miocene	C
V19-209	19°55'	S	41°36'	E	2924		C
V19-226	35°45'	S	23°52'	E	2188		C
V19-250	24°07'	S	05°45'	E	1600		C
V20-25	06°21'	N	105°59.5'	W	3753	Upper Miocene-Pliocene	C
V20-30	08°28'	N	118°29'	W	4069		C/S
V20-32	08°12'	N	121°43'	W	4336	Lower Miocene	C
V20-33	08°53'	N	123°32'	W	4497	Lower Miocene	C
V20-36	11°24'	N	132°07'	W	4843		S
V20-38	12°18'	N	135°25'	W	4885	Lower Miocene	C
V20-40	13°19'	N	138°09'	W	4691		C
V20-41	13°24'	N	138°31'	W	4825		C
V20-45	15°28'	N	143°49'	W	5385	Miocene?	S
V20-47	14°23'	N	145°21'	W	4986		C
V20-80	46°30'	N	135°00'	W	3801	Lower Miocene	C/S
V20-110	49°14'	N	180°00'	W	4334		S
V20-143	14°20'	N	134°13'	E	4029	Lower Miocene	C/S
V20-163	17°12'	S	88°41'	E	2706		C
V20-205	25°27'	S	06°28'	E	1626		C
V20-219	29°02'	S	29°13'	W	3092		C
V21-16	22°43'	N	84°24'	W	2078	Lower Miocene	C/S

TABLE 5—(*Continued*)

Core number	Position					Depth in meters	Remarks	
	Latitude		Longitude					
V21-34	05°22′	S	93°22′	W		3081	Middle Miocene	C
V21-45	07°08′	S	119°54′	W		4199		C
V21-46	08°06′	S	122°22′	W		4136		C
V21-48	09°31′	S	126°22′	W		3922		C
V21-49	10°29′	S	129°08′	W		4160	Pliocene-lower Miocene	C
V21-53	17°39′	S	136°43′	W		3391		C
V21-54	18°58′	S	137°36′	W		4071		C
V21-196	09°48′	N	136°11′	W		4819	Lower Miocene	C
V21-197	08°38′	N	130°11′	W		4890	Upper Miocene	S
V21-198	08°00′	N	126°49′	W		4631	Lower Miocene	C
V21-199	06°46′	N	122°57′	W		4508	Middle Miocene	C
V21-243	24°21′	N	73°01′	W		2564	Lower Miocene	C
V22-4	30°19′	N	74°35′	W		4303		C
V22-10	24°43′	N	73°46′	W		5130	Lower Miocene	C
V22-RD10	16°03′	S	05°50′	W		2310–2096		C
V22-23	14°55′	N	48°03′	W		2845	Miocene-Pliocene	C
V22-58	28°37′	S	29°08′	W		3442		C
V22-63	28°58′	S	29°26.5′	W		2722		C
V22-65	28°34′	S	30°34′	W		2339		C
V22-67	28°34′	S	30°34′	W		2361		C
V22-68	28°34′	S	30°34′	W		2274		C
V22-70	28°46.5′	S	32°38′	W		2750		C
V22-71	29°35′	S	33°25′	W		3314		C
V22-94	51°31′	S	43°30′	W		2164	Miocene?	C
V22-106	46°08′	S	10°54′	W		3037	Miocene-Pliocene	C
V22-121	39°38′	S	24°35′	E		3592		C
V22-122	39°35′	S	24°35′	E		3272		C
V22-123	39°32′	S	24°50′	E		2961	Lower Miocene	C
V22-130	40°08′	S	25°42′	E		2428		C
V22-131	40°00′	S	25°02′	E		2801		C
V22-135	38°05′	S	21°21′	E		5115	Miocene?	C
V22-142	33°15′	S	01°55′	E		4502+		C
V22-146	32°21′	S	02°10′	E		2177		C
V22-153	31°15′	S	02°31′	E		1721		C
V22-155	31°12′	S	02°46′	E		1618		C
V22-159	28°43′	S	01°55′	E		3471		C
V22-172	12°40′	S	09°49′	W		4127		C
V22-178	05°01′	S	15°39′	W		3290	Upper Miocene	C
V22-181	02°21′	S	16°54′	W		4012–4438		C
V22-190	06°02′	N	21°16′	W		3491		C
V22-203	15°02′	N	23°05′	W		2219	Upper Miocene	C
V22-204	15°01′	N	23°14′	W		1723	Upper Miocene	C
V22-206	16°25′	N	24°05′	W		1240	Middle Miocene	C
V22-219	27°55′	N	43°38′	W		2582	Upper Miocene	C
V22-227	30°23′	N	47°14′	W		3860	Upper Miocene	C
V23-14	43°24′	N	45°15′	W		3177		C
V23-91	29°35′	N	28°34′	W		2758**		C
V23-114	17°13′	N	49°56′	W		4177	Upper Miocene	C
V23-129	17°24′	N	58°17′	W		4870	Upper Miocene	C
V24-6	24°58′	N	71°06′	W		5524		C
V24-52	01°49′	N	127°00′	W		4480		C/S
V24-63A	03°27′	N	155°32′	W		4711		C/S
V24-81	11°51′	N	169°41′	E		5137	Miocene?	C
V24-82	14°08′	N	166°48′	E		5587		C
V24-164	13°52′	S	148°58′	E		4526	Lower Miocene	C
V24-178	14°06′	S	148°50′	E		3997	Lower Miocene	C
V24-201	30°55′	S	58°10′	E		2917		C
V24-207	36°18′	S	46°13′	E		3449		C
V25-20	26°29′	N	45°23′	W		3594		C
V25-53	00°30.9′	S	39°16.7′	W		2425		C
V25-54	01°25.2′	S	37°22.7′	W		3056		C
V25-55	01°53.6′	S	37°09.4′	W		2012		C
V25-62	03°25′	N	39°41.4′	W		4321		C
V26-68	30°21.3′	S	15°48′	W		3233	Lower Pliocene-upper Miocene?	C
V27-38	61°22.2′	N	11°29.7′	W		1317	Lower Miocene	C

* Approximate
** Water depth at time corer was lowered

TABLE 6. PLIOCENE CORES

Core Number	Position Latitude		Longitude		Depth in meters	Remarks	
A150-24	29°02′	N	51°02′	W	5009		C
A153-144	33°08′	N	48°08′	W	4850		C
A153-CC163	14°42′	N	49°33′	W	4000	Miocene-Pliocene or Neogene	C
A156-1	28°35.5′	N	77°10′	W	1005	Neogene (Pliocene)	C
A156-10	39°25′	N	71°53′	W	1400	Upper Pliocene or lowest Pleistocene	C
A158-1	38°12′	N	70°40′	W	3390	Upper Pliocene-lower Pleistocene	C
A164-2	38°27.5′	N	70°59′	W	3475		C
A164-8	37°56′	N	70°44′	W	3823	Upper Miocene, possibly lower Pleistocene (Pliocene)	C
A167-28	28°42′	N	76°46′	W	1262	Pliocene?	C
A167-29	28°26.5′	N	76°40′	W	1728	Miocene-Pliocene	C
A167-41	25°39′	N	76°56′	W	3109	Miocene-Pliocene	C
A167-43	25°27′	N	77°03.5′	W	2578	Miocene-Pliocene	C
A167-44	25°39.5′	N	77°21′	W	2487	Miocene-Pliocene	C
A167-49	24°36′	N	77°34′	W	1737	Upper Pliocene-lower Pleistocene	C
A179-11	23°56.5′	N	75°25′	W	2177		C
A180-32	29°07′	N	26°15′	W	5079		C
A180-35	28°56.5′	N	25°45′	W	5029	Pliocene-Miocene?	C
A180-107	19°39′	S	36°04′	W	4023		C
A180-113	20°36.5′	S	34°32′	W	2651		C
A185-7	21°07′	N	72°51.5′	W	2469		C
A185-61	37°17′	N	72°15′	W	3502		C
C10-3	33°39.4′	N	62°26.7′	W	2840		C
C10-13	38°33′	N	70°56′	W	3570		C
C25-5	32°43.3′	N	61°34.5′	W	1710	Miocene-Pliocene-Oligocene?	C
E5-14	61°07′	S	67°52′	W	2145		S
E6-6	57°10′	S	58°50′	W	1995		S
E6-11	55°44′	S	56°03′	W	2140		S
E7-3	55°03′	S	44°40′	W	1910		S
E7-10	63°15′	S	44°56.5′	W	2078		S
E8-18	58°31′	S	22°24′	W	2450		S
E10-29	58°08.4′	S	79°08.1′	W	5081		S
E10-30	56°58.1′	S	78°52.7′	W	4620		S
E10-32	58°18.4′	S	78°39.9′	W	4238		S
E11-5	58°56.6	S	114°43.2′	W	5180		S
E11-6	59°53.8′	S	114°56′	W	5189		S
E11-8	61°56.7′	S	115°09.5′	W	5150		S
E11-9	62°45′	S	115°04′	W	5130		S
E11-11	64°50.6′	S	114°20.3′	W	4969		S
E13-3	57°06.3′	S	89°29′	W	5225		S
E13-6	59°35.8′	S	89°23.1′	W	4463		S
E13-7	61°13.9′	S	89°41.3′	W	4898		S
E13-8	61°50.2′	S	90°08.2′	W	48.6		S
E13-17	65°41′	S	124°06.3′	W	4821	Pliocene-Miocene	S
E14-7	58°03.1′	S	160°09′	W	4238		S
E14-8	59°40′	S	160°17.4′	W	3943	Pliocene-Miocene	S
E14-9	60°47.1′	S	160°12.8′	W	3236		S
E14-13	30°01.9′	S	145°16.9′	W	3459		S
E15-1	61°58′	S	95°00′	W	4898		S
E15-7	61°03′	S	99°58′	W	5130		S
E15-8	61°04′	S	104°58′	W	4971		S
E15-11	60°07′	S	109°55′	W	4971		S
E15-13	57°50′	S	108°39′	W	4936		S
E15-28	56°01′	S	149°49′	W	3367		S
E17-27	64°00′	S	95°00′	W	4834		S
E17-28	63°00′	S	95°00′	W	4947		S
E17-29	62°00′	S	95°00′	W	4997		S
E18-4	58°01′	S	99°19′	W	4882		S
E19-7	62°05′	S	109°25′	W	5172		S
E19-8	61°03′	S	109°39′	W	5147		S
E20-6	58°05′	S	144°57′	W	3153		S

TABLE 6—(*Continued*)

Core number	Position				Depth in meters	Remarks	
	Latitude		Longitude				
E20-11	57°14′	S	104°30′	W	4459		S
E23-2	62°22′	S	95°32′	W	5021		S
E23-3	61°29′	S	95°58′	W	4551		S
E23-4	60°30′	S	95°05′	W	5033		S
E23-5	62°27′	S	101°30′	W	4936		S
E23-15	64°03′	S	115°51′	W	4975		S
E27-22	64°58.2′	S	160°37.4′	E	2970		S
R9-3	44°33.2′	N	47°33.1′	W	3658		C
RC3-2	31°26′	N	66°20.5′	W	4762		C
RC7-RD1	17°38′	N	65°28.5′	W	1606		C
RC8-15	19°20.5′	S	20°32′	W	4707		C
RC8-17	23°50′	S	15°35.5′	W	4235		C
RC8-20	24°30.5′	S	14°12.5′	W	3446		C
RC8-41	43°38′	S	51°16′	E	2540		C
RC8-49	51°04′	S	81°33′	E	3908		C
RC8-93	29°22′	S	105°14′	W	3157		C
RC8-94	27°17′	S	102°05′	W	3074		C
RC8-96	19°45′	S	95°37′	W	3334		C
RC9-77	17°5918′	S	79°09′	W	2908		C
RC9-96	22°47′	S	110°58.7′	W	3577		C
RC9-97	23°29.6′	S	112°46.4′	W	3394		C
RC9-99	24°35.9′	S	115°27.2′	W	2569–2681		C
RC9-102	26°23.1′	S	119°56.4′	W	3294–3442		C
RC9-217	44°30.5′	N	15°27.7′	W	5266	Pliocene?	C
RC10-11	25°31.5′	N	55°14.5′	W	4923		C
RC10-75	06°50′	N	110°28′	W	2696		C/S
RC10-76	06°38.5′	N	110°56.6′	W	4316	Pliocene?	C/S
RC10-77	07°14.7′	N	111°21.3′	W	4136		C
RC10-94	05°39.6′	N	127°20′	W	4356		C/S
RC10-95	03°30.6′	N	129°43.2	W	4471		C/S
RC10-97	00°55′	S	134°18.6′	W	4305		C/S
RC10-98	02°52.7′	S	136°47.4′	W	4308		C/S
RC10-100	03°35.2′	N	140°48′	W	4296		C/S
RC10-109	17°15.3′	S	152°53.2′	W	4438		C
RC10-114	11°11′	S	162°55′	W	2791		C
RC10-116	08°42′	S	164°20′	W	4916	Miocene-Pliocene	C/S
RC10-117	06°49′	S	165°22′	W	3523		C/S
RC10-118	03°46.5′	S	166°57′	W	5497		S
RC10-119	00°30.5′	S	168°46.5′	W	5447		S
RC10-161	33°05′	N	158°00′	E	3587		C/S
RC10-172	32°08′	N	154°37.5′	E	4387		C
RC10-203	41°42′	N	171°57′	W	5883	Pliocene?	S
RC10-205	44°37′	N	170°03′	W	6081	Pliocene?	S
RC10-210	50°48′	N	172°38′	W	7284	Pliocene?	S
RC10-260	19°27′	N	89°10.3′	W	1545	Lower Pliocene?	C
RC10-262	23°26.1′	N	86°17.5′	W	1787	Lower Pliocene?	C
RC10-274	24°26.8′	N	74°14.2′	W	5231		C
RC11-33	30°58′	S	31°36.5′	W	3252	Lower Pliocene	C
RC11-72	48°51′	S	30°52′	W	5561		S
RC11-90	56°38′	S	25°43′	E	5334		S
RC11-101	44°04′	S	59°50′	E	4806		S
RC11-102	43°42′	S	58°48′	E	4709		S
RC11-105	38°47′	S	58°50′	E	5256*	Miocene-Pliocene	S
RC11-125	33°38′	S	91°56′	E	4305		C
RC11-127	30°58′	S	94°16′	E	1393		C
RC11-208	05°21′	N	139°58′	W	4720		C/S
RC11-209	03°39′	N	140°04′	W	4400		C/S
RC11-213	06°08′	S	140°51′	W	4343		C/S
RC11-220	14°49′	S	139°58′	W	2950		C
RC11-224	03°32′	S	122°05.5′	W	4319		C/S
RC11-227	05°59′	S	114°37′	W	4158		C/S
RC11-234	13°19′	S	100°57′	W	3645		C
RC11-235	11°36′	S	95°38′	W	3702		C
RC11-237	01°32.2′	S	85°48.8′	W	2776		S
RC12-43	20°59.5′	N	111°59′	W	3336		C/S
RC12-84	02°20′	N	165°12′	W	5365		C/S
RC12-85	00°39.2′	N	164°52′	W	5106		C/S

TABLE 6—(*Continued*)

Core number	Latitude		Longitude		Depth in meters	Remarks	
RC12-88	04°33.3'	S	163°17'	W	4839		C/S
RC12-90	12°58.3'	S	161°13.7'	W	2860		C
RC12-91	13°30.7'	S	161°36.8'	W	2959		C
RC12-92	13°39'	S	161°37'	W	3281		C
RC12-121	03°44'	S	168°23'	E	3519	Upper Pliocene	C
RC12-122	01°16'	S	166°43'	E	4250	Upper Pliocene	C/S
RC12-123	01°37.9'	N	164°49.4'	E	4285	Upper Pliocene	C/S
RC12-124	01°36.4'	N	163°19.5'	W	4424		C/S
RC12-143	29°45.8'	N	133°16.6'	E	2350	Lower Pliocene	C/S
RC12-173	20°47'	N	157°55.5'	W	1176		C
RC12-241	43°38'	S	57°39.5'	W	3499		C/S
RC12-327	01°44'	N	57°50'	E	4446		C/S
RC12-328	03°57'	N	60°36'	E	3087		C/S
RC12-329	02°59'	N	65°12'	E	3864		C/S
RC12-377	37°35'	N	132°15'	E	2226		S
RC12-378	36°57'	N	134°32.5'	E	1401		S
RC12-380	37°15'	N	135°12.5'	E	1622		S
RC12-384	39°59.5'	N	133°16.8'	E	2677		S
RC13-64	00°09.5'	S	152°53'	W	4766		C/S
RC13-65	01°54.1'	S	152°51'	W	48887		C/S
RC13-77	18°54.9'	S	137°12.6'	W	3005		C
RC13-78	19°00.7'	S	134°11.5'	W	2725		C
RC13-83	19°01.6'	S	117°33.3'	W	3418		C
RC13-85	17°08.7'	S	111°16.2'	W	3349		C
SP8-13	32°44'	N	46°48.5'	W	4480		C
V3-37	27°26.5'	N	85°31'	W	2372		C
V3-130	23°11.8'	N	90°19'	W	1803		C
V3-139	24°12'	N	83°39'	W	1103		C
V4-15	35°11'	N	15°20.5'	W	2439	Miocene-Pliocene	C
V4-19	35°11'	N	15°12'	W	3006	Miocene-Pliocene	C
V4-20	35°07.5'	N	13°04'	W	1770	Neogene, probably Pliocene	C
V5-2	32°29'	N	65°00'	W	2361	Pliocene or Miocene	C
V5-31	32°17.2	N	65°07.2'	W	1597	Neogene, probably Pliocene	C
V9-2	01°45.9'	S	35°38.7'	W	3115**		C
V9-32	14°10.5'	N	45°43.7'	W	3623**		C
V10-89	23°01.5'	N	43°48'	W	3523	Pleistocene-Pliocene	C
V10-91	23°23'	N	46°24'	W	3540		C
V10-94	24°56'	N	48°59'	W	4372		C
V10-98	31°25.5'	N	64°10.5'	W	4299		C
V12-2	32°54.9'	N	64°22.2'	W	4376		C
V12-3	31°57.4'	N	64°03.2'	W	4616		C
V12-4	24°16.9'	N	53°04.1'	W	5009		C
V12-5	21°12'	N	45°21'	W	3003		C
V12-18	28°41.7'	S	34°29.6'	W	4021		C
V14-4	15°29'	N	40°31'	W	4473		C
V15-137	50°23.2'	S	47°24'	W	2681		S
V15-164	09°45'	S	32°24'	W	3588	Neogene, probably Pliocene	C
V15-198	25°19.5'	N	77°09.5'	W	2545		C
V15-205	29°05'	N	76°51'	W	1580		C
V16-14	31°57.5'	N	65°12.8'	W	57	Probably Pliocene	C
V16-19	19°04'	N	53°46.5'	W	4815**		C
V16-20	17°56'	N	50°21'	W	4539		C
V16-21	17°16.5'	N	48°25'	W	3975		C
V16-23	13°15'	N	40°40'	W	4886		C
V16-35	17°39.5'	S	15°46'	W	3891		C
V16-37	21°20'	S	08°57'	W	3908		C
V16-38	22°59'	S	06°06'	W	4925		C
V16-40	26°16'	S	03°01'	W	4740		C
V16-66	42°39'	S	45°40'	E	2985		C/S
V16-70	32°06'	S	55°51'	E	4649		C
V16-84	2°44.5'	S	79°34'	E	3938	Probably Pliocene	C
V16-95	28°01'	S	95°11'	E	4071	Probably Pliocene-Miocene	C
V16-117	53°24'	S	153°59'	E	3992		S

TABLE 6—(*Continued*)

Core number	Position Latitude		Longitude		Depth in meters	Remarks	
V16-137	58°53′	S	71°57′	W	4045		S
V16-187	31°28′	S	40°05′	W	3643		C
V16-197	15°56′	S	35°17′	W	4078		C
V16-205	15°24′	N	43°24′	W	4043		C
V16-208	27°44′	N	49°55′	W	4861		C
V17-8	25°20′	N	84°31′	W	978		C
V17-9	24°33′	N	86°51′	W	1966		C
V17-10	23°03.5′	N	90°46′	W	2244		C
V17-38	18°32′	N	81°31′	W	3803		C
V17-124	48°34′	S	36°04′	W	5176		S
V17-125	50°15′	S	35°53′	W	4689		S
V17-162	24°58′	N	28°56′	W	5480		C
V17-166	34°56′	N	45°21′	W	4210		C
V18-5	27°08′	N	68°03′	W	5174		C
V18-8	18°37.5′	N	63°54.5′	W	2935	Miocene-Pliocene?	C
V18-38	36°35′	S	50°42′	W	4319		C
V18-71	59°30′	S	78°36′	W	5008		S
V18-113	51°00′	S	49°08′	W	2747		S
V18-192	31°12′	S	48°05′	E	4396	Pliocene with Eocene	C
V18-201	21°02′	S	65°56′	E	3654	Pliocene?	C
V18-203	22°23′	S	74°22′	E	4014		C
V18-272	12°47′	S	161°03.5′	W	3160		C
V18-312	02°51′	S	126°12′	W	4614		S
V18-313	02°05.5′	S	124°37′	W	4555		S
V18-316	01°03′	N	120°46′	W	4429		C/S
V18-318	03°10′	N	118°27.5′	W	4191		C/S
V18-320	05°20′	N	115°24′	W	4091	Pliocene?	C/S
V18-322	07°12′	N	111°25′	W	3882		C/S
V18-324	08°46′	N	107°09′	W	3517		C/S
V18-325	09°24′	N	105°54′	W	3206		C/S
V18-350	05°41.5′	N	85°16′	W	1838		C
V18-370	34°27′	N	65°17′	W	4876		C
V19-7	27°28′	N	68°27′	W	5362		C
V19-24	03°12′	N	80°08′	W	1712		C
V19-37	12°16′	S	84°13′	W	4368	Pliocene?	C
V19-40	13°13′	S	92°53′	W	3693		C
V19-41	14°06′	S	96°12′	W	3248		C
V19-44	17°01′	S	108°52′	W	3621		C
V19-45	17°01′	S	110°23′	W	3446		C
V19-46	17°00′	S	110°51′	W	3484		C
V19-47	17°00′	S	111°12′	W	3422		C
V19-59	16°58′	S	115°33′	W	3309		C
V19-61	16°57′	S	116°18′	W	3422		C
V19-63	16°59′	S	117°53′	W	3446		C
V19-65	16°39′	S	124°23′	W	3867		C
V19-88	11°06′	S	174°53′	W	4497		C
V19-96	00°52′	S	172°00′	E	4252		C/S
V19-98	02°22′	N	168°02′	E	4396		C/S
V19-110	11°51′	N	140°03′	E	3532		C
V19-169	10°13′	S	81°37′	E	5110		S
V19-170	07°54′	S	81°25′	E	5218		S
V19-171	07°04′	S	80°46′	E	5053		S
V19-300	06°53′	N	19°28′	W	4263		C
V19-302	10°15′	N	25°22′	W	5583		C
V19-307	26°22′	N	38°50′	W	4715		C
V20-2	18°55′	N	66°04′	W	2902		C
V20-20	07°44′	N	101°21′	W	3288		C
V20-25	06°21′	N	105°59.5′	W	3753	Upper Miocene-Pliocene	C
V20-27	06°28′	N	111°45′	W	4076	Pliocene?	C
V20-28	07°33′	N	114°29′	W	3946	Lower Pliocene	C
V20-30	08°28′	N	118°29′	W	4069		C
V20-168	21°21′	S	71°14′	E	3957		C
V20-192	22°45′	S	41°24′	E	3587		C
V20-200	34°36′	S	28°06′	E	4023		C
V20-207	22°06′	S	00°19′	E	5349		C
V20-238	16°28′	N	36°19′	W	5233		C
V20-241	22°08′	N	41°30′	W	4372		C

TABLE 6—(*Continued*)

Core number	Position				Depth in meters	Remarks	
	Latitude		Longitude				
V20-242	23°22′	N	43°39′	W	4565?		C
V20-251	36°45′	N	65°50′	W	4903		C
V21-35	07°31′	S	95°19′	W	3939		C
V21-43	04°57′	S	114°01′	W	4164		C/S
V21-44	06°10′	S	116°58.5′	W	4535		S
V21-98	23°06′	N	134°26′	E	2135		C
V21-121	14°46′	N	134°22′	E	3521**		C
V21-148	42°05′	N	160°35′	E	5477		S
V21-200	06°31′	N	119°31′	W	3913		C/S
V21-201	05°45′	N	116°45′	W	4232		C/S
V22-11	24°43′	N	73°46′	W	5130		C
V22-23	14°55′	N	48°03′	W	2845	Miocene-Pliocene	C
V22-24	12°45′	N	45°38′	W	4321		C
V22-38	09°33′	S	34°15′	W	3797		C
V22-53	28°32′	S	29°00′	W	3607		C
V22-60	28°42′	S	29°09.5′	W	3469		C
V22-61	28°41′	S	29°08′	W	3493		C
V22-62	29°11′	S	29°16′	W	3043		C
V22-69	28°46.5′	S	32°38′	W	2801		C
V22-72	29°18′	S	34°42′	W	3120		C
V22-85	39°45′	S	49°40′	W	5411	Pliocene?	C
V22-88	45°04′	S	40°20′	W	4980		C
V22-106	46°08′	S	10°54′	W	3037	Miocene-Pliocene	C
V22-128	40°29′	S	26°45′	E	2487		C
V22-144	32°16′	S	01°39′	E	1357		C
V22-152	31°37′	S	00°58′	E	4319		C
V22-154	31°17′	S	02°32′	E	1796		C
V22-158	28°52′	S	01°55′	E	3499		C
V22-160	28°56′	S	02°13′	E	3147		C
V22-163	26°22′	S	00°56′	S	4442		C
V22-167	18°43′	S	03°54′	W	6020	Pliocene?	C
V22-170	14°38′	S	07°34′	W	4131		C
V22-171	13°06′	S	09°20′	W	4155		C
V22-184	00°21′	N	17°31′	W	1712		C
V22-185	02°34′	N	19°14′	W	4587		C
V22-189	04°56′	N	21°07′	W	2525		C
V22-209	19°01.5′	N	29°09′	W	4735		C
V22-211	20°42′	N	31°27′	W	4402		C
V22-230	32°39′	N	52°18′	W	5048		C
V23-103	17°42′	N	29°52′	W	4645?		C
V23-104	17°13′	N	32°21′	W	4953		C
V23-105	17°12′	N	35°50′	W	5009		C
V23-108	17°24′	N	43°14′	W	4367*	Lower Pliocene	C
V23-110	17°38′	N	45°52′	W	3746		C
V23-113	17°16′	N	47°21.5′	W	4142		C
V23-139	29°01′	N	64°22′	W	4510		C
V24-53	01°51′	N	129°01′	W	4473	Pliocene?	C/S
V24-55	02°03′	N	134°38′	W	4189		C/S
V24-58	02°16′	N	141°40′	W	4490		C/S
V24-59	02°34′	N	145°32′	W	4662		C/S
V24-60	02°48′	N	149°00′	W	4859		C/S
V24-61	02°51′	N	150°10′	W	4484		C/S
V24-62	03°04′	N	153°35′	W	4834		C/S
V24-63	03°45′	N	157°07′	W	4495		C/S
V24-104	04°51′	N	170°55′	E	4501		C/S
V24-105	02°49′	N	168°11′	E	4409	Lower Pliocene	C/S
V24-107	02°04′	N	165°19′	E	4160		C/S
V24-108	01°13′	N	162°12′	E	4113		C/S
V24-111	05°38′	N	155°00′	E	4041		C/S
V24-117	18°36′	N	142°22′	E	3706		C
V24-152	03°18′	S	153°32′	E	2410		C
V24-186	10°53′	S	122°02′	E	1252		C
V24-187	11°43′	S	120°12′	E	4266		C
V24-236	32°42′	S	24°05′	W	4089	Upper Pliocene	C
V24-238	31°47′	S	29°00′	W	3585	Lower Pliocene	C
V24-240	31°44′	S	28°12′	W	4327	Upper Pliocene	C
V25-9	27°40′	N	50°15′	W	4773		C

TABLE 6—(*Continued*)

Core number	Position				Depth in meters	Remarks	
	Latitude		Longitude				
V25-12	26°55'	N	47°00'	W	4387		C
V25-17	23°35'	N	46°16'	W	3983		C
V25-23	26°24.5'	N	45°21'	W	3504		C
V25-25	26°33'	N	44°47'	W	2479		C
V25-46	09°19'	N	42°29.6'	W	4310		C
V25-73	08°39'	N	53°09'	W	4133	Pliocene?	C
V26-11	30°21.2'	N	48°36'	W	4680		C
V26-12	29°53.9'	N	45°06.9'	W	3244		C
V26-13	29°53.9'	N	45°06.9'	W	3244	Lower Pliocene (TW)	C
V26-14	29°41.7'	N	45°11'	W	2604	Lower Pliocene	C
V26-15	30°23.8'	N	44°54'	W	3869		C
V26-20	27°03.6'	N	40°38.6'	W	4519		C
V26-24	26°28'	N	40°29.1'	W	4213		C
V26-40	19°40.1'	N	26°07.3'	W	4530		C
V26-60	28°33.2'	S	30°33.4'	W	2593		C
V26-68	30°21.3'	S	15°48'	W	3223	Lower Pliocene- Upper Miocene	C
V26-74	28°36.3'	S	20°41.2'	W	4513	Upper Pliocene	C
V26-77	28°19.1'	S	20°54.4'	W	4308		C
V26-78	27°33.5'	S	22°07.7'	W	4336	Pliocene?	C
V26-84	30°11.5'	S	35°01.4'	W	1897	Middle upper Pliocene	C
V26-128	20°27'	N	83°22'	W	3878		C

* Approximate
** Water depth at time corer was lowered

PHYSICAL CHEMISTRY OF CARBONATES IN THE OCEANS

ROBERT A. BERNER

Yale University, New Haven, Connecticut

ABSTRACT

A large proportion of deep sea water is undersaturated with respect to both calcite and aragonite. This conclusion is based upon laboratory studies of the effects of temperature and pressure on carbonate equilibria in sea water combined with shipboard measurements of water properties as well as upon actual measurements of dissolution rates of calcium carbonate samples held at various depths. Undersaturation is caused by biological production of CO_2 at shallower depths and by the effect of increased pressure on the solubility of $CaCO_3$ at greater depths. The so-called compensation depth below which $CaCO_3$ disappears from deep sea sediments does not simply represent a downward change from supersaturated to undersaturated water. This is proven by the presence of undersaturated water above the compensation depth and by the fact that the compensation depth may be located thousands of meters below depths where $CaCO_3$ shows definite signs of dissolution.

About 1000 metres above the compensation depth, the rate of dissolution shows an abrupt downward increase. This zone, called the lysocline, has been predicted from laboratory measurements of dissolution rate as a function of the degree of undersaturation of sea water. The sudden rate increase can be explained by a change in the mechanism of dissolution at the surface of calcite. Dissolution at all depths is too slow to be controlled by transport of material from particle surfaces by either diffusion, turbulence, or changes in water velocity. This is due to the inhibiting effects of ions and/or organic molecules adsorbed onto the carbonate surfaces from the surrounding sea water.

Surface sea water, in contrast to deep water, is generally supersaturated with respect to both calcite and aragonite. However, inorganic precipitation rarely occurs due to the inhibiting effects of Mg^{++}, phosphate, organic matter and possibly other substances both as dissolved species and as adsorbed coatings on mineral grains.

INTRODUCTION

Before one can undertake meaningful speculation on the chemical history of the oceans and their associated sediments, it is necessary to have a reasonable understanding of the processes occurring in the present ocean and the physical and chemical laws governing these processes. A good case in point is the dissolution and precipitation of calcium carbonate. Carbonate sediments are found in great abundance beneath the ocean floors and on the continents. A complete understanding of the processes whereby these sediments are formed entails knowledge of ecology and biochemistry, as they relate to the secretion of shells and tests and to subsequent dissolution by biogenically produced CO_2; physical oceanography, as it relates to the circulation of nutrients, transport of shells, and movements of undersaturated and supersaturated water masses; and physical chemistry as it relates to the actual processes of dissolution and (inorganic) precipitation. The purpose of this paper is to briefly outline the third topic, i.e. the physical chemistry of calcium carbonate in sea water. In this way speculations regarding the geologic past may be held accountable to physicochemical observations of the present.

STATE OF SATURATION OF SEA WATER WITH RESPECT TO CALCIUM CARBONATE

Direct methods.—The direct approach to the problem of determining whether a sample of sea water is saturated, undersaturated, or supersaturated with respect to a given carbonate mineral involves suspension of the carbonate mineral in the sea water sample in situ, using a ship, buoy, or a deep diving submersible vessel. Evidence for the state of saturation is then obtained by observing whether the sample goes into solution or whether $CaCO_3$ is precipitated upon it. The evidence may consist of a change in weight of the sample, a change in pH of the water in contact with the sample, or by a change in the radioactivity of a sample whose surface has been previously tagged with C^{14} tracer. An example of the first method is given by the work of Peterson (1966) and Berger (1967; 1970) who determined rates of dissolution in the North Pacific by measuring the loss in weight, respectively, of polished spheres of calcite and pelagic foraminiferal tests which were suspended at various depths for four months on a taut wire buoy anchored to the bottom.

Ben-Yaakov and Kaplan (1971) have adapted

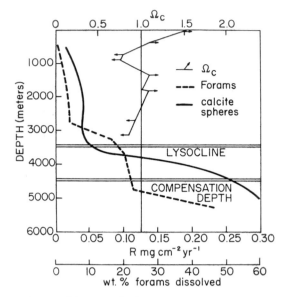

Fig. 1.—Direct methods of determining the relative saturation state of $CaCO_3$ in the ocean. Ω_c = degree of saturation with respect to calcite determined by in situ saturometry (Ben-Yaakov and Kaplan, 1971), R = rate of dissolution of calcite spheres (Peterson, 1966). Foraminiferal dissolution values for 4 months exposure in situ (Berger, 1967). All data for the Pacific Ocean at 20–30°N; Peterson and Berger data for 170°W; Ben-Yaakov and Kaplan data for 120°W. The arrows on the Ω_c curve denote directions which points should move to reach equilibrium. Lysocline and compensation depth from Berger (1970).

the carbonate saturometer of Weyl (1961) so that it can be used at great depths in the ocean. The principle behind the saturometer is that $CaCO_3$ dissolution or precipitation causes a rise or drop, respectively, in pH as can be seen by the following reaction:

$$H^+ + CaCO_3 \lessgtr Ca^{++} + HCO_3^-$$

In the saturometer, pH of a water sample is measured, the calcium carbonate sample added to the water, and then the pH measured until the water has reached equilibrium with the carbonate. By means of mass and charge balance and equilibria calculations the change in pH can be related to the degree of undersaturation or supersaturation. One problem, however, is that the dissolution and precipitation of $CaCO_3$ in sea water are very complicated processes (as will be pointed out later), and, as a result, it is very difficult to determine the pH at which the water becomes truly equilibrated with $CaCO_3$. Thus the carbonate saturometer method is best used as a qualitative or semi-quantitative tool for determining the state of saturation.

The radioactive tracer technique has not yet been applied successfully to the deep oceans,

but it has considerable promise as a qualitative method for checking the other methods (R. Horowitz, personal communication).

Indirect methods.—Indirect methods for determining the state of saturation consist basically of laboratory measurements of the solubility of $CaCO_3$ and the dissociation of H_2CO_3 in sea water at various temperatures, pressures and salinities combined with shipboard measurements of parameters from which the ion product for calcium carbonate:

$$IP = m_{Ca^{++}} m_{CO_3^{--}} \tag{1}$$

can be calculated. (The symbol m refers to molal concentrations of total ions, i.e. free ions plus ion pairs.) Then, if $IP > K'_{sp}$ (where K'_{sp} represents the equilibrium ion or solubility product for the P-T conditions under consideration), the water is supersaturated, and if $IP < K'_{sp}$, the water is undersaturated. The degree of saturation is represented by the symbol $\Omega = IP/K'_{sp}$ and only where $\Omega = 1$ is the water in equilibrium with calcium carbonate. The measurements from which IP is calculated are temperature, pressure (depth), salinity, and any two of the four parameters: pH, P_{CO_2}, A_c, and ΣCO_2. The symbol A_c represents the carbonate alkalinity, which is defined as:

$$A_c = m_{HCO_3^-} + 2m_{CO_3^{--}} \tag{2}$$

A_c is determined by titrating the carbonate and bicarbonate ions with strong acid. ΣCO_2 is the total dissolved carbonate defined as:

$$\Sigma CO_2 = m_{H_2CO_3} + m_{HCO_3^-} + m_{CO_3^-} \tag{3}$$

where H_2CO_3 refers to the sum of dissolved CO_2 along with true H_2CO_3. ΣCO_2 is determined indirectly by titration (Edmond and Gieskes, 1970) or directly by acidification and conversion of all species to gaseous CO_2 which is then measured. The parameter P_{CO_2} is the partial pressure of CO_2 gas in equilibrium with the sea water sample and is determined by a gas-liquid equilibration technique (Li and others, 1969). Values of pH are determined through the use of the glass electrode.

Once the proper measurements have been made, the value of IP is calculated as follows: the concentration of calcium $m_{Ca^{++}}$, is calculated from the salinity (with which it is directly related) and the value for $m_{CO_3^-}$ is calculated, by means of appropriate equilibrium expressions from the two chosen parameters. For example consider pH and A_c. The proper equation for CO_3^- is:

$$m_{CO_3^{--}} = \frac{A_c}{2 + \dfrac{a_{H^+}}{K_2'}} \tag{4}$$

where $a_{H^+} = 10^{-pH}$ and K_2' is the second dissociation constant of H_2CO_3 is sea water expressed as:

$$K_2' = \frac{a_{H^+}m_{CO_3^{--}}}{m_{HCO_3^-}} \qquad (5)$$

Values of K_2' are obtained from laboratory measurements for the same temperature, pressure, and salinity as the sea water sample. Corresponding to K_2' are:

$$K_1' = \frac{a_{H^+}m_{HCO_3^-}}{m_{H_2CO_2}} \qquad (6)$$

and

$$K_0' = \frac{m_{H_2CO_3}}{P_{CO_2}} \qquad (7)$$

In the laboratory K'_{sp}, K_0', K_1', and K_2' are usually determined by direct measurement at different temperatures, pressures, and salinities. A summary of direct measurements is presented by Edmond and Gieskes (1970). An additional technique, however, is available to check the measurements. This consists of determining the partial molal volume v' and partial molal enthalpy h' of Ca^{++}, HCO_3^-, CO_3^{--}, and H_2CO_3 in sea water (Millero, 1969; Millero and Berner, 1972) and calculating the effects of temperature and pressure on the equilibrium constants for a given salinity representative of most of the oceans. The thermodynamic expressions used for this are:

$$\left.\frac{d \log K'}{dP}\right|_T = \frac{-\Delta v'}{2.3RT} \qquad (8)$$

$$\left.\frac{d \log K'}{dT}\right|_P = \frac{\Delta h'}{2.3RT^2} \qquad (9)$$

where $\Delta v'$ and $\Delta h'$ refer to the change in partial molal volume and partial molal enthalpy respectively for the reaction to which K' corresponds. An earlier attempt in this direction, when direct measurements of K' at high pressures were not available, was made by Berner (1965). The advantage of this technique is that relatively few measurements need be made.

Results.—Results of both direct and indirect methods are shown in figures 1–3 for various profiles in the Atlantic and Pacific Oceans. Methods used are described in the figure captions. In a very broad sense all methods are in agreement with each other. Surface sea water is supersaturated with respect to calcite whereas deep sea water is undersaturated with respect to calcite and all other forms of $CaCO_3$ (since calcite is least soluble). Undersaturation is brought about by the biological production of CO_2 at shallow depths and by the increased solubility of $CaCO_3$ at great depths due to increased pressure. Disagreement arises about the depth where Ω drops below one. Most workers,

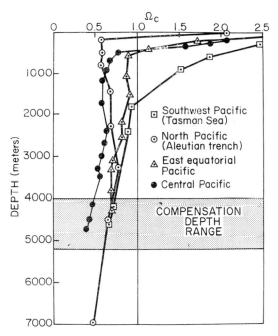

FIG. 2.—Plot of the degree of saturation with respect to calcite, Ω_c, versus depth for some representative stations from various parts of the Pacific Ocean. East equatorial Pacific data from Li and others (1969) corrected for subsequent determinations of equilibrium constants in deep sea water (Hawley and Pytkowicz, 1969). Southwest Pacific data from Edmond (1970). North Pacific data from Hawley and Pytkowicz (1969). Central Pacific data from Berner and Wilde (1972). Li and others measured P_{CO_2} and ΣCO_2, Edmond A_v and ΣCO_2, and Hawley and Pytkowicz and Berner and Wilde used measurements of pH and A_c. Range of compensation depth from Pytkowicz (1970).

however, are of the opinion that the "crossover" or saturation depth is distinctly shallower than the so-called compensation depth below which calcite, due to dissolution, disappears from the sediments or is reduced to a low constant value (e.g. see Pytkowicz, 1970). This is shown in Figures 1–3. (The compensation depth has also been defined as the depth where a sudden decrease in $CaCO_3$ content occurs due to dissolution. However, Heath and Culberson (1970) have pointed out that this "sudden decrease" is often an artifact due to the plotting of percent $CaCO_3$ rather than accumulation rate.)

If the saturation depth does not fall at the same point as the carbonate compensation depth, then considerable calcium carbonate in pelagic sediments must persist in the presence of undersaturated water. This indicates that above the compensation depth the dissolution process is slow relative to the rate of sedimentation

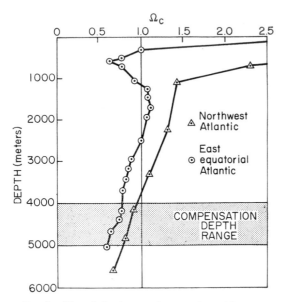

Fig. 3.—Plot of the degree of saturation with respect to calcite, Ω_c, versus depth for some representative stations in the Atlantic Ocean. East equatorial Atlantic data from Edmond (1970); Northwest Atlantic data from Li et al. (1969) corrected for subsequent determinations of equilibrium constants in deep sea water. Edmond measured A_c and ΣCO_2^- whereas Li and others measured P_{CO_2} and ΣCO_2. Range of compensation depth from Turekian (1964) and Edmond (1970).

Thus, explanation of the position of the compensation depth, where dissolution and sedimentation rates are equal, must include along with climatic, oceanographic, and biological factors, study of the dissolution kinetics of $CaCO_3$ in sea water and not simply depend on determinations of the state of saturation.

DISSOLUTION OF CaCO₃ IN SEA WATER

Direct measurements in the ocean.—As in the determination of the state of saturation, there are two basic approaches to studying the kinetics of the dissolution of $CaCO_3$ in sea water, the direct or in situ method and the indirect or laboratory method. Direct techniques using samples attached to moorings are illustrated by the work of Peterson (1966) and Berger (1967) alluded to earlier and to the more recent work of Berger (1970). In the latter paper Berger showed that in the central Pacific at a depth of about 2000 meters (which is 2500 meters above the compensation depth) dissolution of calcite can be delineated in the form of incipient etching and solution damage of less resistant foraminiferal tests, and dissolution of aragonite by the complete disappearance of pteropods. At a depth of about 3500 meters a sudden increase in the percentage of damaged specimens and decrease

in the weight of foraminiferal calcite occurs. To this zone of rapid increase in the rate of dissolution Berger has applied the term *lysocline* (see figure 1). Berger found that between the lysocline and the compensation depth all forms were attacked and most were completely dissolved during the four months exposure of the experiment. Peterson (1966) found that calcite spheres attached to the same mooring used by Berger also showed a lysocline or rapid increase in dissolution rate beginning at 3500–3800 meters.

The rates of dissolution measured by Peterson and Berger, although very useful in a qualitative sense for showing relative changes with depth, cannot be used quantitatively for calculating actual dissolution rates of $CaCO_3$ in the ocean if most dissolution takes place while the particles are resting on the bottom (Bramlette, 1961) and not while they are settling out. Barring resuspension, foram tests should settle out very rapidly requiring only a few days to reach the bottom (Langhus and others, 1970) which is insufficient time for appreciable dissolution. Coccoliths, which constitute an important calcitic component of some sediments, although extremely small, also can be sedimented relatively rapidly because they are often contained within much larger fecal pellets and aggregates (McIntyre and Bé, 1967). Also the organic matrices of the coccoliths serve as a coating material which protects them from dissolution during sedimentation (McIntyre and McIntyre, 1971).

Particles resting on the bottom should not dissolve at the same rate as particles suspended in the water column because of differences in chemistry between interstitial water and overlying water (e.g. see Morse, 1971). If the pore water of sediments with depth becomes saturated with $CaCO_3$, as is likely, and if the depositional rate is high enough, the particles may be buried and immersed in saturated pore water before they are completely dissolved. This would explain why foraminiferal tests are found at water depths where they should have disappeared if the rates obtained by Berger (1970) were applicable to dissolution on the bottom.

The data of Peterson (1966), although not applicable to bottom conditions, can be used to elucidate the mechanism by which calcite dissolves in undersaturated sea water, especially since spheres of calcite were used. The equation for the diffusion controlled dissolution of a sphere suspended in undersaturated solution is:

$$R = \frac{D(C_s - C_\infty)}{r} \qquad (10)$$

where

R = rate of dissolution per unit surface area
C_s = concentration of dissolved carbonate at the surface of the sphere assumed to be that in equilibrium with calcite
C_∞ = concentration of dissolved carbonate in the surrounding water
D = diffusion coefficient in sea water
r = radius of sphere

Using Peterson's rate data and sphere size and calculations of the degree of undersaturation of sea water at each depth in terms of ($C_s - C_\infty$) the writer (Berner, 1971) has shown that values of D calculated from equation (10) are all far less than 10^{-5} cm²/sec. This value is that expected for simple ionic diffusion in stagnant water. Since oceanic turbulence and water flow should cause dissolution to be faster than that predicted for ionic diffusion, the finding that D is less than 10^{-5} cm²/sec. must mean that dissolution rate is controlled by the detachment of ions from the calcite surface and not by the rate of transport away from the surface. Thus, the rate of dissolution of calcite suspended in sea water is not affected by changes in flow rate or turbulence.

Laboratory experiments.—If the rate of dissolution of CaCO₃ in sea water is controlled by reaction rates occurring at the surface of calcareous particles, then the nature of this surface must be an important factor. Terjesen and others (1961) have shown that various ions are capable of strongly inhibiting the dissolution of calcite even at concentrations as low as 10^{-7} molar. Thus, adsorption of inhibiting species (including organics) from sea water may be responsible for retarding dissolution. Because adsorption is a complex process, it also might be expected that rate of dissolution is not related in a simple manner to the degree of undersaturation such as shown by equation (10). Laboratory experiments (Morse and Berner, 1972) have shown this to be the case for both reagent grade calcite and natural deep sea carbonate sediments. If the degree of undersaturation is expressed in terms of ΔpH, which for sea water is given by:

$$\Delta pH = -1/2 \log \Omega$$

a sudden increase in rate of dissolution is found at a ΔpH of 0.14–0.16. This increase is independent of P_{CO_2}. Although there is no simple explanation for this sudden change in rate, it must be related somehow to the degree of blockage of dissolution sites on the crystal surface by adsorbed inhibiting ions. The rates determined in the laboratory before and after the sudden increase, as in Peterson's experiment, are far slower than predicted for ionic diffusion.

Origin of the lysocline.—Two principal hy-

potheses have been advanced to explain the presence of the lysocline. Edmond (1971) and Berger (1970) have suggested that the sudden increase in rate of dissolution is due to crossing of boundaries between water masses and that the deeper water mass (e.g. Antarctic Bottom Water) because of greater flow velocities and turbulence causes dissolution to be faster. For suspended particles, this hypothesis has already been shown to be untenable because CaCO₃ dissolves too slowly to be affected by the transport of dissolved material away from grain surfaces. It is more feasible if dissolution is dependent upon resuspension of sedimented particles which otherwise lie on the bottom in semi-saturated pore water. However, preliminary studies of

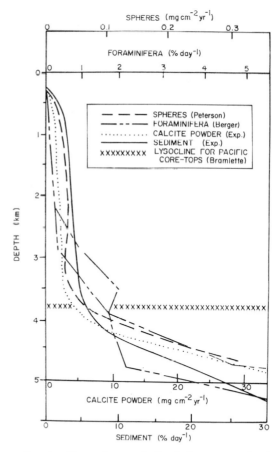

Fig. 4.—Plots of rate of dissolution versus depth showing the measurements of Peterson (1966) for calcite spheres and Berger (1967) for foraminifers, and the predictions of Morse and Berner (1972) based on laboratory rate experiments (using calcite powder and natural sediments) plus the saturation state values of Berner and Wilde (1972). All data are for the Pacific Ocean at 18°49′N; 160°31′W. The position of the lysocline is the average for the Pacific (after Morse and Berner, 1972).

Morse (1971) suggest that pore waters near the sediment-water interface are even more undersaturated than the overlying water.

An alternative hypothesis, advanced by Morse and Berner (1972) is that the lysocline represents the depth zone where a degree of undersaturation is reached which is equal to the value found in the laboratory for the onset of highly accelerated dissolution. In order to test this critical undersaturation hypothesis, values of Ω and ΔpH have been calculated (Berner and Wilde, 1972) for each depth where the dissolution experiments of Peterson (1966) and Berger (1967) were conducted. This was possible because pH and alkalinity data were available for subsurface water at this site. Upon combining the calculated values of ΔpH versus depth with the laboratory results of Morse and Berner (1972) for rate of dissolution versus ΔpH, predicted curves of rates of dissolution versus depth have been constructed. These are shown in figure 4 and compared with the empirical results of Peterson and Berger. Note the very good agreement. This shows that the critical undersaturation hypothesis can successfully predict the position of the lysocline (disagreement in absolute rate between our results and those of Peterson and Berger can be explained in terms of different particle sizes and different surface configurations and compositions). Thus, the origin of the lysocline can be attributed to changes in dissolution kinetics and surface chemistry, and an origin based solely on the hydrographic properties of sea water is not necessitated.

PRECIPITATION OF $CaCO_3$ FROM SEA WATER

All workers are in agreement that shallow sea water above about 100 meters is supersaturated with respect to calcite and usually aragonite. Values of Ω for calcite in surface waters of the open ocean range from about 1.5 to 5. Because of this supersaturation, one might expect to find ubiquitous inorganic $CaCO_3$ precipitation in shallow water regions of the ocean. However, there is little evidence for inorganic precipitation and at least 90% of the calcium carbonate in sediments is instead derived from the skeletal debris of calcareous organisms. Many areas of supposed inorganic precipitation, including the needle muds west of Andros Island in the Bahamas (e.g. Smith, 1940; Cloud, 1962), can be equally well explained in terms of biological processes, such as the secretion of aragonite needles by algae (Neumann and Land, 1968).

Why is there so little inorganic precipitation? The most reasonable explanation is similar to that given for inhibited dissolution. Dissolved organic molecules and inorganic ions interfere with the nucleation and growth of $CaCO_3$. This has been abundantly shown by laboratory experiments. For instance working with CO_2^- enriched seawater Pytkowicz (1965) has demonstrated that removal of Mg^{++} greatly increases the rate of nucleation of $CaCO_3$, and Chave and Suess (1970) have shown that as little as 3 ppm dissolved organic carbon has a pronounced retarding effect on the rate of precipitation (assuming that their results were actually caused by organic matter and not by associated dissolved phosphate). In addition Simkiss (1964) has shown that dissolved phosphate also acts to inhibit $CaCO_3$ precipitation from sea water. Seeding by suspended biogenic carbonate particles does not greatly aid the process because of adsorbed molecules and ions on the surfaces of the particles. Only where there is a high density of seeds is unequivocal evidence for inorganic precipitation found in the form of relatively rare occurrences of recent sub-tidal carbonate cements (see Mackenzie and others, 1969). Thus, shallow sea water is insufficiently supersaturated at the existing concentration level of dissolved Mg^{++}, phosphate, organic compounds, and possibly other species for appreciable inorganic $CaCO_3$ precipitation to occur.

CONCLUSIONS

In conclusion it can be stated with reasonable assurance that:

1. Surface sea water is supersaturated with respect to calcite and (except, perhaps in isolated polar regions) also supersaturated with respect to aragonite.

2. A large portion of the oceans, that below about 2500 meters, is undersaturated with respect to both aragonite and calcite.

3. The calcium carbonate compensation depth does not correspond to the depth where sea water becomes undersaturated. This is because dissolution is not instantaneous and the complete removal of calcareous tests requires considerable time.

4. Rapid change in the rate of dissolution with depth can be correlated with the attainment of a critical degree of undersaturation where a change occurs in the surface chemistry of $CaCO_3$ in sea water.

5. Rates of dissolution in the deep ocean are slower than that predicted for simple diffusion of Ca^{++} and HCO_3^- away from the dissolving particles.

6. Rates of precipitation in shallow water are much lower than that expected for the measured state of saturation.

7. The most probable cause for lowered rates of both dissolution and precipitation in sea water is that dissolved ions and/or organic compounds are readily adsorbed onto CaCO₃ which inhibits the processes of crystal dissolution, nucleation, and growth.

ACKNOWLEDGMENTS

This work was supported by a fellowship grant from the Alfred P. Sloan Foundation and N.S.F. Grants GA-1441 and GA-30288X. The writer acknowledges the helpful discussions and critical comments of J. Morse of Yale University.

REFERENCES

Ben-Yaakov, S., and Kaplan, I. R., 1971, Deep-sea *in situ* calcium carbonate saturometry; Jour. Geophys. Research, v. 76, p. 722–731.

Berger, W. H., 1967, Foraminiferal ooze: Solution at depths: Science, v. 156, p. 383–385.

———, 1970, Planktonic foraminifera: selective solution and the lysocline: Marine Geology, v. 8, p. 111–138.

Berner, R. A., 1965, Activity coefficients of bicarbonate, carbonate, and calcium ions in sea water: Geochimica et Cosmochimica Acta, v. 29, p. 947–965.

———, 1971, Principles of chemical sedimentology: New York, McGraw-Hill, 240 p.

———, and Wilde, P., 1972, Dissolution kinetics of CaCO₃ in sea water. I. Saturation state parameters for kinetic calculations: Am. Jour. Sci., v. 272, p. 826–839.

Bramlette, M. N., 1961, Pelagic sediments, *in* Sears, M., Oceanography: Am. Assoc. Adv. Sci. Pub. 67, p. 345–366.

Chave, K. S., and Suess, E., 1970, Calcium carbonate saturation in sea water: effects of dissolved organic matter: Limnology and Oceanography, v. 15, p. 633–637.

Cloud, P. E., 1962, Environment of calcium carbonate deposition west of Andros Island, Bahamas: U.S. Geol. Survey Prof. Paper 350, 138 p.

Edmond, J. M., 1970, The carbonic acid system in sea water (Ph.D. dissertation): San Diego, Univ. California, 174 p.

———, 1971, An interpretation of the calcite spheres experiment: Am. Geophys. Union, EOS Trans., v. 52, p. 256.

———, and Gieskes, J. M. T. M., 1970, On the calculation of the degree of saturation of sea water with respect to calcium carbonate under *in situ* conditions: Geochimica et Cosmochimica Acta, v. 34, p. 1261–1291.

Hawley, J., and Pytkowicz, R. M., 1969, Solubility of calcium carbonate in sea water at high pressures and 2°C: *ibid.*, v. 33, p. 1557–1561.

Heath, G. R., and Culberson, C., 1970, Calcite: Degree of saturation, rate of dissolution, and the compensation depth in the deep oceans: Geol. Soc. America Bull., v. 81, p. 3157–3160.

Langhus, B. G., Medioli, F. and Watkins, C., 1970, Foraminiferal tests as sedimentary particles: *ibid.*, Abs. with Programs, N. 2, p. 601.

Li, Y. H., Takahashi, T. and Broecker, W. S., 1969, Degree of saturation of CaCO₃ in the oceans: Jour. Geophys. Research, v. 74, p. 5507–5525.

McIntyre, A., and Be, A. W. H., 1967, Modern coccolithophoridae of the Atlantic Ocean. I. Placoliths and cyrtoliths: Deep-Sea Research, v. 14, p. 561–597.

———, and McIntyre, R., 1971, Coccolith concentrations and differential solution in oceanic sediments, *in* Funnell, B. M., and Riedel, W. R., (eds), The micropaleontology of oceans. Cambridge, England, Cambridge Univ. Press, p. 253–261.

Mackenzie, F. T., Ginsburg, R. N., Land, L. S., and Bricker, O. P., 1969, Carbonate cements: Bermuda Biol. Sta. for Research Special Pub. 3, 325 p.

Millero, F. J., 1969, The partial molal volumes of ions in sea water: Limnology and Oceanography, v. 14, p. 376–385.

———, and Berner, R. A., 1972, Effect of pressure on carbonate equilibria in sea water: Geochimica et Cosmochimica Acta, v. 36, p. 92–98.

Morse, J. W., 1971, pH and alkalinity gradients across the sediment-water interface in the eastern Atlantic and the implications for the deep-water carbonate system: Geol. Soc. America, Abs. with Programs, N. 3, p. 651–652.

———, and Berner, R. A., 1972, Dissolution kinetics of calcium carbonate in sea water. II. A kinetic origin for the lysocline: Am. Jour. Sci., v. 272, p. 840–851.

Neumann, A. C., and Land, L. S., 1968, Algal production and lime mud deposition in the Bight of Abaco: a budget: Geol. Soc. America, Abs. of Annual Meetings, p. 219.

Peterson, M. N. A., 1966, Calcite: Rates of dissolution in a vertical profile in the central Pacific: Science, v. 154, p. 1542–1544.

Pytkowicz, R. M., 1965, Rates of inorganic calcium carbonate precipitation: Jour. Geology, v. 73, p. 196–199.

———, 1970, On the carbonate compensation depth in the Pacific Ocean: Geochimica et Cosmochimica Acta, v. 34, p. 836–839.

Simkiss, K., 1964, The inhibitory effects of some metabolites on the precipitation of calcium carbonate from artificial and natural sea water: Jour. Cons., Cons. Perm. Int. Explor. Mer, v. 29, p. 6–18.

Smith, C. L., 1940, The Great Bahama Bank: II. Calcium carbonate precipitation: Jour. Marine Research, v. 3, p. 171–189.

Terjesen, S. G., Erga, O., Thorsen, G. and Ve, A., 1961, II Phase boundary processes as rate determining steps in reactions between solids and liquids: Chem. Eng. Sci., v. 74, p. 277–288.

Turekian, K. K., 1964, The geochemistry of the Atlantic Ocean basin: New York Acad. Sci. Trans., ser. 2, v. 26, p. 312–330.

Weyl, P. K., 1961, The carbonate saturometer: Jour. Geology, v. 69, p. 32–43.

CARBONATE DISSOLUTION ON THE WESTERN FLANK OF THE EAST PACIFIC RISE

WALLACE S. BROECKER AND SUZANNE BROECKER

Lamont-Doherty Geological Observatory, Palisades, New York

ABSTRACT

The study of a series of closely spaced radiometrically dated cores down the west flank of the East Pacific Rise at 17°S reveals a very sharp elevation boundary separating cores which show little evidence of dissolution effects from those which have lost more than 95% of their $CaCO_3$ to dissolution. This transition occurs over an interval of no more than 80 meters and lies at about 3950 meters depth. Cores from below this boundary have a $CaCO_3$-rich layer a few tens of centimeters thick at their tops. It is not possible to say definitely whether this zone results from a kinetic lag in dissolution or a brief downward shift in the elevation of the compensation level at the peak of the last glacial period. C^{14} dates do, however, preclude the possibility that this layer was deposited in postglacial time. Solution attack on the foraminiferal tests contained in this layer demonstrates that the compensation level now lies within a few meters of where it has on the average over the last several hundred thousand years.

INTRODUCTION

There is little doubt that in areas isolated from the margins of continents the average $CaCO_3$ content of marine sediments decreases with increasing water depth. It is also clear that this change in sediment composition is the result of an increase with depth in the degree to which $CaCO_3$ debris is redissolved (rather than in the extent to which the $CaCO_3$ is diluted with other components of the sediment). Here the agreement ends. A wide range of recent opinion has been expressed both with regard to the nature of the transition from sediment rich in $CaCO_3$ to sediment poor in $CaCO_3$ content and as to the reason for the depth dependence in the degree of dissolution (Peterson, 1966; Li and

others, 1969; Edmond and Gieskes, 1970: Chave and Suess, 1970; Heath and Culberson, 1970; Ben-Yaakov, 1970; Berger, 1967, 1968, 1970; Cooke, 1971; Parker and Berger, 1971; Edmond, 1971; Pond and others, 1971; Morse and Berner, 1972). The purpose of this paper is to present detailed data from one area on the ocean floor (the west flank of the East Pacific Rise) and to use these to place some limits on the nature of the processes at work.

MEASUREMENTS

The measurements reported here were carried out on a series of closely spaced cores collected

TABLE 1.—LOCATION AND DEPTH OF CORES
ANALYZED IN THIS STUDY

Core no.	Latitude (°S)	Longitude (°W)	Depth (m)
V19-54	17°02'	113°54'	2964
V19-55	17°00'	114°11'	3177
V19-56	17°00'	114°32'	3147
V19-57	17°00'	114°53'	3168
V19-58	16°58'	115°12'	3334
V19-59	16°58'	115°33'	3309
V19-60	16°58'	115°56'	3329
V19-61	16°57'	116°18'	3422
V19-62	16°58'	116°48'	3422
V19-63	16°59'	117°53'	3446
V19-64	16°56'	121°12'	3570
V19-65	16°39'	124°23'	3867
V19-66	16°24'	127°38'	4096
V19-67	16°10'	129°52'	3952
V19-68	15°37'	131°58'	4199
V19-69	15°55'	134°17'	3970
V19-70	15°39'	138°35'	3939

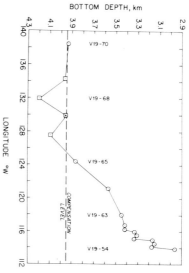

FIG. 1.—Plot of bottom depth at coring sites versus longitude.

44

on cruise 19 of the R/V VEMA in 1963 in connection with a study of the distribution of heat flow across the East Pacific Rise. The locations of the cores are given in table 1 and displayed on a longitude-bottom depth plot in figure 1. Measurements of $CaCO_3$ content as a function of depth in the sediment (see table 2) were carried out on 17 of these cores (by a gasometric technique modified after that of Hülsemann, 1966), and sedimentation rates based on uranium series disequilibrium measurements (table 3; fig. 2) were determined on four of the cores. In addition the Al, Si, Fe, Mn, and Cl content of three of the dry cores were determined (Bender and others, 1971). These results are summarized along with the $CaCO_3$, Th, and U data for the four dated cores in

table 4. These latter data permit the determination of the relative proportions of the ferromanganese oxide, alumino silicate, opal, sea salt, and calcium carbonate components in the core.

PATTERN OF SEDIMENTATION

To understand the factors controlling the distribution of $CaCO_3$ in these sediments it is necessary to determine the geographic and temporal variation in the rate of accumulation of all the contributing components. A general impression can be obtained by considering the four cores for which data on the sedimentation rate were obtained. The chemical data in table 4 allow rough estimates to be made of the relative proportions of major sedimentary components

TABLE 2.—$CaCO_3$ RESULTS

Depth (cm)	CaCO₃ (%)	Depth (cm)	CaCO₃ (%)	Depth (cm)	CaCO₃ (%)	Depth (cm)	CaCO₃ (%)	Depth (cm)	CaCO₃ (%)	Depth (cm)	CaCO₃ (%)
V19-54		*V19-59*		*V19-64*		*V19-65*		*V19-66TW**		*V19-67*	
(2964 m)		(3309 m)		(3570 m)		(3867 m)		0	69	(3952 m)	
0	61	10	86	150	87	110	84	2	66	270	71
10	63	30	89	160	86	120	86	4	69	280	62
15	55			170	89	130	87	6	64	290	56
30	64	*V19-60*		180	90	140	87	8	46	300	49
40	68	(3329 m)		190	91	150	84	12	41	310	56
53	66	10	89	200	92	160	91	16	39	320	76
60	63	30	91	210	90	170	86	20	33	330	87
68	62			230	88	180	89	22	21	340	91
80	64	*V19-61*		240	86	190	87	24	11	350	91
93	59	(3422 m)		250	86	200	86	28	11	360	77
101	61	10	90	260	91	230	78			370	70
108	59	30	90	270	88	260	87	*V19-67*		380	80
120	61			280	79	290	92	(3952 m)		390	83
130	56	*V19-62*		290	85	320	92	10	78	400	68
140	60	(3422 m)		300	85	350	86	20	61	410	76
148	59	10	90	310	87	380	92	30	32	420	80
160	62	30	90	320	89	410	91	40	17	430	84
170	62			350	93	440	92	50	20	440	89
180	55	*V19-63*		380	89	470	93	60	22		
		(3446 m)		410	91	500	92	70	21	*V19-68*	
V19-55		10	92	440	84	530	88	80	15	(4199 m)	
(3177 m)		30	95	470	90	560	86	90	12	10	33
10	76			490	86			100	6	30	9
30	82	*V19-64*		520	85	*V19-66*		110	6	200	9
		(3570 m)		550	86	(4096 m)		120	6		
V19-56		10	93	580	93	10	61	130	7	*V19-69*	
(3147 m)		20	90			15	42	140	7	(3970 m)	
10	78	30	91	*V19-65*		20	18	150	8	10	83
30	84	40	91	(3867 m)		25	16	160	9	20	76
		50	89	10	92	30	18	170	14	30	76
V19-57		60	90	20	91	60	13	180	18	40	10
(3168 m)		70	90	30	91	90	10	190	21	50	6
10	84	80	91	40	87	120	10	200	23		
30	86	90	87	50	79	140	9	210	30	*V19-70*	
		100	86	60	80	180	10	220	57	(3939 m)	
V19-58		110	91	70	73	210	9	230	62	10	85
(3334 m)		120	85	80	80	240	9	240	57	30	95
10	85	130	87	90	78	270	10	250	82	200	56
30	87	140	84	100	83	300	9	260	84		

* Trigger weight gravity core.

TABLE 3.—URANIUM AND THORIUM ISOTOPE CONCENTRATIONS

Core No. and depth	Depth in core (cm)	[CaCO₃] (%)	[U] (ppm)	$\frac{^{234}U}{^{238}U}$	^{232}Th (ppm)	^{230}Th (dpm gm⁻¹)	Unsupported ^{230}Th (dpm gm⁻¹)
V19-54	18	59	4.76	1.13	<0.2	17.5	13.6
2964 m	48	67	3.96	1.15	<0.2	14.0	9.8
	86	61	4.93	1.09	<0.2	11.2	7.3
	114	64	4.30	1.13	<0.3	10.8	7.2
	150	60	5.25	1.12	<0.2	11.1	6.8
	200	60	6.90	1.11	0.1	10.1	4.5
	305	60	5.60	1.07	0.1	6.68	2.3
	400	58	4.55	1.03	0.8	3.79	0.4
V19-61	15	90	.37	—	<0.3	17.5	17.2
3422 m	53	—	.71	—	<0.3	12.1	11.6
	93	—	.47	—	0.2	5.35	5.0
	128	—	.45	—	0.1	3.23	2.9
	160	—	.41	—	0.1	2.05	1.8
	208	—	.56	—	0.1	1.04	0.6
	260	—	77	—	0.1	0.64	0.1
V19-64	11	93	.20	—	0.05	15.4	15.2
3570 m	35	91	.27	—	0.1	14.3	14.1
	60	90	.35	—	0.1	11.4	11.1
	85	89	.32	—	0.2	5.35	5.1
	157	86	.52	—	0.6	1.53	1.15
	218	89	.34	—	0.3	.35	.10
	265	89	.36	—	0.4	.36	.10
V19-66	10	61	1.74	1.05	2.16	41.5	40.2
4096 m	30	10	3.55	1.04	4.54	14.3	11.5
	49	15	4.50	1.02	3.18	6.7	3.3
	70	11	3.87	1.05	1.80	4.2	1.2
	96	10	5.24	1.07	1.83	4.0	−0.1

(i.e., calcium carbonate, alumino silicate, ferromanganese oxides, opal, and sea salt). If the following assumptions are made: 1) the opal and CaCO₃ fractions are free of Fe, Al, U, and Th; 2) the ferromanganese oxide fraction is free of Al and of Th and contains 15 ppm U; 3) the alumino silicate fraction is 15% by weight Al₂O₃ and 60% by weight SiO₂ and contains 3 ppm U and 12 ppm Th; the data yield the self-consistent results shown in table 5. The ridge crest sediment (V19-54) consists of a mixture of 2.5 parts CaCO₃ and 1 part Fe-Mn oxide with minor amounts of opal and sea salt and no detectable alumino silicate material. The two flank cores from above the compensation level are roughly 90% CaCO₃ with minor amounts of Fe-Mn oxide, opal and sea salt and, again, no detectable alumino silicate. Finally the core (V19-66) from below the compensation level consists of roughly 3 parts alumino silicate to one part of Fe-Mn oxide with minor amounts of CaCO₃ and sea salt (the data needed to calculate the opal content of this core are not available).

By combining these results with the sedimentation rate data and estimates of the dry density of the cores it is possible to obtain the absolute accumulation rate of each component (as a function of water depth and of distance from the ridge crest). The densities given in table 6 were not directly measured and hence are only approximate. They are based on previous observations of the dependence of porosity on CaCO₃ content. CaCO₃-free cores have on the average at least twice the water content (and hence less than half the dry density) of cores with high CaCO₃ content. However, because plots of CaCO₃ content against dry density show considerable scatter, the densities adopted could be in error by as much as 25%. Fortunately this uncertainty does not affect the conclusions to be drawn.

The absolute accumulation rates of the various components show the patterns indicated in table 6. The rate of CaCO₃ accumulation decreases slowly west from the ridge crest and then falls by a factor of 100 between 3570 and 4096 meters, the rate of Fe-Mn oxide accumulation decreases rapidly away from the ridge crest reaching the ambient oceanic value of 10 to 20 mg/cm² 10³ yrs by a depth of 3422 meters. The rate of alumino silicate accumulation rises from less than 10 mg/cm² 10³ yrs on the higher portions of the ridge to 40 ± 10 mg/cm² 10³ yrs

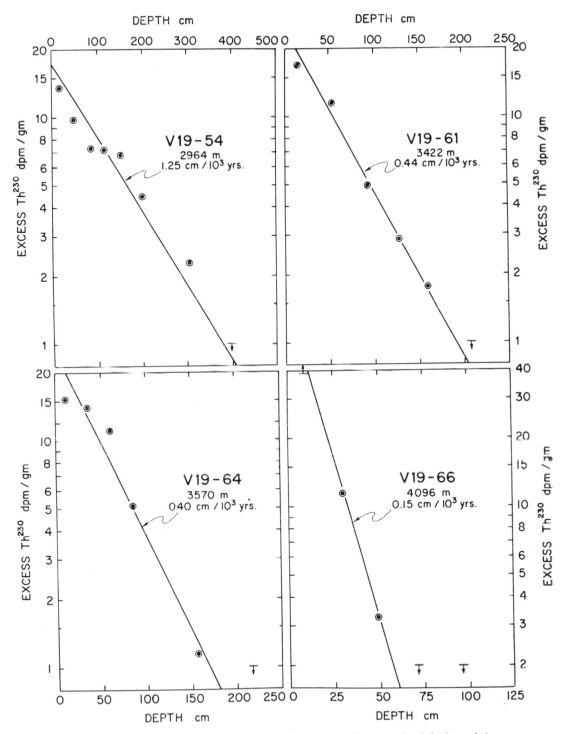

FIG. 2.—Plots of excess Th230 activity (i.e., total U234 supported) versus depth in four of the cores studied. The slope of the best fit line is a measure of the average rate of sedimentation.

TABLE 4.—CHEMICAL COMPOSITION MEASUREMENTS (AS REPORTED BY BENDER AND OTHERS (1971) FOR V19-54, -61, AND -64 AND REPORTED HERE FOR V19-66)

	$MnO_2+Fe_2O_3$ %	Al_2O_3 %	SiO_2 %	$CaCO_3$ %	NaCl %	Th^{232} ppm	U^{238} ppm
V19-54	26	<0.3	5	65	4	<0.2	5
V19-61	5	0.6	3	90	—	<0.2	0.5
V19-64	2	<0.3	2	90	4	<0.5	0.3
V19-66	—	—	—	10	—	3 ± 1	4.3 ± 0.8

TABLE 5.—COMPONENT DISTRIBUTION IN DRY CORE MATERIAL AS ESTIMATED FROM THE CHEMICAL DATA

Core	Depth (m)	$CaCO_3$ %	Opal %	Fe-Mn oxides %	Al-silicates %	Salt %
V19-54	2964	65	5	26	<2	4
V19-61	3422	90	3	5	<2**	4*
V19-64	3570	90	2	2	<2	4
V19-66	4096	10	?	25 ± 10*	70 ± 15*	8*

* Calculated using assumptions outlined in text.
** Based on Th rather than Al content.

TABLE 6.—ACCUMULATION RATES OF VARIOUS SEDIMENTARY COMPONENTS AS A FUNCTION OF WATER DEPTH

Core no.	Water depth (m)	Sedimentation rate cm/10^3 yrs	Dry density gm/cm^3	Sedimentation rate mg/cm^2 10^3 yrs	$CaCO_3$	Fe+Mn oxides	Alumino-silicates	Opal
V19-54	2964	1.25	0.8	1000	650	260	<20	50
V19-61	3422	0.44	1.0	440	400	20	<10	13
V19-64	3570	0.40	1.0	400	360	8	<10	8
V19-66	4096	0.15	0.3	45	4	15 ± 5	40 ± 10	?

at a depth of 4096 meters, the rate of opal deposition appears to decrease away from the ridge crest.

These results indicate that (1) the deposition of the Fe-Mn oxide on the ridge crest is associated with ridge crest volcanism, (2) a very large change in the degree of dissolution of $CaCO_3$ occurs at the "level of compensation," (3) the alumino silicate debris is transported from adjacent ocean margins in the nepheloid horizon rather than by the wind or surface currents and, (4) the rate of productivity of both calcium carbonate and opal-producing organisms decreases to the west of the ridge crest.

DISTRIBUTION OF CaCO₃

In figure 3 and table 7 the $CaCO_3$ content of two depth horizons (10 and 30 cm) in the sediment column are shown as a function of bottom depth. The increase from 65 to 90 percent $CaCO_3$ away from the ridge crest is the result of the decrease in the accumulation rate of Fe-Mn oxide as a function of distance from the spreading center. The very sharp decrease from more than 80 to less than 20 percent $CaCO_3$ close to

3950 meters reflects a major change in the rate of dissolution of $CaCO_3$.

Vertical changes in $CaCO_3$ content in a single core are also interesting. Results for 4 cores are shown in figure 4. V19-54 from the crest of the rise shows a remarkably constant $CaCO_3$ content over a depth interval of 180 cm. Because the percentage is determined by the relative rates of $CaCO_3$ and of Fe-Mn oxide accumulation, this constancy can be taken to indicate that neither the rate of volcanic emanation nor that of $CaCO_3$ rain has varied significantly over this interval of time (about 150,000 years). This has significance both to theories of sea floor spreading and to theories regarding the response of the ocean to major climatic cycles. If the generation of Fe-Mn oxides in the ridge crest zone is directly related to the rate of sea floor spreading then these results would suggest that the plates have been moving at a nearly constant rate for the last 150,000 years. Because a complete major climatic cycle has occurred in the last 150,000 years these results indicate that the rates and patterns of oceanic mixing are not significantly altered by glacial to interglacial

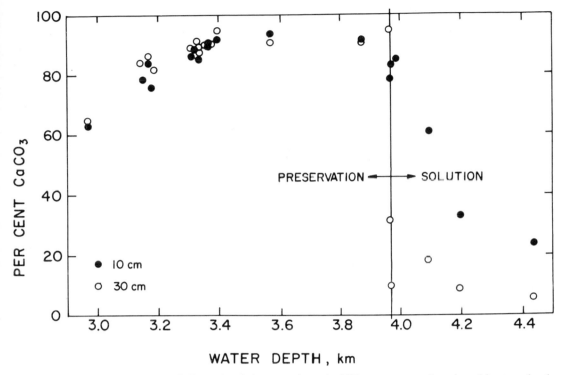

FIG. 3.—CaCO₃ content at 10 and 30 cm depth in cores along the V19 traverse as a function of bottom depth.

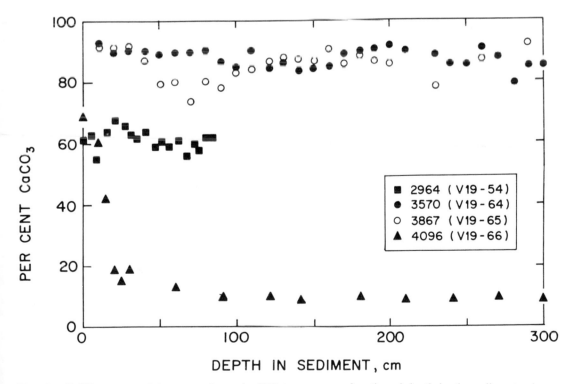

FIG. 4.—CaCO₃ content of four cores from the V19 traverse as a function of depth in the sediment column.

TABLE 7.—CaCO₃ CONTENT OF CORES FROM
VARIOUS OCEAN DEPTHS

Depth in ocean	Depth in sediment		
	10 cm	30 cm	120 cm
3867 m	92%	91%	86%
3939 m	85%	95%	56%
3952 m	78%	32%	6%
3970 m	83%	76%	6%
4096 m	61%	18%	10%

climatic changes (see Broecker, 1971a). The alternate interpretation that sympathetic changes in CaCO₃ and Fe-Mn oxide accumulation rates have occurred cannot be excluded, but it would demand a correlation between tectonic and climatic cycles for which there is no current explanation.

The cores from the flank of the ridge are not as useful in this respect. Their very high CaCO₃ content makes their composition less sensitive to changes in the rate of deposition of the major components. For example, a twofold increase in CaCO₃ accumulation rate would change the CaCO₃ content by only about 5% and a twofold increase in Fe-Mn accumulation rate would decrease the CaCO₃ content by only about 4%. Thus the near constancy in CaCO₃ content of these cores only allows broad limits to be placed on the constancy of the rate of rain of the major components.

Below the "level of compensation" a CaCO₃-rich layer exists at the core top. The variation of CaCO₃ content with depth in the upper meter of one such core (V19-66 from 4096 meters) is shown in figure 5. Two possible explanations can be given this layer. The first is that it reflects a kinetic lag in the dissolution of the CaCo₃ (in other words, the dissolution time of CaCO₃ falling to the sea floor below the "compensation horizon" is tens of thousands of years). The second is that it is caused by a change in the elevation of the "level of compensation" during the last few tens of thousands of years.

The species composition of foraminifera in the tops of cores from below the compensation horizon are very different from those for cores taken above this level (Luz, pers. comm.). In the two cores V19-67 and V19-68, from well below the compensation level evidence for extensive dissolution exists. Cores from above the level show little evidence for dissolution.

C¹⁴ measurements were made on samples from a similar CaCO₃-rich zone at the top of piston core V19-67. Samples centered at 2.2, 7.0, 11.0, and 19.0 cm depth yielded ages of 10,700, 14,700, 15,600, and 14,500 years. A check measurement at the top companion gravity core yielded an age of 11,400 years, confirming that the high age at the top of the piston core is real and not an artifact of coring. Either the CaCO₃ was deposited during late glacial time and/or mixing has largely homogenized the CaCO₃ deposited over several tens of thousands of years. If the CaCO₃ was deposited during late glacial time and has not been extensively mixed then the accumulation rate as determined from the C¹⁴ ages is 2.2 cm/10³ years. This rate is five times faster than the average obtained from the Th²³⁰ measurements on cores V19-61 and V19-64 from above the compensation level.

Core V19-67, from 3952 meters (just below the level of compensation), shows a sharp increase in CaCO₃ content below a depth of 220 cm (fig. 6). The region of the sea floor from which this core was taken must have subsided below the level of compensation at this time. From our evidence on accumulation rates we would estimate the age of this event to be at least one million years. Paleontologic examination by Saito (pers. comm.) reveals that the sediment at 220 cm is Late Miocene in age (i.e., ∼5 million years in age). If sedimentation has been continuous since that time the average rate cannot have been greater than .05 cm/10³ years. Taking a density of 0.3 gm/cm³ this corresponds to about 15 mg/cm² 10³ years.

Since the lithosphere on the flanks of oceanic rises is sinking at the rate of about 30 meters per million years, the elevation of this region of the sea floor must have been about 150 meters shallower at the end of the Miocene than it is today. Thus about 5 million years ago the

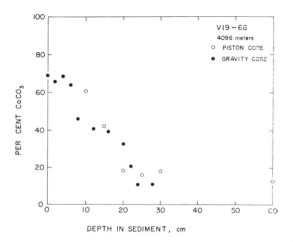

FIG. 5.—Comparison of CaCO₃ versus depth data near the top of the piston and the gravity cores from station V19-66.

compensation level must have been at about 3800 meters depth.

THE NATURE OF THE COMPENSATION HORIZON

The results on samples taken 30 cm below the top of cores from various water depths show a remarkably sharp decrease in $CaCO_3$ content close to 3950 meters depth. A core from a depth of 3870 meters shows a nearly uniform high $CaCO_3$ content over a depth range of at least 560 cm while one from 3950 meters shows a decrease to 17% $CaCO_3$ at a depth of 40 cm. Thus for sediments older than 15,000 years (the radiocarbon age of the base of the $CaCO_3$-rich top layer) a 100-fold contrast in the degree of dissolution exists between a depth of 3870 and 3950 meters! In this region of the ocean the level of compensation is indeed a very sharp feature (complete within an elevation range of less than 80 meters). The fact that the roughness in bottom topography (see fig. 1) causes this level to be recrossed during the traverse demonstrates that *elevation* rather than *distance from the ridge crest* is the controlling factor. Core top samples alone would suggest a far more gradual transition (over an elevation range of several hundred meters). This could be an artifact of a kinetic lag in $CaCO_3$ dissolution or of a recent shift in the level of compensation.

THE KINETIC LAG HYPOTHESIS

In the kinetic lag hypothesis solution is envisioned as occurring within the pore waters of the sediment. Transport of the products of solution to the overlying ocean would logically be by molecular diffusion.

A quantitative model of this process will permit the determination of the chemical gradients within the pore fluids required to dispose of the dissolving $CaCO_3$. In order to do this we make the following simplifying assumptions: 1) the rates of rain onto the sea floor of the carbonate and of the non-carbonate fractions are uniform with geographic location and with time (respectively, 400 and 40 mg/cm^2 10^3 yrs), 2) each unit of $CaCO_3$ reaching the sea floor undergoes solution according to a first order rate law (a fixed fraction of the residual $CaCO_3$ is destroyed each year), and 3) the effects of mechanical mixing are negligible.

If this is the case then the thickness, x, of material above any given time horizon, t, is given by the following relationship:

$$x = \int_0^t \frac{S_C}{\rho_C} e^{-t/\tau} dt + \frac{S_{NC}}{\rho_{NC}} t$$

where S_C and S_{NC} are the masses of carbonate and non-carbonate matter reaching the sea floor per unit area and unit time, ρ_C and ρ_{NC} the dry densities of carbonate and non-carbonate matter, and τ the mean solution time for $CaCO_3$ after arrival at the sea floor.

Integrating,

$$x = \frac{S_C \tau}{C} (1 - e^{-t/\tau}) + \frac{S_{NC}}{\rho_{NC}} t$$

Further, the $CaCO_3$ content, f_C, of sediment of any given age would be,

$$f_C = \frac{S_C e^{-t/\tau}}{S_{NC} + S_C e^{-t/\tau}}$$

or

$$f_C = \frac{1}{1 + \frac{S_{NC}}{S_C} e^{+t/\tau}}$$

From these two relationships it is possible to predict the variation in $CaCO_3$ content with depth for any given values of τ, S_{NC}, S_C, ρ_C, and ρ_{NC}.

The value of τ can be estimated by integrating the total amount of $CaCO_3$ per unit area of sea floor in a given core and dividing this amount by the rate of $CaCO_3$ rain, i.e.;

$$\tau = \frac{\rho_C}{S_C} \int_0^\infty f_C dx$$

For cores V19-66 (4096 m) and V19-67 (3950 m) the results of this calculation yield τ values of 15,000 years and 45,000 years, respectively (note that less excess $CaCO_3$ is present in the core 150 meters below the compensation level than in the core just below this horizon).

Using these time constants the $CaCO_3$ content of cores V19-66 and V19-67 have been calculated as a function of depth in the core and of

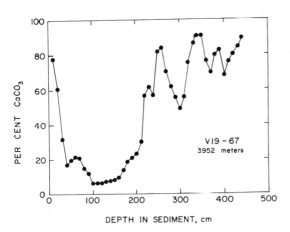

FIG. 6.—$CaCO_3$ versus depth in the sediment column for core V19-67 taken just below the present day compensation horizon.

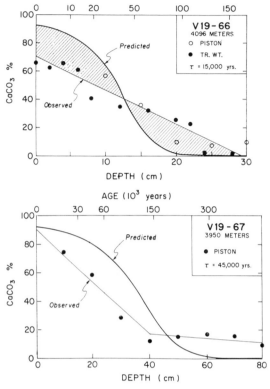

FIG. 7.—Comparison of CaCO₃ versus depth in sediment curve predicted from the first order kinetic solution model with the observed distributions in cores V19-66 and V19-67.

age of the core material. The results are plotted in figure 7 along with the actual CaCO₃ content data.

Because of the complex nature of the relationship between the CaCO₃ content of the core and the fraction of CaCO₃ destroyed by solution (see table 8) and between age and depth in

TABLE 8.—PERCENT CaCO₃ AS A FUNCTION OF THE FRACTION, f, OF THE CaCO₃ SURVIVING DISSOLUTION FOR TWO DIFFERENT RATIOS OF CARBONATE TO NONCARBONATE SEDIMENTATION RATE

f	% CaCO₃	
	$S_\Sigma = 1.1\ S_{CaCO_3}$	$S_\Sigma = 2\ S_{CaCO_3}$
1.00	91	50
.80	89	44
.50	84	33
.20	67	17
.10	50	9
.03	23	3
.01	9	1
.003	3	0.3

the core (see fig. 8), it is not intuitively obvious that the depth distribution of CaCO₃ predicted should take the form it does. Instead of the exponential fall-off which might be expected for first order kinetics we predict a sharp transition from a region of high to a region of low CaCO₃ content.

The failure of the model to yield the observed roughly linear drop-off in CaCO₃ content indicates that the actual processes must differ from the simple model proposed here.

Although not entirely adequate the model nevertheless allows us to get a first approximation as to the magnitude of the changes in pore water concentrations necessary to eliminate the products of CaCO₃ solution. At any depth, x, in the core the flux of Ca (and of C) must equal the integrated amount of underlying CaCO₃ divided by the mean solution time, i.e.;

$$\text{Flux} = D\frac{dc}{dx} = \frac{\rho c \int_x^\infty f_c dx}{\tau}$$

Thus from a knowledge of the depth dependence of the CaCO₃ content, the mean solution time and the rate of molecular diffusion, D, it is possible to calculate the gradients of Ca (and ΣCO_2) content at various depths in the core.

$$\frac{dc}{dx} = \frac{\rho c}{D\tau} \int_x^\infty f_c dx$$

Knowing the profile of these gradients and the composition of near bottom water it is then

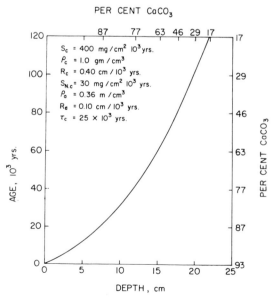

FIG. 8.—Predicted age versus depth plot for one set of deposition rate and solution time parameters.

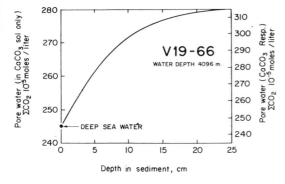

Fig. 9.—Predicted total dissolved inorganic carbon, ΣCO_2, content of pore waters as a function of depth in core V19-66 assuming that only $CaCO_3$ solution occurs (left hand axis) and that $CaCO_3$ solution is in response to the release of CO_2 by the oxidation of organic debris.

possible to calculate the composition of the pore fluid at various depths in the core. This has been done for core V19-66. The ΣCO_2 content versus depth in the core is shown in figure 9 and the chemical composition at the base of the $CaCO_3$-rich layer in table 9 (case A).

The results pose a serious problem. Water at 4000 meters depth in the South Pacific is within a few tens of percent of saturation with calcite (Li and others, 1969; Culberson, 1972). In the absence of any other chemical reactions solution of $CaCO_3$ would generate pore waters highly supersaturated with calcite. If solution does take place within the core then there must be some complementary reaction. One possibility is that oxidation of organic material produces sufficient CO_2 to trigger the $CaCO_3$ solution:

$$CO_2 + CaCO_3 + H_2O \Rightarrow 2HCO_3^- + Ca^{++}$$

Then the chemistry of the pore water at the base of the $CaCO_3$-rich zone would be as shown in table 9 (case B). It is highly unlikely that an adequate supply of organic matter is available for this process.

Another possibility is that SiO_2 reacts with the $CaCO_3$ to yield a silicate mineral (table 9, case C). The following reaction illustrates the type of process envisioned:

$$Mg^{++} + SiO_2 + 2CaCO_3 \Rightarrow 2Ca^{++} + MgSiO_3 + 2HCO_3^-$$

This process can be ruled out because the destruction of the $CaCO_3$ is *not* matched mole to mole by the appearance of any silicate material.

As suggested by Lohmann (pers, comm.) the need for large pore water gradients could be eliminated by calling on mechanical mixing in the sediment to bring the carbonate close to the interface. If mixing were sufficiently rapid and if it proceeded deep enough, active dissolution could be confined to the uppermost centimeter or so of sediment. The high C^{14} age (11,000 years) for the top of the sediment can be taken as evidence that such mixing is indeed taking place. Thus an adequate model of the kinetic lag hypothesis would have to take into account both diffusion and mechanical stirring. The pore water gradients calculated above are hence *upper* limits.

THE SHIFTING COMPENSATION LEVEL HYPOTHESIS

If a shift in the level of $CaCO_3$ compensation has taken place during the last few tens of thousands of years, then it most likely was associated with the changes in climate which have occurred over this time interval. As shown by Broecker (1971a) evidence from three regions of the world ocean (i.e., the Caribbean, the equatorial Indian and the east equatorial Pacific) indicates that dissolution was more intense during interglacial than during glacial periods. This means that the level of compensation stood

TABLE 9.—PREDICTED CHEMICAL COMPOSITIONS OF PORE WATERS AT THE BASE OF THE $CaCO_3$-RICH LAYER COMPARED WITH THAT FOR DEEP PACIFIC WATER

	Pacific deep water	Pore water Case A	Pore water Case B	Pore water Case C
Mg^{++} $(10^{-5}$ m/l)	5000	5000	5000	4982
Ca^{++} $(10^{-5}$ m/l)	1000	1035	1035	1035
Alk $(10^{-5}$ eq/l)	249	319	319	284
ΣCO_2 $(10^{-5}$ m/l)	245	280	315	280
HCO_3 $(10^{-5}$ m/l)	235	241	305	270
$CO_3^=$ $(10^{-5}$ m/l)	7	39	7	7
CO_2 $(10^{-5}$ m/l)	3	0	3	3
$Ca^{++} \times CO_3^=$ $(10^{-7}$ m²/l²)	7	40	7	7

Case A: $CaCO_3 \Rightarrow Ca^{++} + CO_3^=$
Case B: $CO_2 + H_2O + CaCO_3 \Rightarrow Ca^{++} + 2HCO_3^-$
Case C: $Mg^{++} + SiO_2 + 2CaCO_3 \Rightarrow 2Ca^{++} + MgSiO_3 + 2HCO_3^-$

deeper during glacial than during interglacial periods. Then the most logical time for the generation of the core top $CaCO_3$ observed below the compensation level on the west flank of the East Pacific Rise would have been during late glacial rather than postglacial time. The C^{14} data on core V19-67 support this conclusion. If the drop in compensation level were to have occurred at the end of the last period of glaciation (i.e., 11,000 years ago) and the $CaCO_3$-rich layer deposited during postglacial time, then the mean age of the layer would be 5000 years and no age should exceed 11,000 years. The fact that the youngest age observed was 10,700 years eliminates the possibility of wholly postglacial deposition (regardless of the degree of mechanical mixing). If the $CaCO_3$-rich layer is the result of a climate-induced shift in the compensation level then this shift must have occurred at some point during the long climatic decline which occurred between 80,000 and 11,000 years ago. A return to approximately 3950 meters must have taken place early in postglacial time. The $CaCO_3$ currently falling on this area must be dissolving and the buried $CaCO_3$ subject to dissolution through diffusion of undersaturated bottom waters into the pores of the sediment.

Since the core from 4096 meters (V19-66) also contains a $CaCO_3$-rich layer the compensation level must have dropped from 3950 to at least 4100 meters depth during late glacial time. A shift of at least 150 meters between late glacial and postglacial time is required.

The absence of a $CaCO_3$-free layer at the core top is not hard to explain. In 10,000 years only a fraction of a centimeter of $CaCO_3$-free material would be deposited. Mixing would certainly make such a thin layer difficult to detect at the core top. It should, however, be sought by detailed core top sampling.

One serious objection to this hypothesis is that this event is not repeated deeper in the core. Previous glacial periods should, by analogy, have generated similar $CaCO_3$-rich layers. Their absence requires either that dissolution of the late glacial layer occurs during the subsequent interglacial or that the last glacial period produced an unusually large and long drop in the compensation level.

WHY IS THE COMPENSATION LEVEL SO SHARP?

If solution takes place in direct contact with bottom water then the transition from supersaturated to undersaturated water can be used to explain the abrupt nature of the boundary. $CaCO_3$ falling onto sediments bathed in unsaturated water will dissolve and that falling nto supersaturated water will be preserved. An

other explanation is that a change in the *rate* of solution resulting from differences in current velocity takes place at 3950 meters (Edmond, 1971). If, on the other hand, dissolution of $CaCO$ takes place *within* the sediment rather than at the interface, then a very difficult problem arises. Destruction of the $CaCO_3$ several centimeters or more below the sediment-water interface would require changes in pore water composition of sufficient magnitude to allow transport of the products of solution back to the sea. These changes would *overwhelm* the small differences in degree of saturation resulting from pressure. The buried sediment would also be immune to the effect of currents.

Our data clearly demonstrate that a 100-fold increase in the degree of dissolution takes place between 3870 meters and 3950 meters depth. This seemingly eliminates the possibility that solution takes place within the pores of the sediment. Instead it must occur in contact with the bottom water.

Chung (1971) and Craig and others (1972) have pointed out that an abyssal thermocline is present in the South Pacific west of the East Pacific Rise. The depth of this feature in the area of our study is estimated to be about 3900 meters. It is possible that more active flow in the underlying water could be called upon to provide the needed 100-fold difference in solution rate (Edmond, 1971). On the other hand, the depth of the transition from super- to undersaturation has also been estimated to occur at roughly this depth (Li and others, 1969; Ben-Yaakov, 1970; and, by inference, from experiments carried out by Cooke, 1971). Until detailed chemical and hydrographic measurements are available in the water column of this area it will prove difficult to choose between the kinetic and thermodynamic explanations.

FACTORS CONTROLLING THE DEPTH OF $CaCO_3$ COMPENSATION

As pointed out by Li and others (1969) marine organisms are producing $CaCO_3$ roughly five times more rapidly than carbon is being supplied for this purpose by rivers (see fig. 10). Loss of carbon from the sea must balance the gain on a time scale not exceeding the residence time of carbon in the sea. Thus there must be some mechanism operating within the sea which destroys the excess carbonate manufactured by marine organisms. This mechanism involves a feedback between net $CaCO_3$ production and the carbonate ion content of the sea. If the net production (total production minus that redissolved) exceeds the rate of supply of carbon then there will be a net decrease in the amount of carbon stored in the sea (i.e., the mean ΣCO_2

content of sea water will fall). The carbonate alkalinity of the sea will fall by twice the rate the ΣCO_2 falls (i.e., $\Delta A = 2\Delta\Sigma CO_2$). Since

$$\sum CO_2 \cong HCO_3^- + CO_3^-$$

and

$$A \cong HCO_3^- + 2CO_3^-$$

we have

$$CO_3^- \cong A - \sum CO_2$$

Since the alkalinity of the sea drops faster than the ΣCO_2 the difference between these quantities (i.e., CO_3^-) will also decrease. Thus an imbalance in the removal and supply rate of carbon due to too *high* a rate of $CaCO_3$ storage in sediments will cause the mean carbonate ion in the sea to fall. This in turn would cause all sea water to decrease in degree of saturation with respect to $CaCO_3$. The fraction of the $CaCO_3$ produced by marine organisms subjected to dissolution would rise and the magnitude of the overstorage rate of $CaCO_3$ would drop. This would continue until loss and gain had once again been balanced. This negative feedback would always drive the compensation level to that place where the overproduction of $CaCO_3$ was balanced by dissolution. This argument holds regardless of whether compensation is a kinetic or a thermodynamic phenomenon and whether or not the transition from $CaCO_3$-rich to $CaCO_3$-poor sediment is sharp or gradational. The rate of $CaCO_3$ solution in the sea must be inversely related to the mean CO_3^- ion concentration (because the concentration of Ca in sea water exceeds, on the average, that of ΣCO_2 by a factor of 4.5 and that of CO_3^- ion by a factor about 18, it will be the CO_3^- ion content rather than the Ca^{++} ion content that responds to any short term change in the economics of carbon).

In this connection it is important to state what we mean by the "carbon entering the sea destined to become $CaCO_3$". Rivers carry two types of carbon, that derived from weathering and that from the atmosphere. As most weathering reactions involve CO_2 derived from the atmosphere the latter is often the major fraction of the total. As this carbon is being recycled within the ocean-atmosphere system it is not of interest. Only the carbon from carbonate minerals and organic compounds weathered from the earth's crust are potentially available for new oceanic sedimentary $CaCO_3$. Of this some will be lost from the sea as organic tissue. The question then becomes: how does the sea proportion the carbon it receives between organic tissue loss and $CaCO_3$ loss?

As pointed out by Broecker (1971b) the amount of carbon lost as organic tissue is limited by the availability of the element phosphorus. Aquatic organisms use C and P in the atomic ratio of roughly 100 to 1. The tissue that is lost to the sediment, although perhaps not of this same composition, has a similar C:P ratio. Thus only about 100 carbon atoms can leave the sea in the form of organic tissue for each phosphorus atom added to the sea. The carbon to phosphorus ratio in the rivers feeding the sea is on the order of 1000 to 1. Thus only one carbon atom in ten released by weathering is destined to be lost to organic tissue; the rest must leave the sea as $CaCO_3$. It is this fraction of the carbon carried by rivers that we designate to be that "destined to become $CaCO_3$".

Since the CO_3^- ion content of deep Pacific

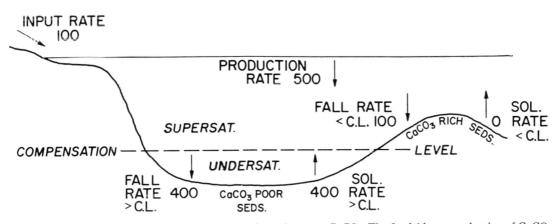

Fig. 10.—Cycle of carbon "destined" to be lost from the sea as $CaCO_3$. The fivefold overproduction of $CaCO_3$ by organisms is compensated by dissolution of $CaCO_3$ in the deep sea. The boundary between undersaturated and supersaturated assumes that level such that only an amount of $CaCO_3$ equal to that supplied by rivers reaches sediments bathed in supersaturated waters. Positive feedback between the input-loss difference and the carbonate ion content of the sea drives the compensation level toward that level yielding material balance.

ocean water is only about 3% the total dissolved inorganic carbon content of this water (Li and others, 1969), the response time for $CO_3^=$ ion change will be only 3% the residence time for carbon in the sea. Since the latter is on the order of 100,000 years the former will be only 3000 years. Thus the sediments can respond to changes in the production rate of calcite to the input rate of carbon destined to become calcite on the time scale demanded for the late glacial to postglacial change proposed here.

Thus if the results presented here are to be explained by a drop in the level of compensation during late glacial time then there must have been a decrease in the ratio of the rate of calcite production to the rate of supply of carbon (destined to become $CaCO_3$) at that time. This could have been the result of: 1) a decreased rate of vertical mixing in the sea; 2) a decrease in the amount of calcite generated per unit of phosphorus reaching the surface ocean; 3) an increase in the rate of supply of carbon destined to become $CaCO_3$; 4) a change in the pattern of deep mixing leading to a drop in the level of compensation in some basins and a rise in others. In the absence of additional evidence it is not possible to select among these possibilities.

THE RELATIONSHIP BETWEEN THE LYSOCLINE AND COMPENSATION DEPTHS

Ruddiman and Heezen (1967) and Berger (1968, 1970) introduced the concept of a lysocline (i.e., the depth at which dissolution of sedimentary $CaCO_3$ becomes easily apparent) in addition to that of a compensation horizon (the depth at which total dissolution occurs). In the area we studied below a depth of 30 cm in the sediment column the lysocline and compensation depth are one and the same (both lie at about 3950 meters). Above 30 cm and hence for core top material the lysocline would lie at about 3950 meters and the compensation horizon at greater than 4100 meters. If the kinetic lag hypothesis is adopted to explain our results then these horizons are consistent with Berger's ideas as to their origin. However, if a late glacial shift in compensation depth is called upon to produce the high carbonate tails found at the tops of the cores from below 3950 meters, then Berger's explanation is incorrect. In this case, the separation between the lysocline and compensation depth has a far more complex origin (at least in the area we have studied). Only with the kind of detailed study presented here can the bottom depth dependence of solution phenomena begin to be understood. Studies of the degree of dissolution confined to core tops could prove to be very misleading.

CONCLUSIONS

We have tried to integrate a wide range of chemical, radiometric, and paleontologic information toward the resolution of questions as to the nature and origin of the calcite compensation depth. The results suggest that either a kinetic lag in dissolution or temporal shifts in the level of compensation (or a combination of the two effects) greatly complicate the situation. Until similar studies have been carried out at a variety of locations along the boundary between $CaCO_3$-rich and $CaCO_3$-poor sediments conclusions as to the nature of the transition will be impossible.

ACKNOWLEDGMENTS

The authors wish to thank Richard Pardi for carrying out the C^{14} measurements. We also are grateful to Boaz Luz of Brown University for allowing us to quote his unpublished data on the degree of dissolution of the foraminifers in the tops of the cores studied here. Discussions with George Lohmann, Joris Gieskes, John Edmond, Robert Cooke, Taro Takahashi, William Hay, Andrew McIntyre and Michael Bender have been very helpful in formulating some of the ideas presented here. A very thoughtful review of the paper by John Edmond was much appreciated. Seminars given at Woods Hole, Princeton and in the LDGO core laboratory were particularly stimulating in this regard. Financial support was provided by the Atomic Energy Commission grant AT(11-1) 2185 and National Science Foundation grant GA 27119.

This paper is Contribution Number 2084 of the Lamont-Doherty Geological Observatory.

REFERENCES

BENDER, M., BROECKER, W., GORNITZ, V., MIDDEL, U., KAY, R., SUN, S.-S., AND BISCAYE, P., 1971, Geochemistry of three cores from the East Pacific Rise: Earth and Planet. Sci. Letters, v. 12, p. 425–433.
BEN-YAAKOV, S., 1970, An oceanographic instrumentation system for *in situ* measurements (Ph.D. thesis): Los Angeles Univ. California.
——, AND KAPLAN, I. R., 1971, Deep-sea *in situ* calcium carbonate saturometry: Jour. Geophys. Research, 76, p. 722–731.
BERGER, W. H., 1967, Foraminiferal ooze: solution at depths: Science, v. 156, p. 383–385.
——, 1968, Planktonic foraminifera: Selective solution and paleoclimatic interpretation: Deep-Sea Research, v. 15, p. 31–43.
——, 1970, Planktonic foraminifera: selective solution and the lysocline: Marine Geology, v. 8, p. 111–138.

BROECKER, W. S., 1971a, Calcite accumulation rates and glacial to interglacial changes in oceanic mixing, *in:* TUREKIAN, K. K. (ed.), The late Cenozoic glacial ages: New Haven, Connecticut, Yale Univ. Press, p. 239–265.

————, 1971b, A kinetic model for the chemical composition of sea water: Quaternary Research, v. 1, p. 188–207.

CHAVE, K. E. AND SUESS, E., 1970, Calcium carbonate saturation in sea water: Effects of organic matter: Limnology and Oceanography, v. 15, p. 633–637.

CHUNG, Y., 1971, Pacific deep and bottom water studies based on temperature, radium and excess-radon measurements (Ph. D. thesis): San Diego, Univ. California.

COOKE, R. C., 1971, The lysocline and calcium carbonate compensation depth in the sea (Ph. D. thesis): Halifax, Nova Scotia, Dalhousie Univ.

CRAIG, H., CHUNG, Y., AND FIADEIRO, M., 1972, A benthic front in the South Pacific: Earth and Planetary Sci. Letters, v. 16, p. 50–65.

CULBERTSON, C., 1972, Processes affecting the oceanic distribution of carbon dioxide (Ph. D. thesis): Corvallis, Oregon St. Univ.

EDMOND, J. M., 1970, The carbonic acid system in sea water (Ph. D. thesis): San Diego, Univ. California.

————, 1971, An interpretation of the calcite spheres experiment: Am. Geophys. Union, EOS Trans., v. 52, p. 256.

————, AND GIESKES, J. M. T. V., 1970, On the calculation of the degree of saturation of sea water with respect to calcium carbonate under *in situ* conditions: Geochimica et Cosmochimica Acta, v. 34, p. 1261–1291.

HEATH, G. R. AND CULBERSON, C., 1970, Calcite: degree of saturation, rate of dissolution, and the compensation depth in the deep oceans: Geol. Soc. America Bull. v. 81, p. 3157–3160.

HULSEMANN, J., 1966, On the routine analysis of carbonates in unconsolidated sediments: Jour. Sed. Petrology, v. 36, p. 622–625.

LI, Y.-H., TAKAHASHI, T. AND BROECKER, W. S., 1969, The degree of saturation of $CaCO_3$ in the oceans: Jour. Geophys. Research, v. 74, p. 5507–5525.

MORSE, J. W., 1972, Dissolution kinetics of calcium carbonate in sea water: II. A kinetic origin for the lysocline: Am. Jour. Sci., v. 272, p. 840–851.

PARKER, F. L. AND BERGER, W. H., 1971, Faunal and solution patterns of planktonic foraminifera in surface sediments of the South Pacific: Deep-Sea Research, v. 18, p. 73–107.

PETERSON, M. N. A., 1966, Calcite: rates of dissolution in a vertical profile in the central Pacific: Science, v. 154, p. 1542–1544.

POND, S., PYTOWICZ, R. M. AND HAWLEY, J. E., 1971, Particle dissolution during settling in the oceans: Deep-Sea Research, v. 18, p. 1135–1139.

RUDDIMAN, W. F AND HEEZEN, B. C., 1967, Differential solution of planktonic foraminifera: *ibid.*, v. 14, p. 801–808.

THE DISTRIBUTION OF CALCIUM CARBONATE IN DEEP SEA SEDIMENTS

A. T. S. RAMSAY
University College of Swansea, Wales

ABSTRACT

Fluctuations in the rate of solution of calcium carbonate, and in the calcium carbonate compensation depth have occurred since the Jurassic. The alternating dissolution facies in calcareous sequences in oceanic basins show that fluctuations in the rate of solution can have a duration of 250,000 years or less. The oscillatory nature of the calcium carbonate compensation depth is attributed primarily to changes in plankton productivity, particularly in the high latitude fertile belts which result from global variations in temperature, through time. Warm periods, which are associated with high productivity and possibly with increased oceanic mixing, are characterized by an increase in the removal of carbonate by organisms, deposition of carbonates in high latitudes, and the enhanced solution of calcareous tests and an elevated compensation level in mid-latitudes. Cold periods correspond to intervals of low surface productivity which in high latitudes leads to a decrease in the diversity of calcareous species and a reduction in the rate of carbonate deposition; in the mid-latitudes these changes in surface productivity are reflected by a decrease in the rate of carbonate solution, depression of the compensation depth, and an increase in the distribution of carbonates.

The areal distribution of carbonates at any one time is attributed to a combination of surface topography and the position of the calcium carbonate compensation depth. Palaeobathymetric models of the Tertiary Atlantic indicate an approximately twofold increase in the areal extent of sediments of the hololytic facies (red clays and/or biogenic siliceous ooze) in this basin during periods of maximum elevation of the calcium carbonate compensation depth.

Changes in surface productivity and the associated fluctuations in the compensation depth may provide a unifying concept for pelagic sedimentation in the Mesozoic to Recent oceans. Apart from the carbonate cycles which are differentially developed in high and mid-latitudes, increases in the extent of organic siliceous ooze and the formation of cherts in Late Cretaceous and Eocene equatorial sequences correspond with intervals when the compensation depth was elevated. It is also possible that submarine lithification and the formation of hardgrounds in the oceanic environment may be related to the low rates of sedimentation which accompanied periods of enhanced carbonate solution.

INTRODUCTION

Prior to the Deep Sea Drilling Project deep-sea sediments were recovered from the oceans in dredge hauls and by piston and gravity cores. These relatively short cores have provided an adequate record of pelagic sedimentation during the Pleistocene epoch, and have been used by several workers to determine changes in the plankton faunas (Emiliani, 1969), chemistry (Arrhenius, 1952; Broecker, 1971), and surface temperature (Emiliani, 1964) which have occurred in the oceans during the past two million years. In the case of pre-Pleistocene deposits, however, the sampled localities were too dispersed, the piston and gravity cores too short, and most dredge hauls were too incomplete to provide detailed information. Sediment samples dated palaeontologically at the level of epoch or stage provided information on the minimum age of the sea floor at a given locality and the distribution of these ages (see Funnell and Smith, 1968) had a profound influence on development of ideas concerning the formation of ocean basins; they generally supported the concept of

sea floor spreading. The nature of these samples, that is whether they contain calcium carbonate or not, also provided information on their depth of deposition relative to the calcium carbonate compensation depth, but did not provide information on the stability of this level through time.

Many of the sites cored by the Deep Sea Drilling Project have yielded long sections containing a more complete biological and sedimentary record of the pre-Quaternary deposits. They also show the transition from one sediment type to another. Perhaps the most spectacular transitions are from the Pliocene and Pleistocene calcareous oozes which often overlie red clay in the Atlantic (Peterson and others, 1970); the alternating sequences of red clay and carbonate ooze in the Pliocene of the Caribbean (Bader and others, 1970), and of calcareous and pure radiolarian oozes in the sediments from the East Pacific (McManus and others, 1970). These alternations in sediment type are highly significant in that they reflect fluctuations in the calcium carbonate compensation depth and hence in the productivity and chemistry of the oceans. The purpose of this paper is to identify these alternations and to describe the fluctuations in the calcium carbonate compensation depth in space and time.

FACTORS WHICH INFLUENCE THE DEPOSITION OF CARBONATES IN THE OCEAN

Calcium carbonate is the dominant biogenic constituent of Mesozoic and younger deep-sea sediments. Modern deep ocean carbonates are derived almost entirely from the skeletal elements of planktonic organisms: foraminifers, coccolithophores, and to a lesser extent the pteropoda. The dominance of any one of these groups in Recent pelagic carbonates is determined, however, by chemical and physical factors, such as selective dissolution winnowing and the planetary temperature gradient.

With the exception of their pteropod content, Cenozoic and late Cretaceous pelagic carbonate fossils are similar to their modern counterparts. The dominance of coccoliths in late Jurassic and early Cretaceous carbonates recovered by DSDP from the Atlantic and Pacific is an artifact of organic evolution because planktonic foraminifers were not an important element of the calcareous plankton until the Albian.

In the modern oceans the accumulation rate of pelagic carbonates is determined initially by the abundance of members of the calcareous plankton, particularly the planktonic foraminifers, in the photic zone. This in turn is a function of global temperatures and atmospheric and hydrospheric circulation. On the basis of a comparison between the absolute mass of calcium carbonate in bottom sediments and the quantitative distribution of calcareous plankton in suspension, Lisitzin (1971) defined three latitudinal belts characterized by high plankton productivity and high rates of carbonate accumulation (10–30 grams per square centimeter per 10^3 years). These zones, which coincide with the northern, equatorial, and southern humid zones, are separated by the less productive arid zones (central water masses) characterized by carbonate accumulation rates of 0.1–1 gram per square centimeter per 10^3 years or less. In the temperate, arctic and antarctic zones the rate of carbonate accumulation decreases. According to McIntyre and Bé (1967) and Bé and Tolderlund (1971), the temperate zones are subject to seasonal variations in foraminiferal and coccolith productivity. Although the seasonal changes in calcareous plankton productivity probably result in a reduction in the rate of carbonate sedimentation in these areas relative to the equatorial zone, as implied by Bé and Tolderlund (1971), the fluctuations in productivity which accompany

changes in temperature on a global scale have a more profound influence on the rate of sedimentation and distribution of oceanic carbonates through geological time.

A vertical zonation, which is associated with the solution of calcium carbonate within the progressively undersaturated oceanic deep water, is superimposed on and interferes with the development of the climatically controlled accumulation zones on the ocean floor. At varying depths within the undersaturated zone the rate of calcium carbonate solution exceeds its rate of supply to the ocean floor and no calcareous plankton accumulate within the sediment; this depth is defined as the calcium carbonate compensation depth. The position of the calcium carbonate compensation depth changes with latitude within an ocean, and in the Atlantic, Pacific and Indian Oceans it shoals from the equator to the poles (Lisitzin, 1970; 1971; 1972). The position of the calcium carbonate compensation depth also differs for the same latitudinal zone from ocean to ocean (see table 1).

Li and others (1969) have investigated the variations in the transition from supersaturation to undersaturation for species of calcium carbonate in the North Atlantic and Pacific oceans. Their data show that the crossover from supersaturation to undersaturation occurs at a water depth between 4,000 and 5,000 meters for calcite and between 1,000 and 2,000 meters for aragonite in the North Atlantic, and between 1,500 and 3,000 meters for calcite and approximately 300 meters for aragonite in the Pacific. These results are in accord with the results of the buoy experiments which were undertaken in the Pacific by Peterson (1966) and Berger (1967), and with the known distribution of aragonitic pteropod ooze in the ocean (Chen, 1971).

The development of the undersaturated zone and calcium carbonate compensation depth in the oceans has a marked effect on the nature and composition of the pelagic sediments accumulating on the ocean floor. The original proportions of skeletal calcite and aragonite produced in the calcium carbonate saturated photic zone are modified by solution during and following deposition. In the undersaturated zone dissolution leads to the progressive removal of the less resistant species of both the planktonic foraminifers (Berger, 1968, 1970) and calcareous nannoplankton (McIntyre and McIntyre, 1971; Ramsay, 1971) and ultimately to the total dissolution of the skeletal elements of both groups. The planktonic foraminifers which as a group are less resistant to solution than the calcareous nannoplankton (Hsu and Anderson, 1970) are removed at a higher level in the water column.

TABLE 1.—VARIATIONS IN THE CALCIUM CARBONATE COMPENSATION DEPTH (in meters)
FOR LATITUDINAL ZONES IN THE WORLD OCEAN (FROM LISITZIN, 1971)

Ocean	Zone								
	North latitude				South latitude				
	>70	70–40	40–20	20–10	10–20	10–20	20–40	40–70	>70
Atlantic	3,650	5,000	5,900	6,000	5,600	5,500	5,400	5,000	—
Indian	—	—	3,400	5,000	5,500	5,200	5,100	5,000	—
Pacific	—	4,100	4,300	4,850	5,300	4,750	4,500	4,500	—

The progressive dissolution of biogenic calcareous elements with depth results in an increase in the proportion of the non-soluble terrigenous clay sized components and/or biogenic opaline siliceous tests in the bottom sediments. Consequently the nature of the sediments which accumulate below the calcium carbonate compensation depth is primarily a function of the biological productivity of the surface waters. Red clays accumulate in areas characterized by low biological productivity, while almost pure biogenic siliceous ooze characterizes the highly productive regions of the oceans.

Hsu and Anderson (1970) recognized and defined five facies of pelagic sediments according to their degree of calcium carbonate dissolution. The two end members of their series comprise sediments which are either unaffected by dissolution (alytic facies) or sediments from which almost all the calcium carbonate has been dissolved (hololytic facies). In this report the pure siliceous oozes are included with the red clays in the hololytic facies. Their three intermediate facies were defined according to the percentage of terrigenous material and the percentage of planktonic foraminiferal tests contained in the sediment. The eolytic facies has a terrigenous component of 10 percent or less, and contains more than 10 percent foraminiferal tests; the oligolytic facies contains 10 to 30 percent terrigenous matter, and less than 10 percent foraminiferal tests; the mesolytic facies contains 30 to 70 percent terrigenous matter and less than 3 percent foraminiferal tests.

FACTORS WHICH CONTROL THE SOLUTION OF
BIOGENIC CARBONATE AND THE DEVELOPMENT
OF COMPENSATION LEVELS IN THE OCEAN

As is discussed extensively by Berner and by Broecker and Broecker in this volume, the dissolution of calcium carbonate in the deep-sea maintains a balance between its rate of supply to the oceans via continental runoff and its excessive removal by organisms (see fig. 1). Li and others (1969) have suggested that the proportion of the ocean floor bathed in undersaturated water (i.e. not only the area below the compensation level) is determined by the rate at which organisms utilize calcium carbonate.

The rate of calcium carbonate solution, together with the areal distribution of pelagic dissolution facies, is determined by 1) the tectonically controlled bottom relief, 2) the production rate of organically derived carbon dioxide, and 3) the influence of low temperature and high hydrodynamic pressure on its solubility in the bottom waters. The production of excess carbon dioxide in the ocean is achieved by the oxidation of suspended organic matter and is related to surface productivity. Berger (1971) recorded higher rates of solution of foraminiferal tests at shallower depths in the fertile equatorial region of the Pacific than at the center of the comparatively infertile South Pacific Gyre. The level of concentration of organic carbon dioxide in the ocean, however, is primarily a function of deep water circulation which influences both the rate of oceanic mixing and the residence time of the bottom water

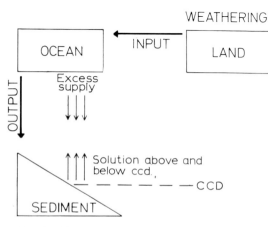

FIG. 1.—The relationship between the rate of supply of calcium carbonate to the ocean, its excess removal by organisms, and solution. CCD = calcium carbonate compensation depth.

within an ocean basin. Consequently the differences in the levels of dissolved carbon dioxide for the Pacific and North Atlantic (values for dissolved carbon dioxide are almost twice as high for the Pacific) and the variation in the compensation depths for calcite and aragonite between these oceans results from the more efficient flushing of the North Atlantic.

FACTORS WHICH INFLUENCED THE RATE OF SOLUTION, AND LEVELS OF COMPENSATION IN THE ANCIENT OCEANS

Evidence of past changes in the rate of dissolution of calcium carbonate and for fluctuations in the calcium carbonate compensation depth is provided by the carbonate cycles recorded in Quaternary sediments from the equatorial Pacific (Arrhenius, 1952; Hays and others, 1969) and by the alternations of pre-Quaternary carbonates showing various degrees of dissolution in cores recovered by the Deep Sea Drilling Project from the Atlantic, Pacific and Caribbean. The carbonate cycles and alternating dissolution facies in pelagic sequences presumably reflect periodic adjustments in oceanic chemistry to changes in the supply rate of calcium carbonate, organic productivity and oceanic mixing (Broecker and Broecker, in this volume). Variations in one or more of these parameters would enhance or depress the solution rate of calcium carbonate and would lead to fluctuations in the calcium carbonate compensation depth.

Figure 2 summarizes, in a series of simple models, possible changes in the combinations of factors which have influenced the rate of calcium carbonate solution and the level of the calcium carbonate compensation depth. The orogenic state of the continents is critical since it influences the rate of supply of weathered products to the oceans. Organic productivity and the rate of oceanic mixing, which are related, influence the rate of carbonate removal by organisms, fluctuations in these parameters are attributed to oscillations in global temperatures. These models must be compared with the record of pelagic sedimentation in the oceans and the record of global climatic changes determined by oxygen isotope data.

THE QUATERNARY RECORD

Analyses of Quaternary pelagic sequences from mid-latitudes (45° N to 45° S) indicate that accumulation rates for calcium carbonate were higher during glacial periods. During interglacial periods conditions which involve a reduction in the rate of carbonate sedimentation are indicated by the carbonate cycles which are described for the equatorial Pacific (Arrhenius,

1952; Hays and others, 1969) and Indian Oceans (Olausson, 1971). Cores from these oceans and from the Caribbean offer evidence for the enhanced solution of calcareous tests during interglacial intervals. In Pacific and Indian Ocean cores obtained close to the modern calcium carbonate compensation depth, carbonate ooze deposited during glacial cycles alternates with interglacial siliceous ooze. In areas which remained above the compensation depth the carbonates deposited during interglacial cycles are characterized by a deficit in the number of whole planktonic foraminiferal tests (Olausson, 1971), and enrichment of solution resistant species. In Caribbean deposits, the aragonitic tests of pteropods occur only in glacial intervals (Chen, 1968), and the tests of planktonic foraminifers show evidence of solution in the interglacial sediments (Zobel in Berger, 1971).

The record of pelagic carbonate sedimentation in the high latitudes of the North Atlantic is the reverse of that described for the mid and equatorial latitudes of the Pacific, Indian Ocean and Caribbean. Olausson (1971) and McIntyre and others (1972) demonstrated that less carbonate accumulates during glacial cycles than during interglacial cycles. Olausson interpreted this record in terms of enhanced solution during glacial events. McIntyre and others, however, argued convincingly that the glacial carbonate minima are associated with low biological productivity which accompanied the southward penetration of cold polar water during glacial intervals. Less fertile glacial events are characterized either by the total elimination of coccolith carbonate, by a severe reduction in the amount deposited, and by a reduction in the species diversity of the planktonic foraminifera. These authors also suggested that the southern limit for polar water incursions is defined by the northern boundary of the subtropical gyre (approximately 45° N). During interglacial cycles the retreat of the polar water is accompanied by coccolith carbonate maxima, increased species diversity and increased productivity in high latitudes. If these data are equally valid for the fertile belts aligned on the convergences in the high latitudes of the Pacific and southern oceans, then the fluctuations in the calcium carbonate compensation depth and in the solution rates of skeletal carbonate in the equatorial belt and mid-latitudes are mainly a consequence of changes in plankton productivity in the temperate zones. It is possible that an increase in the ratio of the deep-sea to littoral accumulation rates during glacial events could also have contributed to the greater quantities of calcium carbonate deposited in mid-latitudes.

OROGENIC

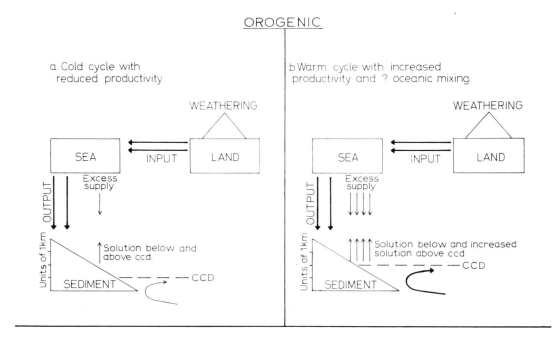

a. Cold cycle with reduced productivity

b. Warm cycle with increased productivity and ? oceanic mixing.

OROGENIC QUIESCENCE

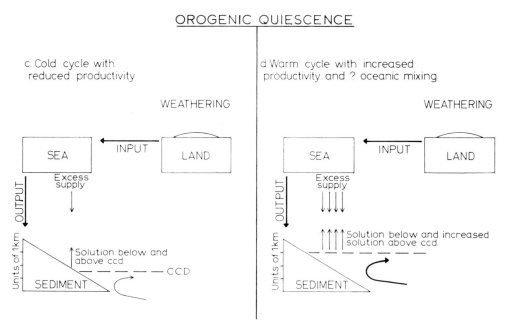

c. Cold cycle with reduced productivity

d. Warm cycle with increased productivity and ? oceanic mixing.

Fig. 2.—Models of parameters which may influence the relationship between the rate of supply of calcium carbonate to the ocean, its excess removal by organisms, and solution, and lead to fluctuations in the calcium carbonate compensation depth (CCD). The thickness of the curved arrow expresses the degree of oceanic mixing.

Quaternary data tend to conform to models a and b, outlined on figure 2.

VERTICAL MOVEMENTS OF THE SEA FLOOR AND THE DEVELOPMENT OF PELAGIC SEDIMENTARY FACIES

In the model of sea floor spreading it is postulated that the ocean basins are generated by the spreading and subsidence of new ocean crust away from the elevated crests of mid-ocean ridges (Hess, 1962; Menard, 1969). Assuming a zone of calcium carbonate compensation which is fixed and does not fluctuate in depth through time, sites at increasing distances from a ridge crest should contain a sequence of sediments which have undergone increasing degrees of dissolution. Data from DSDP Leg 3 in the South Atlantic (Hsu and Anderson in Maxwell and others, 1970) and Leg 5 in the East Pacific (McManus and others, 1970) show that this is not the case. At site 42, in the East Pacific, sediments of the hololytic and mesolytic facies alternate and one complete cycle of mesolytic through hololytic to mesolytic sediments can occur within a period of 250,000 years or less (see fig. 3). The same is true for the Atlantic and Caribbean (see fig. 4). At South Atlantic sites 15 and 17 oligolytic and eolytic Upper Miocene and younger sediments are superimposed on mesolytic sediments. Hsu and Anderson (in Maxwell and others, 1970) interpreted the facies changes in the South Atlantic in terms of significant vertical movements of the mid-ocean ridge system, considering the calcium carbonate compensation depth to remain at a constant depth in the oceans. This interpretation requires the elevation and depression of broad areas of the ocean floor by as much as 1 kilometer within relatively short intervals of time. The facies changes can be explained more realistically by assuming that the only significant vertical motion of points on the ocean floor has been downwards as they moved away from the mid-ocean ridge crests, and that the calcium carbonate compensation depth has fluctuated through considerable distances in the water column.

Frehrichs (1970) suggested a combination of vertical tectonics, intermittent convection in the mantle, and global fluctuations in temperature to explain similar changes in Cenozoic pelagic sediments exposed on the continents.

An interpretation of the DSDP cores and other sequences which contain the most complete record of alternating dissolution facies is presented on figures 3 and 4. The curves which illustrate fluctuations in the calcium carbonate compensation depth are based primarily on the cores indicated, although other data were considered. The Pacific (fig. 3) and Atlantic (fig. 4) curves have been adjusted for the depth changes of the site which would be expected as a result of sea floor spreading. In making these adjustments it was assumed that the respective mid-ocean ridges have maintained a constant angle of slope since the Late Cretaceous; the following spreading rates define the position of a point on the surface of the slope at any given time: Central Atlantic 1.5 cm/yr (Talwani and others, 1969); South Atlantic 2 cm/yr (von Herzen and Maxwell in Maxwell and others, 1970) North Pacific 4 cm/yr; Central Pacific 8 cm/yr from the Eocene to the Middle Miocene followed by 4 cm/yr for the Middle Miocene to the Recent (Hayes and others, 1970). In the absence of precise information for depth changes in the Caribbean Basin since the Cretaceous the present depths of sampled localities are used.

Although it is easy to distinguish sediments deposited above or below the calcium carbonate compensation depth, it is sometimes difficult to recognize this surface in fossil sediments. For this paper sediments which contain only a few species of calcareous nannoplankton and less than 10 percent calcium carbonate are considered to have been deposited at or near the calcium carbonate compensation depth.

The paleotemperature graph on figure 4 is compiled from the oxygen isotope data of Lowenstam and Epstein (1954), Bowen and Fontes (1963), Fritz (1965), Devereaux (1967), and Douglas and Savin (1971). This graph is based on the actual determinations rather than on averaging results and is constructed from individual records which in some instances are separated by several degrees of latitude (e.g. New Zealand and Western Europe). Nevertheless it is assumed that the fluctuations recorded on the graph provide an indication of oscillations of global temperatures since the Jurassic.

THE TERTIARY RECORD

Figures 3 and 4 indicate remarkable synchroneity between the fluctuations in the calcium carbonate compensation depth recorded for the Tertiary mid-latitude sequences in the Atlantic, Caribbean and Pacific basins. The shallower compensation depth in the Pacific basin throughout the Tertiary, which is the only significant difference between the graphs, is analogous to the modern situation, and probably has a similar cause, namely higher concentrations of carbon dioxide in the Pacific bottom waters.

There is a good correlation between changes in the compensation level and the fluctuations in global temperatures which are recorded in the graph on figure 4. With the exception of the

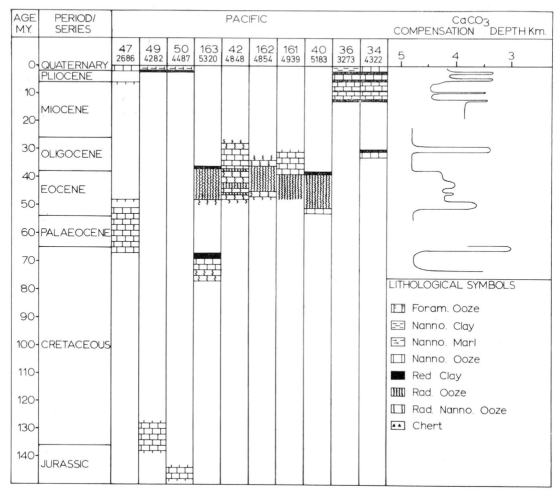

FIG. 3.—Schematic representation of the vertical fluctuations in the calcium carbonate compensation depth for the Pacific plotted against time. Time scale after Berggren in Maxwell and others (1970) and Harland and others (1964).

peak in the compensation level at 9 million years before present, corresponding to a cold cycle, and the Eocene troughs which correlate with a warm interval, the relationship between changes in the compensation level and changes in global temperature during the Tertiary is identical to the relationship observed for the Quaternary period. During cold cycles the mid-latitudes are characterized by a depressed compensation level and an increased distribution of carbonates; during warm cycles they are characterized by an elevated compensation level, a decrease in the distribution of carbonates, and an increase in the rate of solution of calcium carbonate. These changes are clearly reflected in the vertical distribution of red clay, siliceous ooze, carbonate ooze and the intermediate dissolution facies in

the cores illustrated on figures 3 and 4. The only exceptions to this pattern, i.e. the peak in the compensation depth at 9 million years, and the depressions in this level during the Eocene, may be fortuitous and result from our present state of knowledge of paleotemperatures for these intervals of time.

Few data are available for the Tertiary record of pelagic sedimentation in high latitudes. In a study of subantarctic deep-sea cores, Margolis and Kennett (1971) interpreted variations in the abundance of glacially attrited quartz grains together with changes in the species diversity of the planktonic foraminifera in terms of a series of Antarctic glaciations. Their results, which indicated periodic cooling in the early Eocene, late Middle Eocene, and Oligocene correspond with the interpretation presented here. Unfortunately, these authors did not determine the percentage of calcium carbonate, but the reduction in species diversity during cold intervals, which they noted, is analogous to similar changes in foraminiferal diversity accompanying reduced surface productivity during the Quaternary glacial cycles in the North Atlantic (McIntyre and others, 1972). It is also significant that the fluctuations in the compensation depth in the mid-latitudes correlate with the changes in phytoplankton abundance and produc-

tivity recorded by Tappan (1968) and Tappan and Loeblich (1971).

It is probable that the Tertiary cold cycles, like those of the Quaternary, were accompanied by an increase in the distribution of carbonates at equatorial and mid-latitudes, and a decreased distribution in high latitudes. The reverse would be true for warm intervals. Because the Cenozoic was a period of continuous orogeny it appears that models a and b, outlined on figure 2 are also applicable to the Tertiary patterns of deep-sea sedimentation.

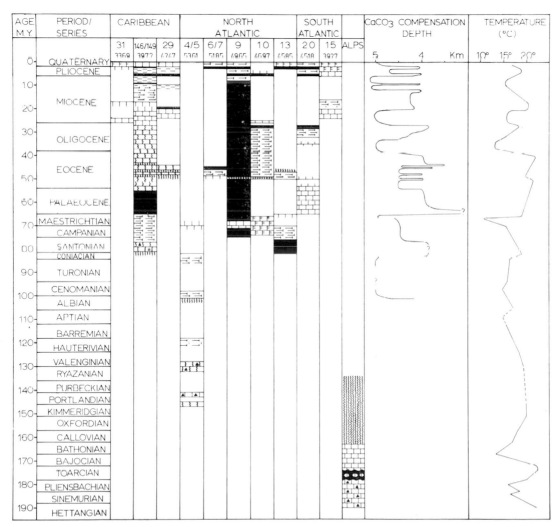

Fig. 4.—An interpretation of the record of fluctuations in the calcium carbonate compensation depth for the Atlantic and Caribbean plotted against time, and compared with a paleotemperature graph for the Jurassic sequence which contains sedimentary evidence for fluctuations in the calcium carbonate compensation depth. Time scale after Berggren in Maxwell and others, 1970, and Harland and others, 1964. Data from Peterson and others, 1970; Maxwell and others, 1970; Bader and others, 1970; Ramsay, 1970; Bernoulli and Jenkyns, 1970; Laughton and others, 1970; Hayes and others, 1971; Edgar and others, 1971.

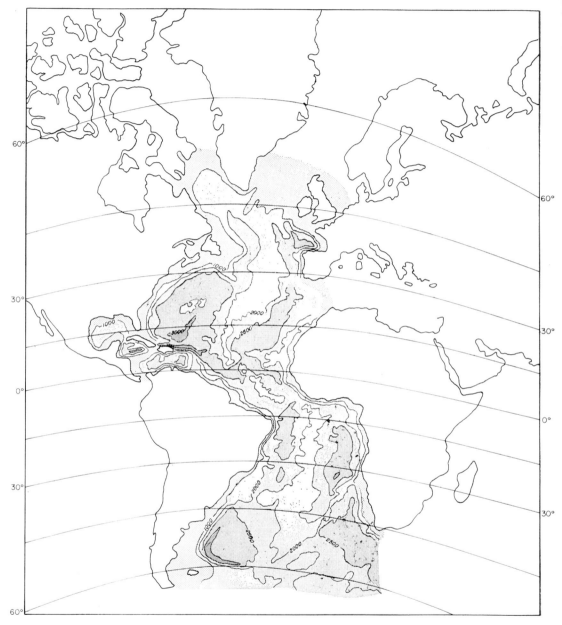

FIG. 5.—A physiographical model of the Eocene Atlantic of 40 million years ago, superimposed on a continental reconstruction by Francheteau (1970). Depth in fathoms.

THE INFLUENCE OF BOTTOM TOPOGRAPHY AND FLUCTUATIONS IN THE CALCIUM CARBONATE COMPENSATION DEPTH ON PELAGIC SEDIMENTATION IN THE TERTIARY ATLANTIC

The distribution of carbonate ooze and red clay in the modern Atlantic is influenced to a large extent by bathymetry. To postulate the effect of the fluctuations in the calcium carbon-ate compensation depth during the Eocene, late Oligocene and early Miocene on the areal distribution of pelagic sediments it is necessary to formulate physiographic models of the Terti-ary Atlantic ocean. Figures 5 and 6 are physio-graph models for the Middle Eocene and early Miocene based on Francheteau's (1970) recon-structions of the Atlantic of 40 and 20 million years ago. Both models are founded on two as-

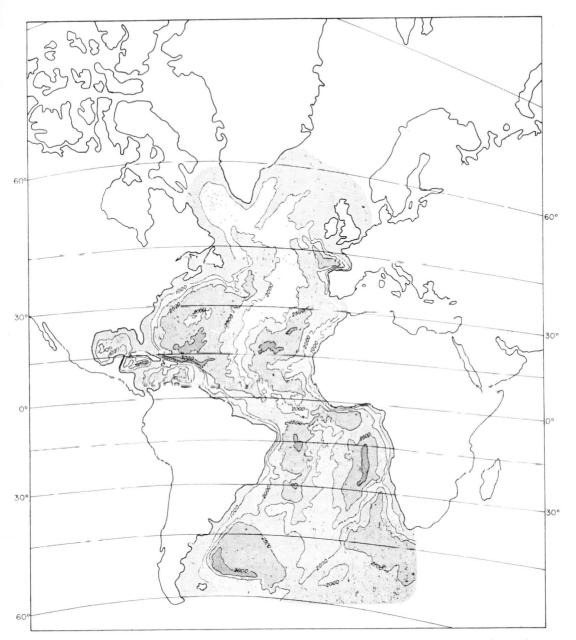

FIG. 6.—A physiographical model of the Miocene Atlantic of 20 million years ago, superimposed on a continental reconstruction by Francheteau (1970). Depths in fathoms.

sumptions: 1) that the height and width of the Eocene and Miocene mid-Atlantic Ridge are equivalent to these dimensions in their modern counterpart, and 2) that, with the exception of younger areas of the Atlantic (i.e. north of 50° N), there was no appreciable subsidence around the margins of the Atlantic since the Mesozoic. The first assumption is reasoned on the grounds that currently available data (Vogt

and others, 1970; Williams and McKenzie, 1971; Maxwell and others, 1970) show that the Tertiary ridge, like its modern counterpart, was the product of a slow spreading rate (i.e. 1–2 cm/yr.). Various authors (Vogt and Ostenso, 1967; Menard, 1967; Le Pichon and Langseth, 1969) have demonstrated a causal relationship between width, local topography and the spreading rate of mid-ocean ridges. There is no con-

68 A. T. S. RAMSAY

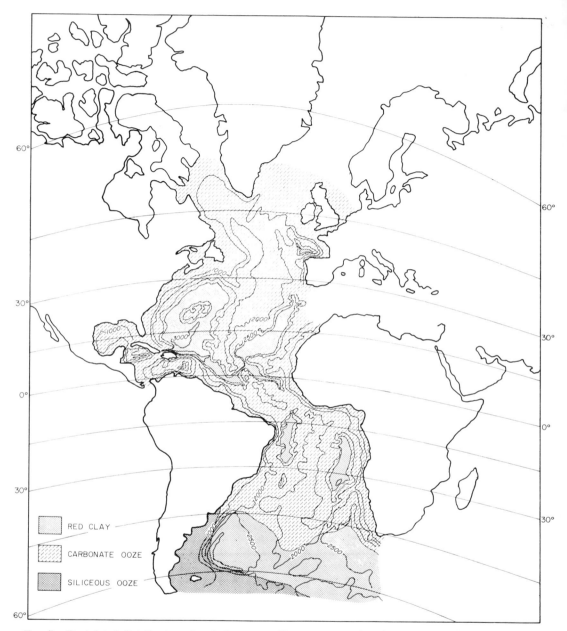

Fig. 7.—Postulated distribution of red clay, pure siliceous ooze and carbonate ooze in the Early Eocene Atlantic, during an interval when the compensation depth was depressed. Depths in fathoms.

clusive evidence to support or refute the second assumption. If, however, the results obtained at the margins of the North Atlantic during Leg 12 of the Deep Sea Drilling Project are applicable to the whole of the basin, it may be postulated that major vertical movements occur at the periphery of an ocean only during the initial 40 to 50 million years of its formation as an isostatic response to opening.

As in the modern Atlantic, the deep basins in the models are situated on the oldest parts of the ocean floor. Although both models are subject to errors inherent in the reconstructed positions of the continents and to errors of personal interpretation, they do provide a surface on which the hypothetical distribution of pelagic sedimentary facies in the past can be plotted. They serve as hypotheses for future testing.

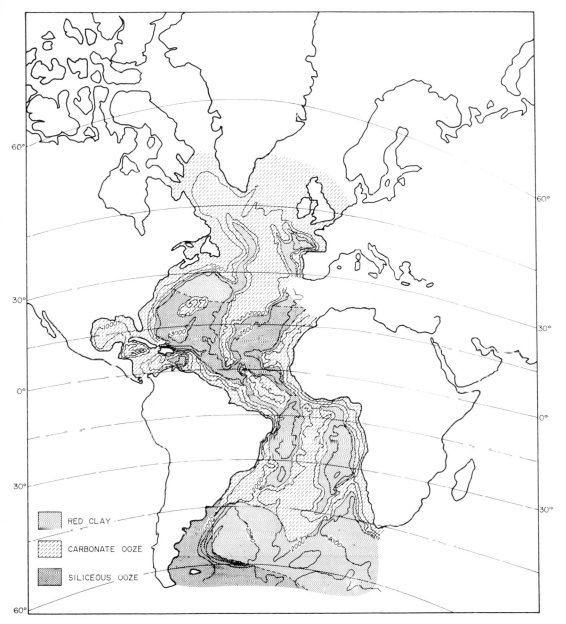

FIG. 8.—Postulated distribution of red clay, pure siliceous ooze and carbonate ooze in the Middle Eocene Atlantic, during an interval characterized by an elevated compensation depth. Depths in fathoms.

The distribution of pelagic facies during the early and middle Eocene (figs. 7 and 8) and during the late Oligocene and early Miocene (figs. 9 and 10) are indicated in terms of fluctuations of 1 kilometer in the calcium carbonate compensation depth (see fig. 1). A comparison of figures 8 and 10 shows that there was an approximately twofold increase in the areal extent of sediments of the hololytic facies during pe-riods of maximum elevation of the calcium carbonate compensation depth. It should be noted that terriginous sediments deposited in areas proximal to the continents are omitted from these figures, so that they represent a simplified picture of sedimentation in the Atlantic during these intervals. The development of a zone of biogenic siliceous sediments in the early Tertiary equatorial Atlantic is attributed to an influx of

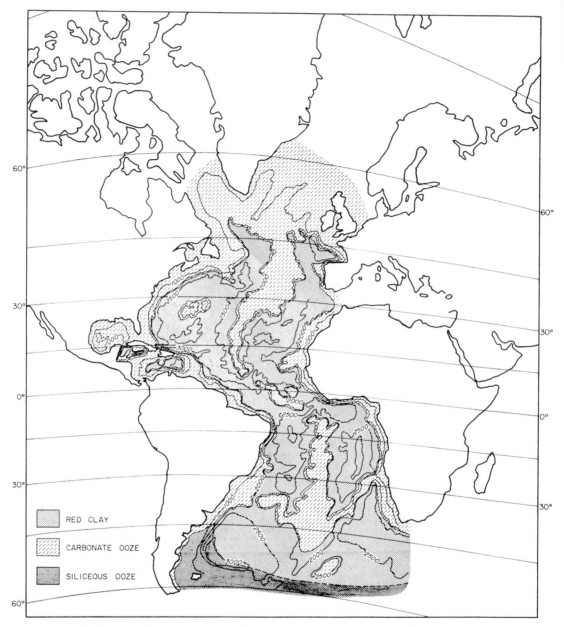

Fig. 9.—Postulated distribution of red clay, pure siliceous ooze and carbonate ooze
in the Late Oligocene Atlantic. Depths in fathoms.

nutrient rich Pacific equatorial water through an open Isthmus of Panama (Ramsay, 1971).

THE CRETACEOUS RECORD

Fluctuations of the calcium carbonate compensation depth in the mid-latitudes during the Upper Cretaceous were also synchronous for the Atlantic, Caribbean and Pacific basins (see figures 3 and 4). They also correlated with changes

in world temperatures, and with the changes in phytoplankton abundance and productivity recorded by Tappan (1968) and Tappan and Loeblich (1971).

On the basis of the relationship between the fluctuating calcium carbonate compensation depth, paleotemperature and changes in oceanic productivity, it would appear that models a and b outlined on figure 2 are also applicable to the

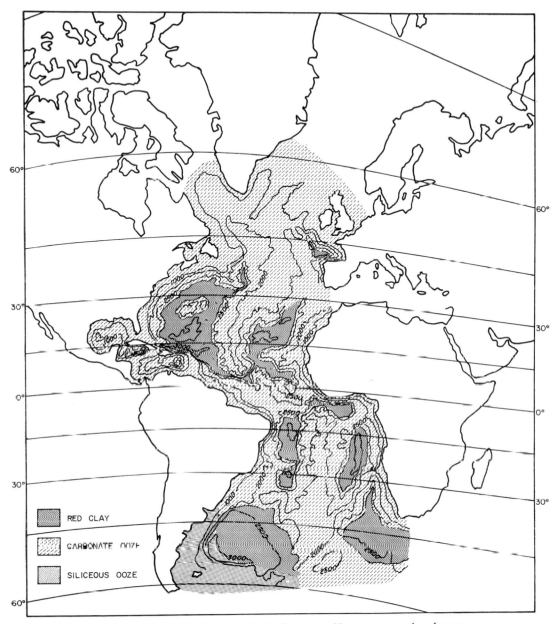

FIG. 10.—Postulated distribution of red clay, pure siliceous ooze and carbonate ooze in the Lower Miocene Atlantic. Depths in fathoms.

RED CLAY

CARBONATE OOZE

SILICEOUS OOZE

Late Cretaceous. Before considering these models, however, we have to consider two alternative models proposed by Tappan (1968) and Worsley (1971), which attempt to account for increased carbonate solution and the faunal and floral extinctions which occur at the close of the Cretaceous.

Tappan's model involves a combination of low continents, minimal influx of terrigenous sedi-

ments and therefore nutrient salts into the oceans, equable climates and sluggish oceanic circulation accompanied by reduced upwelling resulting from the influence of the low physiography of the continents on atmospheric circulation. She suggested that the severe reduction in the microfloras and phytoplankton productivity which resulted from the combined effect of these factors, led to a reduction in the utilization of carbon dioxide by organisms, and hence to a depletion of atmospheric oxygen, an increase in the partial pressure of carbon dioxide a decrease in the pH of the oceans and an increase in the solution of calcium carbonate. The increased partial pressure of carbon dioxide would, she proposed, arise from volcanic outgassing and animal, plant and bacterial respiration.

Worsley's (1971) model entailed a combination of low continents, low input of clastic sediments to the oceans, and pronounced climatic deterioration. Worsley suggested that the change in world climate during the Maestrichtian was caused by a depletion in atmospheric carbon dioxide which resulted from the late Cretaceous phytoplankton bloom and the associated 'worldwide' deposition of chalk. He proposed that the resulting lowering of the planetary temperatures would lead to a decrease in precipitation and associated terrestrial weathering and erosion and would contribute to a reduction in the supply of nutrients and carbonate to the oceans. In Worsley's model enhanced solution in the late Cretaceous oceans resulted from the cooling of seawater and the concomittant increased solubility of carbon dioxide in high latitudes.

Tappan (1968) and Worsley (1971) both suggested that the "hard grounds" and associated phosphatic deposits which characterize the Cretaceous/Tertiary boundary deposits in the shelf sequences of many areas indicate that the calcium carbonate compensation depth approached the photic zone at the end of the Maestrichtian.

Despite the differences between these models, one assumption, namely orogenic quiescence, low Cretaceous continents and an associated reduction in the input of terrigenous sediments to the oceans, is common to both. In the light of plate-tectonics and the disruption of the supercontinent Pangea during the Early Jurassic this assumption is not wholly valid. Apart from the Late Cretaceous Laramide Orogeny which deformed the west coast of the Americas, there are several other instances of Cretaceous orogeny. In the extrapeninsular Himalayas of India, Wadia (1966) described the initiation of orogeny during the Cenomanian, implying that it continued through the Cretaceous. Orogenic movements of this age are also recorded from central Borneo and the western Celebes (Kummel, 1961) and Japan (Takai and others, 1969). In Japan orogenic movements are recorded from the Neocomanian, Albian, Turonian and Maestrichtian. Late Upper Cretaceous earth movements are also reported for almost the whole of the East Indies (Kummel, 1961). The Cretaceous therefore certainly cannot be described

as a period of orogenic quiescence. Worsley viewed the Laramide Orogeny only in terms of the North American Plate, and although, as he suggested, sediments derived from this orogenic belt were deposited in the restricted epicontinental sea to the east of the belt, it is highly probable that flysch sediments were poured into the eastern margin of the Pacific Ocean along the whole length of the Americas. There is, however, some justification for the assumptions made by these authors because during the late Cretaceous wide shelf areas were characterized by minimal terrigenous sedimentation and the accumulation of chalk. The concentration of these shelf areas in the tropics as a result of plate movements undoubtably contributed to the extensive accumulation of shelf carbonates during the Cretaceous. Other factors in the mechanisms proposed by both authors to account for the high rate of solution and elevated calcium carbonate compensation level in mid-latitudes at the end of the Cretaceous also correspond with periods of high oceanic productivity rather than low productivity as implied by Tappan (1968). The same relationship is also true for the Cretaceous (see figures 3 and 4). Worsley's model (1971, and elsewhere in this volume) suggests that the solution of calcium carbonate is enhanced during cold periods. This is not the case in the Quaternary and Tertiary oceans, and increased solution of calcium carbonate during cold periods is not indicated by the currently available data for Cretaceous deep sea carbonates (see figures 3 and 4). Indeed, Maestrichtian carbonates are usually present in most DSDP cores which penetrate mid-latitude late Cretaceous sequences.

Figures 3 and 4 indicate that the elevated compensation depth at the end of the Maestrichtian corresponds with a rise in global temperatures. The absence of a transitional Cretaceous/Tertiary calcareous faunal and floral sequence in the majority of DSDP cores which contain this boundary coupled with the evidence of hard grounds and paraconformities on the continental shelves suggests that the degree of elevation of the compensation depths at this time exceeded subsequent elevations of this level. Whether it reached the photic zone as suggested by Tappan (1968) and Worsley (1971) is a mute point. Submarine lithification and the formation of Recent hardgrounds has been described from the Persian Gulf (Shinn, 1969). Shinn (1969), Fischer and Garrison (1967) and Garrison and Fischer (1969) have suggested that a slow rate of sedimentation may be a crucial factor in submarine lithification. The interpretation of DSDP cores provides conflicting information.

If the transitional Cretaceous/Tertiary sequence described by Bukry and others (1971) from Core 47 on the Shatsky Rise is not a product of Palaeocene reworking or mixing during drilling then the elevation of the compensation depth in the east Pacific did not exceed three kilometers below sea level. On the other hand the Cretaceous/Tertiary hiatus in core 20 from the South Atlantic was developed when this site was almost at the crest of the mid-Atlantic ridge. This suggests that the calcium carbonate compensation depth was elevated above the crest of the mid-ocean ridge at approximately two kilometers below sea level. The increased rate of solution at shallower depths and the concomittant reduction in the rate of carbonate sedimentation which would accompany the elevation of the calcium carbonate compensation depth to depths of three kilometers or less below sea level, though not necessarily into the photic zone, would certainly have led to the formation of extensive hardgrounds in carbonate sequences deposited on the continental shelves.

In the light of the above discussion, the models of factors controlling carbonate sedimentation in the deep sea which are illustrated on figures 2 a and 2 b are equally applicable to the Late Cretaceous. The extreme elevation of the compensation depth to depths shallower than three or even two kilometers at the end of the Maestrichtian is, however, probably due to an additional factor, namely the deposition of carbonate on the extensive continental shelves. In the time interval for which we have the most data (Late Cretaceous to Recent) there is no evidence to support models 2 c and 2 d, in which orogenic quiescence is the primary factor. The depression of the compensation depth during the early Palaeocene, despite evidence of increasing global temperatures, may be due to the substantial extinctions which occurred in the calcareous plankton at the end of the Cretaceous, or alternatively the paleotemperature data may be erroneous.

Unfortunately it is not possible to construct curves for the history of the calcium carbonate compensation depth for the Early Cretaceous. The adjustment of the data provided on figures 3 and 4 for depth changes involved in sea floor spreading, however, suggests that it was certainly situated at a depth in excess of 3.8 kilometers below sea level in the mid-latitudes of the Atlantic and Pacific.

THE JURASSIC PERIOD

There are, as yet, few data available on Jurassic deep-sea carbonates and it is not possible to determine the history of calcium carbonate solution in the oceans for this period with any certainty. The adjustment of DSDP sites 49 and 50 (northwest Pacific) for vertical changes which occurred during sea floor spreading suggests that during the Late Jurassic the compensation depth for calcite was in excess of 3.7 kilometers below sea level. Similar adjustments for Atlantic DSDP sites 4 and 5 indicate that the compensation depth was situated at depths greater than 2.5 km for much of the Late Jurassic.

At present the most complete record of Jurassic pelagic sedimentation is contained in the Alpine ensialic basinal sequences (see fig. 4). The section illustrated on figure 4 is based on the Glasenbach Gorge section (Austria) described by Bernoulli and Jenkyns (1970); I have, however, omitted turbidites which they also record. In this section the Toarcian marly Ammonitico Rosso facies and the Late Jurassic radiolarite probably represent sediments deposited during intervals of increased calcium carbonate solution. There is certainly a good correlation between the development of these facies and elevated temperatures during the Jurassic (see fig. 4). The sequence of pelagic sedimentary facies in the Glasenbach Gorge suggests that the calcium carbonate compensation level was depressed during the early Early Jurassic (Hettangian-Pliensbachian), elevated in the Toarcian, depressed through much of the Middle Jurassic and elevated again in the late Middle Jurassic and through the whole of the Late Jurassic. Garrison and Fischer (1969) also interpreted the development of pelagic facies in Jurassic sediments of the Unken Syncline (Austrian Alps) in terms of a fluctuating compensation depth and in their second model suggested a depression in the compensation zone from 1,500 or 2,000 meters in the Mid-Jurassic to below 4,000 meters in the Late Jurassic. Their interpretation of the possible history of the calcium carbonate compensation depth is very different from the sequence of events outlined for the Glasenbach section. Because both areas have been subject to vertical movements (Bernoulli and Jenkyns, 1970; Garrison and Fischer, 1969) and because vertical tectonics have certainly influenced the nature of carbonate turbidites in the Glasenbach sequence (Bernoulli and Jenkyns, 1970) the differences in interpretation are hardly surprising. Obviously, more complete information from oceanic sequences is required in order to construct a definitive history of the rate of calcium carbonate solution and fluctuations of the compensation depth during the Jurassic. If the relationship between the sequence of sedimentary events in the Glasenbach section and the temperature graph is not fortuitous, this section may provide a reliable indication of carbonate sedimentation in mid-latitudes for this interval of time.

FLUCTUATIONS IN OCEANIC PRODUCTIVITY: A POSSIBLE UNIFYING CONCEPT IN MESOZOIC AND YOUNGER PELAGIC SEDIMENTATION

Analysis of Mesozoic and younger pelagic carbonate sediments shows that changes in oceanic productivity have had a profound influence on the nature and distribution of pelagic sedimentation.

During the Quaternary, changes in surface productivity which are associated with fluctuating global temperatures (cold equals low productivity, warm equals high productivity), have led to the development of carbonate cycles. In the mid and equatorial latitudes the formation of these cycles is a function of oscillations in the rate of solution of calcium carbonate and in the level of the compensation depth as a response to changes in surface productivity in high latitudes. At these latitudes (45° N–45° S) warm periods are characterized by the enhanced solution of calcitic or aragonitic tests in carbonate sequences, or by siliceous ooze or red clay, which accumulated below an elevated compensation level. In high latitudes the situation is reversed and warm intervals are characterized by carbonate maxima, and cold intervals by carbonate minima. Temperature related carbonate cycles, which are caused by fluctuations in the rate of calcium carbonate solution and compensation depth are also recorded in Cenozoic and Mesozoic mid-latitude sections. There are also indications of high latitude Eocene and Oligocene carbonate cycles which are identical with and are of similar origin to the Quaternary high latitude cycles. Unfortunately the paucity of data for high latitude Tertiary and Mesozoic sections does not allow one to draw firm conclusions about the history of pelagic sedimentation in these areas for this interval of time and one can only assume that it was similar to the Quaternary.

During the Cretaceous, Tertiary and Quaternary periods the mid-latitude carbonate cycles are also associated with other phenomena. The extensive development of Early Tertiary cherts in equatorial sequences is almost certainly related to fluctuations in the compensation level. Oscillations of the compensation depth at the equator during this interval resulted in an increase in the areal extent of siliceous ooze during periods of elevation and produced alternating sequences of carbonate and siliceous ooze characterized by interstitial solutions of different alkalinities, and created a potentially ideal environment for the development of chert. Opaline silica will dissolve in an environment of high pH and reprecipitate in one of low pH. The widespread late Cretaceous cherts, recovered by DSDP from the Atlantic, Caribbean and Pacific, probably owe their origin to similar phenomena. One may also speculate that if the 'near future' equatorial sediments of the Pacific and Indian Oceans are deposited through a series of climatic oscillations, these future deposits together with Recent and Quaternary sediments will give rise to widespread chert horizons in the oceans of 50 to 70 million years hence.

The development of lithified carbonates (hardgrounds) in oceanic sediments may also be related to fluctuations in the rate of solution of calcium carbonate. An elevated compensation depth and enhanced solution in the water column and at the sediment water interface above this depth could lead to the solution and reprecipitation of calcite. They would also produce the slow rates of sedimentation which are essential for the submarine lithification of carbonates (Shinn, 1969; Garrison and Fischer, 1969; Fischer and Garrison, 1967). Alternations of Quaternary lithified-nonlithified couplets recovered in drill cores from mid-latitude seamounts in the eastern and western North Atlantic (Bartlett and Greggs, 1969) tend to support this hypothesis. The non-lithified carbonates which presumably represent periods of high sedimentation contain foraminifers of a cold water aspect, whereas the lithified carbonates contain a warm water fauna. This association could also be produced by a decrease in the sedimentation rate due to increased winnowing during intervals of enhanced oceanic circulation which may occur during warm intervals. Since lithified pelagic carbonates are frequently associated with topographic rises this alternative must also be given serious consideration.

ACKNOWLEDGMENTS

This research was undertaken while I was Visiting Assistant Professor of Geology at the University of Illinois. I am grateful to Professor W. W. Hay for his critical reading of the manuscript, and for several stimulating discussions concerning this problem. I am indebted to Dr. T. R. Worsley, Dr. David Bukry, Dr. Stefan Gartner, Dr. W. R. Riedel and Dr. Andrew McIntyre for providing reprints and in some instances unpublished manuscripts which have proved most useful in interpreting the DSDP results. I also wish to acknowledge Dr. Jean Francheteau for his permission to use his unpublished reconstructions of the Eocene and Miocene Atlantic, and Mr. L. Lewis who prepared many of the diagrams.

REFERENCES

ARRHENIUS, G. O. S., 1952, Sediment cores from the east Pacific: Rept. Swedish Deep-Sea Exped., v. 5, no. 1, 227 p.

BADER, R. G., AND OTHERS, 1970, Initial Reports of the Deep Sea Drilling Project: Washington, D.C., U.S. Govt. Printing Office, v. 4, xxi + 753 p.

BARTLETT, G. S., AND GREGGS, R. G., 1969, Carbonate sediments: oriented lithified samples from the North Atlantic: Science, v. 166, p. 740–41.

BE, A. W. H., AND TOLDERLUND, D. S., 1971, Distribution and ecology of living planktonic foraminifera in surface waters of the Atlantic and Indian Oceans, *in* FUNNEL, B. M., AND RIEDEL, W. R. (eds.), The micropalaeontology of oceans: Cambridge, England, Cambridge Univ. Press, p. 105–149.

BERGER, W. H., 1967, Foraminiferal ooze: solution at depths: Science v. 156, p. 383–385.

———, 1968, Planktonic foraminifera: selective solution and palaeoclimatic interpretation: Deep Sea Research, v. 15, p. 31–43.

———, 1970, Planktonic foraminifera: selective solution and the lysocline: Marine Geology, v. 8, 111–138.

———, 1971, Sedimentation of planktonic foraminifera: *ibid.*, v. 11, p. 325–358.

BERNOULLI, D., AND JENKYNS, H., 1970, A Jurassic basin: the Glasenbach Gorge, Salzburg, Austria: Geol. Bundesanst. Verh., v. 4, p. 504–531.

BOWEN, R., AND FONTES, J. C., 1963, Palaeotempératures indiquees par l'analyse isotopique de fossiles du Crétacé inférieur des Hautes-Alps (France): Experimentia, v. 19, p. 268–75.

BROECKER, W. S., 1971, Calcite accumulation rates and glacial to interglacial changes in oceanic mixing, *in* TUREKIAN, K. K. (ed.), The late Cenozoic glacial ages. New Haven, Connecticut, Yale Univ. Press, p. 239–265.

BUKRY, D., DOUGLAS, R. G., KLING, S. A., AND KRASHENINNIKOV, V. V., 1971, Planktonic microfossil biostratigraphy of the northwestern Pacific area, *in* FISCHER, A. G., AND OTHERS, Initial reports of the Deep Sea Drilling Project: Washington, D.C., U.S. Govt. Printing Office, v. 6, p. 1253–1300.

CHEN, C., 1968, Pleistocene pteropods in pelagic sediments: Nature, v. 219, p. 1145–9.

———, 1971, Occurrence of pteropods in pelagic sediments, *in* FUNNELL, B. M., AND RIEDEL, W. R. (eds.), The micropalaeontology of oceans: Cambridge, England, Cambridge Univ. Press, p. 351.

DEVEREAUX, I., 1967, Oxygen isotope measurements on New Zealand Tertiary fossils: New Zealand Jour. Sci., v. 10, p. 988–1011.

DOUGLAS, R. G., AND SAVIN, S. M., 1971, Isotopic analysis of planktonic foraminifera from the Cenozoic of the northwest Pacific, Leg 6, *in* FISCHER, A. G., AND OTHERS, Initial reports of the Deep Sea Drilling Project: Washington, D.C., U.S. Govt. Printing Office, v. 6, p. 1123–1127.

EDGAR, N. T., AND OTHERS, 1971, Deep Sea Drilling Project: Leg 15: Geotimes, v. 16, no. 4, p. 12–16.

EMILIANI, C., 1964, Palaeotemperature analysis of the Caribbean cores A 254-BR-C and CP-28: Geol. Soc. America Bull., v. 75, p. 129–144.

———, 1969, A new paleontology: Micropaleontology, v. 15, p. 265–300.

FISCHER, A. G., AND GARRISON, R. E., 1967, Carbonate lithification on the sea floor, Jour. Geology, v. 75, p. 488–496.

———, AND OTHERS, 1971, Initial reports of the Deep Sea Drilling Project: v. 6, Washington, D.C., U.S. Govt. Printing Office, v. 6, xxii + 1329 p.

FRANCHETEAU, J., 1970, Palaeomagnetism and plate tectonics (thesis): Berkeley, Univ. California.

FREHRICHS, W. E., 1970, Palaeobathymetry, palaeotemperature and tectonism: Geol. Soc. America Bull., v. 81, p. 3445–3452.

FRITZ, P., 1965, O^{18}/O^{16} Isotopenanalysen und Palaeotemparaturbestimmungen an Belemniten aus dem Schwab. Jura: Geol. Rundsch., v. 54, p. 261–269.

FUNNELL, B. M., AND SMITH, A. G., 1968, Opening of the Atlantic Ocean: Nature, v. 129, p. 1328–1333.

GARRISON, R. E., AND FISCHER, A. G., 1969, Deep-water limestones and radiolarites of the Alpine Jurassic: Soc. Econ. Paleontologists and Mineralogists Special Pub. 14, p. 20 56.

HARLAND, W. B., SMITH, A. G., AND WILCOCK, B. (eds.), 1964, The Phanerozoic time-scale: Quart. Jour. Geol. Soc. London, v. 1205, p. 260–261.

HAYS, J. D., SAITO, T., OPDYKE, N. D., AND BURCKLE, L. H., 1969, Pliocene-Pleistocene sediments of the equatorial Pacific: their palaeomagnetic, biostratigraphic and climatic record. Geol. Soc. America Bull., v. 80, p. 1481–1541.

HAYES, D. E., AND OTHERS, 1971, Deep Sea Drilling Project: Leg 9: Geotimes, v. 15, no. 4, p. 11–13.

———, AND OTHERS, 1971, Deep Sea Drilling Project Leg 14: *ibid.*, v. 16, no. 2, p. 14–17.

HESS, H. H., 1962, History of ocean basins, *in* ENGEL, A. E. J., JAMES, H. L., AND LEONARD, B. L. (eds.), Petrologic studies, a volume in honour of A. F. Buddington: Geol. Soc. America, p. 599–620.

HSU, K. J., AND ANDERSON, J. E., 1970, Summary and conclusions: Mid-Atlantic Ridge sequence: lithology, *in* MAXWELL, A. E., AND OTHERS, Initial reports of the Deep Sea Drilling Project: Washington, D.C., U.S. Govt. Printing Office, v. 3, p. 445–452.

KUMMEL, B., 1961, History of the Earth: San Francisco, Calif., W. H. Freeman & Co., 610 p.

LAUGHTON, A. S., AND OTHERS, 1970, Deep Sea Drilling Project: Leg 12: Geotimes, v. 15, no. 9, p. 10–14.

LE PICHON, X., AND LANGSETH, M. G., 1969, Heat flow from the mid-ocean ridges and sea-floor spreading: Tectonophysics, v. 8, p. 319–344.

LI, Y. H., TAKAHASHI, T., AND BROECKER, W. S., 1969, Degree of saturation of $CaCO_3$ in the oceans: Jour. Geophys. Research, v. 74, p. 5507–5525.

LISITZIN, A. P., 1970, Sedimentation and geochemical considerations, *in* WOOSTER, W. S. (ed.), Scientific exploration of the South Pacific: Washington, D.C., Natl. Acad. Sci., p. 89–132.

———, 1971, Distribution of carbonate microfossils in suspension and in bottom sediments, *in* FUNNELL, B. M., AND RIEDEL, W. R. (eds.), The micropalaeontology of oceans: Cambridge, England, Cambridge Univ. Press, p. 197–218.

———, 1972, Sedimentation in the world ocean with emphasis on the nature, distribution and behavior of marine suspensions: Soc. Econ. Paleontologists and Mineralogists, Special Pub. 17, xiii + 218 p.

LOWENSTAM, H. A., AND EPSTEIN, S., 1954, Paleotemperatures of the post-Aptian Cretaceous as determined by the oxygen isotope method: Jour. Geology, v. 62, p. 207–48.

MARGOLIS, S. V., AND KENNET, J. P., 1971, Cenozoic paleoecological history of Antarctica recorded in sub-antarctic deep sea cores: Am. Jour. Sci., v. 271, p. 1–36.

MAXWELL, A. E., AND OTHERS, 1970, Initial Reports Deep Sea Drilling Project: Washington, D.C., U.S. Govt. Printing Office, v. 3, xx + 806 p.

McINTYRE, A., AND BE, A. W. H., 1967, Modern Coccolithophoridae of the Atlantic Ocean—1, Placoliths and cyrtoliths: Deep-Sea Research, v. 14, p. 561–597.

———, AND McINTYRE, R., 1971, Coccolith concentrations and differential solution in oceanic sediments, in FUNNEL, B. M., AND RIEDEL, W. R. (eds.), The micropalaeontology of oceans: Cambridge, England, Cambridge Univ. Press, p. 253–261.

———, RUDDIMAN, W. F., AND JANTZEN, R., 1972, Southward penetrations of the North Atlantic polar front: faunal and floral evidence of large scale surface water mass movements over the last 225,000 years: Deep-Sea Research, v. 19, p. 61–77.

McMANUS, D. A., AND OTHERS, 1970, Initial reports of the Deep Sea Drilling Project: Washington, D.C., U.S. Govt. Printing Office, v. 5, xxi + 827 p.

MENARD, H. W., 1967, Sea floor topography and the second layer: Science, v. 157, p. 923–924.

———, 1969, Elevation and subsidence of oceanic crust: Earth and Planet. Sci. Letters, v. 6, p. 275–284.

OLAUSSON, E., 1971, Quaternary correlations and the geochemistry of oozes, in FUNNELL, B. M., AND RIEDEL, W. R. (eds.), The micropalaeontology of oceans: Cambridge, England, Cambridge Univ. Press, p. 375–398.

PETERSON, M. N. A., 1966, Calcite rates of dissolution in a vertical profile in the central Pacific: Science, v. 154, p. 1542–1544.

———, AND OTHERS, 1970, Initial reports of the Deep Sea Drilling Project: Washington, D.C., U.S. Govt. Printing Office, v. 2, xxi + 491 p.

RAMSAY, A. T. S., 1971, The study of lower Tertiary calcareous nannoplankton from the North Atlantic Ocean by means of scanning electron microscopy, in HEYWOOD, V. H. (ed), Scanning electron microscopy: Systematic and evolutionary applications: Systematics Assoc. Spec. Vol. 4, London, Academic Press, p. 179–209.

———, 1971, Occurrence of biogenic siliceous sediments in the Atlantic Ocean: Nature, v. 233, p. 115–117.

SHINN, E. A., 1969, Submarine lithification of Holocene carbonate sediments in the Persian Gulf: Sedimentology, v. 12, p. 109–144.

TAKAI, F., MATSUMOTO, T., AND TORIYAMA, R., 1963, Geology of Japan: Tokyo, Univ. Tokyo Press, p. 279.

TALWANI, M., PITMAN, W., AND HEIRTZLER, J. R., 1968, Magnetic anomalies in the North Atlantic: Am. Geophys. Union Trans., v. 50, p. 189.

TAPPAN, H., 1968, Primary production, isotopes, extinctions and the atmosphere: Palaeogeography, Paleoclimatology, and Palaeoecology, v. 4, p. 187–210.

———, AND LOEBLICH, A. R., 1971, Geobiologic implications of fossil phytoplankton evolution and time-space distribution, in KOSANKE, R., AND CROSS, A. T. (eds.), Symposium on palynology of the Late Cretaceous and early Tertiary: Geol. Soc. America Special Paper 127, p. 247–339.

TRACEY, J. I., AND OTHERS, 1970, Deep Sea Drilling Project: Leg 8: Geotimes, v. 15, no. 2, p. 15–16.

VOGT, P. R., AND OSTENSO, N. A., 1967, Steady state crustal spreading: Nature, v. 215, p. 810–817.

———, ———, AND JOHNSON, G. L., 1970, Magnetic and bathymetric data bearing on sea floor spreading north of Iceland: Jour. Geophys. Research, v. 75, p. 903–920.

VON HERZEN, R. P., AND MAXWELL, A. E., 1970, Summary and conclusions: Mid-Atlantic Ridge sequence: sea floor spreading, in MAXWELL, A. E., AND OTHERS, Initial reports of the Deep Sea Drilling Project: Washington, D.C., U.S. Govt. Printing Office, v. 3, p. 459–464.

WADIA, D. N., 1966, Geology of India: New York, N.Y., Macmillan, 563 p.

WILLIAMS, C. A., AND McKENZIE, D., 1971, The evolution of the north-east Atlantic: Nature, v. 232, p. 168–173.

WORSLEY, T. R., 1971, The terminal Cretaceous event: ibid., v. 230, p. 318–320.

DISSOLVED SILICA AND DEEP-SEA SEDIMENTS

G. ROSS HEATH

Oregon State University, Corvallis

ABSTRACT

Most of the silica dissolved in sea water comes from silica-rich interstitial waters of marine sediments and from rivers carrying the products of subaerial weathering. Silica-secreting microplankton, diatoms and radiolarians, extract enough opal each year to strip the oceans of dissolved silica in about 250 years. Because most of the microscopic tests dissolve rapidly in the water column and at the sea floor, however, only about 4% survive long enough to be buried, and only about 2% avoid post-depositional dissolution and enter the geologic record. Opal-rich sediments are deposited beneath biologically productive surface regions where nutrient rich deep waters upwell to the photic zone, rather than in areas where the silica enters the sea. The opal-rich deposits ultimately undergo diagenetic transformation to chert. The occurrence of volcanic material with siliceous deposits in the geologic record does not reflect a direct cause-effect relation, but rather the association of volcanism with the same tectonic processes that modify oceanographic and depositional environments so as to induce high productivity of silica-secreting organisms and preservation of the tests in protected basins. At present, 85-90% of the opaline silica incorporated in marine sediments is deposited in near-shore environments where most of it is masked by terrigenous debris. Deposition of silica by inorganic precipitation appears virtually impossible since the late Mesozoic and unlikely since the Precambrian.

INTRODUCTION

At first glance, the sedimentary geochemistries of silica and calcium carbonate have much in common. Both are important constituents of the dissolved load of rivers, both are segregated into relatively pure masses by sedimentary processes, and both are utilized in the construction of tests by important groups of marine microorganisms.

However, the surface water of the open oceans, from which the foraminifers and calcareous nannoplankton extract their tests, is usually saturated and often several times supersaturated with calcite. In contrast, the same seawater may be a thousand times undersaturated with respect to the opaline silica from which the important silica-secreting organisms, the diatoms and radiolarians, construct their tests. The basic geochemical questions are, then, what factors control the concentration and distribution of dissolved silica in the world oceans, why are the silica and carbonate systems so chemically different, and is it possible to interpret ancient non-detrital silica deposits in the light of oceanographic conditions prevailing today?

DISTRIBUTION OF DISSOLVED SILICA IN THE OCEANS

Dissolved silica in seawater has been measured for about a hundred years. However, only since the development of the colorimetric molybdate method (Isaeva, 1958; Riley, 1965) has it been practical to collect the mass of data necessary to map the distribution of silica in the oceans. Even today, the quality of determinations is highly variable. Under optimum conditions (careful analyst, determinations made immediately after collection of samples, and carefully controlled laboratory conditions) the accuracy can be of the order of ± 0.03 ppm (concentrations range from below detection level, <0.01 ppm, to about 11 ppm SiO_2).[1] In general, however, comparison of supposedly identical deep sea profiles determined by different vessels suggests that errors of 10-20 percent are common and 50 percent not unusual. In near surface waters, where the observed range of concentrations frequently exceeds 0.3 to 3 ppm SiO_2, such errors are not particularly important. In deeper waters, however, where much smaller variations must be used to evaluate vertical and horizontal advections of silica, these errors are serious and largely explain the limited value of silica as an oceanographic tracer relative to other parameters such as temperature, salinity and oxygen concentration.

Figure 1 shows four recent vertical profiles of dissolved silica in the Atlantic and Pacific Oceans. The low surface values result from biological extraction of silica. Increasing concentrations at depth reflect dissolution of falling

[1] The literature on dissolved silica in natural waters is complicated by the use of several units of concentration. Most geochemical papers including this one, use parts per million SiO_2 by weight (ppm). Biological and most oceanographic papers use microgram atoms per liter (μ gm at/l) and rarely micrograms Si per liter. The conversions are:

1 ppm SiO_2 = 16.6 μ gm at/l = 467 μ gm Si/l

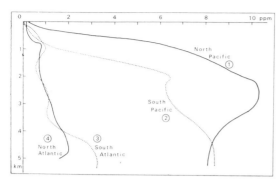

FIG. 1.—Vertical profiles of dissolved silica in the Pacific and Atlantic Oceans. (1) Zetes Stn. 13, 38°05′N, 155°04′W (Scripps Institution of Oceanography, 1970); (2) Eltanin Stn. 28–33, 43°12.6′S, 166°47′W (Scripps Institution of Oceanography, 1969); (3) Circe Stn. 245, 7°8.9′S, 21°21.1′W (Edmond and Anderson, 1971); (4) Baffin Island St. BI–0566–15, 40°51′N, 42°55′W (Grant, 1968).

tests as well as advection of dissolved silica, a subject which will be discussed in more detail in a later section. The striking difference in the concentrations of silica in the two major oceans (fig. 1) reflects the importance of oceanographic phenomena in the marine geochemistry of silica. Berger (1970) has explained this particular difference by pointing out that the Atlantic is "lagoonal" (it looses deep water in exchange for silica-poor surface water from the other oceans) whereas the Pacific is "estuarine" (it gains deep water from other oceans and

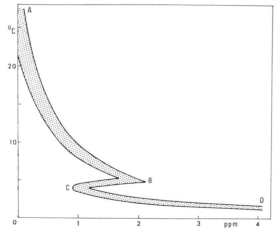

FIG. 2.—Silica content of North Atlantic waters between northeast South America and the Mid-Atlantic Ridge (after Metcalf, 1969). A-B Surface and intermediate water; C North Atlantic Deep Water; D Antarctic Bottom Water.

FIG. 3.—Silica content (ppm) and inferred movement of deep Atlantic water along the 2°C potential temperature surface (after Metcalf, 1969). Stippled areas lie above the 2°C surface. NADW North Atlantic Deep Water; AABW Antarctic Bottom Water.

looses surface water that has largely been stripped of silica by opal-secreting plankton). In general, the "oldest" deep waters, that is, those farthest from their last contact with the photic zone, contain the highest silica concentrations. In the Pacific Ocean, in which all the bottom waters come from the south, there is a south to north increase in silica along isopleths of thermosteric anomaly (roughly, paths of constant potential energy). In the Atlantic, deep water originates both in the arctic and antarctic, and the pattern of silica distribution is more complex. Figure 2, based on about 1500 determinations between northeastern South America and the Mid-Atlantic Ridge (Metcalf, 1969) shows strikingly the influence of hydrography on silica concentration. The maximum at about 5°C is due to Antarctic Intermediate Water that has moved north from the antarctic convergence at about 50°S, the minimum at about 4°C lies in the North Atlantic Deep Water that has moved south from the east coast of Greenland, and the silica-rich coldest and deepest water is Antarctic Bottom Water that originated in the Ross Sea area of Antarctica.

Clearly, any explanation of the marine geochemistry of silica must allow for the dynamic nature of the oceans. Figure 3, based on a criti-

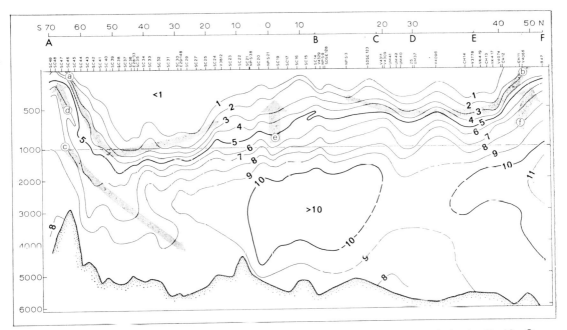

FIG. 4.—Vertical north-south profile of the distribution of dissolved silica (ppm) in the Pacific Ocean (location of profile and stations used shown on Fig. 5). Vertical scale in m, note scale change at 1000m. Station abbreviations: B, Boreas; CH, Chinook; E, Eltanin; NP, Norpac; SC, Southern Cross; SDSE, Swedish Deep Sea Expedition; UM, Ursa Major; V, Vitiaz; VK, Voeikov; Z, Zetes. Original data adjusted for consistency with Eltanin data, as far as possible, but there is probably some mismatch north of B. Stippled arrows show principal water movements determined from other oceanographic parameters (see, for example, Reid, 1965). (a) and (b) Antarctic and Arctic Intermediate Water; (c) Antarctic Bottom Water; (d) upwelling at the Antarctic divergence; (e) upwelling at the equatorial divergence; (f) upwelling south of the Aleutian arc.

cal compilation of deep North Atlantic data by Metcalf (1969) shows the movement of water along the 2°C potential temperature[2] surface, and the corresponding variations in dissolved silica. Such a pattern results from the influx of silica-depleted water from both north and south. At the present time, of the major oceans only the Atlantic displays this pattern.

The distribution of dissolved silica in the Pacific is distinctly different. A longitudinal profile such as figure 4 (location in fig. 5) shows the generally south to north increase in concentration which occurs at any level, but is particularly clear in the deep waters. Overall, the silica pattern mirrors water movements deduced from other criteria (see, for example, Reid, 1965). Upwelling in the antarctic (d), equatorial (e) and arctic (f) areas is marked by rises in the isopleths of silica concentration.

[2] The potential temperature is the temperature the water would have if brought to the surface without loss or gain of heat. Because of adiabatic compression, the *in situ* temperature is about 0.5°C higher in this case.

The surface central water masses, with their deep, stable thermoclines are low in silica due to biologic extraction, particularly in the South Pacific where the "oldest" surface water is drifting south to rejoin the circum-Antarctic mixing system. Perhaps the most convincing evidence in figure 4 for the influence of advection on the distribution of dissolved silica in deep water is the pattern along arrow (c). This arrow, which marks the salinity maximum of the core of the Antarctic Bottom Water (Reid, 1965), coincides with a lobe of relatively silica-poor water that is being carried towards the equator.

POSSIBLE CONTROLS OF THE CONCENTRATION OF DISSOLVED SILICA

Solubility of Solid Silica Species

Figure 6 summarizes the solubility of various silica-bearing phases in seawater. As pointed out by numerous workers, and summarized by Krauskopf (1959), natural seawater at atmospheric pressure is never at equilibrium with amorphous or opaline silica. The effect of pressure on the

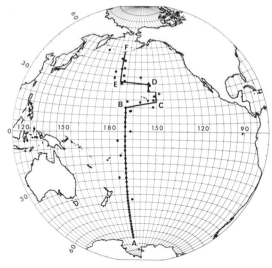

FIG. 5.—Location of stations used to construct Fig. 4, and position of the N-S profile.

Siever (1968b) has suggested that "reverse weathering" is largely restricted to the deeper portions of thick sediment sections along continental margins, where relatively high temperatures and pressures promote intense diagenesis. Finally, the distribution patterns of figures 1 and 4 are readily related to gross oceanic circulation and regions of biological productivity, but make little sense if clay-water interactions control the concentration of silica. The Atlantic Ocean, for example, receives more suspended clay-sized sediment per unit area from the surrounding continents than the other major oceans. However, its concentration of dissolved silica (fig. 1) is markedly less than the experimental values of figure 6 or the values observed in interstitial water from clayey Atlantic sediments (Bischoff and Ku, 1970, 1971). It seems that the clay minerals react too slowly and release too little silica to mask or even modify the distribution pattern resulting from

equilibrium solubility deep in the oceans is slight —at 5000 m, the solubility is only about 10% greater than its surface value at the same temperature (Jones and Pytkowicz, 1973).

Although Eocene opal and cristobalitic deep-sea cherts are less soluble than fresh amorphous silica, they should still readily dissolve in natural seawater. Of the solid silica phases, only quartz is at saturation. The slow equilibration of quartz with water and the complex vertical and horizontal variations of dissolved silica concentrations within the oceans suggest that this phase exerts little control over the silica cycle.

Solubility of Silicates

Within the past decade, Sillén (1961), Siever (1968a) and Mackenzie, Garrels and co-workers (Garrels, 1965; Mackenzie and Garrels, 1965, 1966a, b; Mackenzie and others, 1967) have emphasized the importance of reactions involving clay minerals in the weathering of silicates and in the control of the pH of seawater over geologic time. They propose that "reverse weathering," involving the uptake of silica by clay minerals in seawater, is an important geochemical process tending to maintain the concentration of dissolved silica at its present low value. The short-term importance of this process has been seriously questioned on several grounds. Pytkowicz (1967) has convincingly argued that over periods corresponding to the circulation times of the oceans (hundreds to one or two thousand years), pH is controlled by the carbonate system. In the same vein,

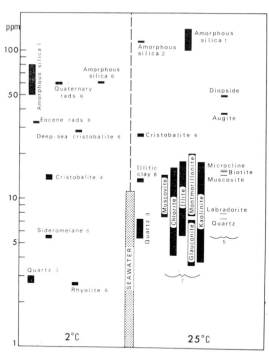

FIG. 6.—Solubility of common silica-bearing minerals at 2° and 25°C, compared to the range of dissolved silica concentrations observed in the oceans (stippled bar). Sources of data: 1—Krauskopf (1959); 2—Morey and others (1964); 3—Morey and others (1962); 4—Fournier and Rowe (1962); 5—Keller and others (1963); 6—Jones and Pytkowicz (1973), Jones (pers. comm.); 7—Mackenzie and Garrels (1965); Mackenzie and others (1967), Jones (pers. comm.); 8—Fanning and Schink (1969). References 2 to 5 refer to fresh water, but are probably also applicable to sea water at the scale plotted.

biological activity (next section) and oceanic circulation.

Biological Activity

If one compares a map of modern deep-sea siliceous sediments (Lisitzyn, 1967, 1972) with almost any measure of biological productivity in surface waters (including such diverse parameters as chlorophyll concentration, zooplankton biomass, or fish catches), the similarity is striking. Clearly, conditions that encourage the synthesis of protoplasm also favor the fixation of opaline silica. As we have seen from figure 4, high concentrations of near-surface silica (as well as nutrients such as phosphate and nitrate) occur in regions of upwelling. These regions lie along continental margins (where their impact on sedimentation is usually masked by terrigenous deposition), and along subarctic, equatorial, and subantarctic latitudinal belts. The latitudinal belts are underlain by deposits rich in calcitic and opaline tests. The accumulation of siliceous oozes requires not only high surface productivity, but also removal of calcite by solution. Thus, such oozes characteristically are found below the calcite compensation depth (a few hundred meters near Antarctica to about five kilometers in the equatorial Pacific).

Since siliceous microplankton can be found in the surface waters of all the oceans, the complete absence of opaline tests from large areas of the sea floor indicates that much of the biologically fixed silica re-dissolves rather than enters the sedimentary record.

THE SILICA CYCLE IN THE OCEANS

Figure 7 shows a number of sources, sinks and transformation processes that might be expected to influence the marine geochemistry of silica. The sources, river influx (a), submarine volcanism (b), submarine weathering (halmyrolysis) including dissolution of siliceous tests prior to burial (c), and upward migration of silica from interstitial waters (d), leave no mark on the geologic record and must be inferred from actualistic data and gross silica budgets of the past. The sinks, regions of accumulation of siliceous tests (h) and of fine detritus that has adsorbed some dissolved silica (i), are the portions of the system than can be preserved and from which past silica cycles must be deduced. Finally, transformations and cycling within the silica system (e, f, g) can be studied only in today's oceans. Our ability to reconstruct plausible ancient systems, therefore, depends exclusively on our understanding of the dynamics and stability of the present system.

In the following sections, an attempt is made

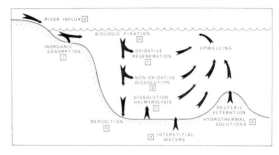

FIG. 7.—Components of the cycle of dissolved silica in the oceans. Letters refer to subdivisions discussed in the text.

to evaluate quantitatively factors (a) through (i) of figure 7. As will become obvious, there are still critical gaps in our knowledge, but a useable model does appear attainable in the not-too-distant future.

1. Sources of Dissolved Silica

River influx.—According to Livingstone (1963) river water, on the average, contains 120 ppm dissolved solids. This is equivalent to an annual supply of 3.91×10^{15} gm to the oceans. Dissolved silica forms 13.1 ppm, which is equivalent to an influx of 4.27×10^{14} gm/yr. More recent data (Gibbs, 1967) suggest that this value may be a few percent high, but such an error will not influence the crude calculations in the following sections.

Submarine volcanic sources.—Because oceanic volcanism is basic in character, it has never been considered a likely source of much silica in today's oceans. However, the association of bedded cherts with large masses of volcanic material (such as spilites) in the geologic record has been taken as evidence of a genetic relationship. Possible factors responsible for this association are considered in a later section. At the present time, primary quartz is known in sediments from the crest of the East Pacific Rise (Peterson and Goldberg, 1962) and from Henderson seamount (J. Dymond, personal communication), suggesting that some silica is supplied to the ocean both at lithospheric plate divergences (mid-ocean ridges) and from the hot spots beneath oceanic seamounts. Such silica could be released in a volatile aqueous fraction left after crystallization of the basalt, or could be freed by deuteric alteration of hot lava by seawater entering fractures resulting from thermal contraction. Both mechanisms are unsupported by experimental or field evidence. Although the work of Corliss (1970) who compared the geochemistry of quenched margins

and slowly cooled interiors of deep-sea tho-
leiites, strongly supports the deuteric release to
seawater of a number of transition metals, any
suggestion that silica is released by the same
mechanism is pure speculation in the absence of
analytical data.

Clearly, there is not yet enough quantitative
information on the subject to support a rigorous
model. However, the possible importance of volcanic silica in our system can be estimated from
the data we do have. The area of new sea floor
created at mid-ocean ridges is about 2 km²/yr
(the figure is about the same regardless of
whether a long term average based on a 200
million year lifespan for exposed sea floor, or a
short term average calculated from the average
spreading rate at active ridges is used). If the
new crust is accessible to alteration to a depth
of 100 m and has a specific gravity of 2.7 the
volume of basalt subject to deuteric alteration
each year is:

$$2 \times 10^{10} \times 10^4 \times 2.7 = 5.4 \times 10^{14} \text{ gm.}$$

Loss of 0.01 to 1 percent silica from this mass
would add 5.4×10^{10} to 5.4×10^{12} gm/yr to
the oceans—about 1/100 to 1 percent of the an-
nual river influx. Even allowing for substantial
errors in the figures used in the calculations
and adding in the effects of eruptions away
from spreading ridges, it is clear that submarine
volcanism cannot be a major source of dissolved
silica in today's oceans.

Low temperature reactions at the sea floor.—
Processes tending to release silica at the sea
floor can be grouped into three main classes:
dissolution of opaline silica tests; low temperature alteration (halmyrolysis) of oceanic basalt; and halmyrolysis of detrital silicate particles.

At the present time, dissolution of opaline
tests at the sea floor cannot be distinguished
from non-oxidative dissolution within the water
column (g of fig. 7). Such a distinction requires further experimental work on the rates
of settling and dissolution of opal in the ocean,
and a better understanding of the near-bottom
circulation. For our model, the two dissolution
components will be considered together under
(g).

In a recent paper, Hart (1970) has studied
the chemical changes accompanying low-temperature alteration of oceanic tholeiitic basalts
over periods of millions of years. For silica, he
suggests an average annual loss of 7.4×10^{-9}
gm/cm³. If we assume that such alteration proceeds to a depth of 100 m and supplies silica to
the ocean only in areas of thin or no sediments
(no more than one third of the deep ocean

basins or 1.1×10^{18} cm²), the annual release is:

$$7.4 \times 10^{-9} \times 1.1 \times 10^{18} \times 10^4$$
$$= 8.1 \times 10^{12} \text{ gm/yr}$$

Thus, although not the major source of silica in
the ocean, halmyrolysis of basalts appears capable of yielding about 20 percent of the amount
annually supplied by rivers.

Low-temperature alteration of detrital material does not appear to be a major source of
dissolved silica. Keller and others (1963)
crushed a number of common silicate minerals
and determined the concentration of silica (and
other elements) in the supernatant liquids after
equilibration (table I). If the values are reduced to allow for a bottom-water temperature
of 2°C rather than the room temperature (about
20°C) of the experiments, it appears that only
the pyroxenes of the common detrital minerals
could supply much soluble silica. The persis-
tence of pyroxenes in Tertiary deep-sea deposits
(Heath, 1969) suggests that little alteration resulting from loss of silica prior to burial actually occurs. It should, perhaps, be emphasized
here that the effects of pressure or the use of
seawater rather than distilled water on the values cited, and the nature of the reactions involved are unknown.

Schutz and Turekian (1965) proposed that
glacigene rock flour from Antarctica supplied
as much dissolved silica to the oceans as all the
rivers of the world. Their estimate was based
on the difference between very poorly known
rates of supply of rock flour and of deposition
of glaciomarine sediments in the circum-Antarctic region. While the value of 5×10^{15} gm/
yr for glacio-marine sedimentation around Antarctica has not been revised (despite the availability of the core data from R/V ELTANIN),
a recent paper by Warnke (1970) suggests that
intense glacial erosion of Antarctica occurred

Table 1.—Silica released to solution by minerals wet ground in distilled water at room tempera-ture (10 gms solid to 100 ml water) (after Keller and others, 1963)

Mineral	Ppm
Quartz	7.5
Labradorite	8.1
Hornblende	10.7
Olivine	12.8
Muscovite	14.8
Biotite	15.6
Microcline	15.8
Enstatite	35.3
Augite	37.9
Diopside	49.8

only during the early development of the icecap, and that modern glaciers are agents of protection rather than erosion. Thus, Schutz and Turekian's value of 14×10^{14} gm/yr for glacial rock flour derived from Antarctica may well be too large, and consequently, their mass imbalance and "missing silica" may not exist. Further evidence against the ability of glacial rock flour to add large quantities of silica to seawater comes from Muir Inlet, a branch of Glacier Bay, Alaska. The inlet, which is more than 300 m deep, is fed by outflow from five glaciers and is visibly turbid. The water column is stably stratified during the summer, with its salinity increasing from 2.6 percent at the surface to 3.1 percent at depth. Thus, below sill depth (60 m) the deep water does not suffer biologic loss of silica over a period of several months. In the fall, the concentration of glacially derived silica in the inlet should be at its highest value, yet a vertical profile of seven samples collected below sill depth by R/V YAQUINA late in August 1970 contained only 1.6 to 2.0 ppm dissolved silica.

Release of interstitial water from deep-sea sediments.—Over the past decade, an enormous number of silica determinations have been made on interstitial waters from deep-sea sediments (see, for example, Bischoff and Ku, 1970, 1971; Bruyevich, 1966; Fanning and Schink, 1969; Harriss and Pilkey, 1966; Kaplan and Presley, 1970; Manheim and others, 1970; Manheim and Sayles, 1971; Presley and Kaplan, 1970, 1971, 1972; Presley and others, 1970; Sayles and others, 1970, 1972; Siever and others, 1965). Although integration of the data is complicated by non-uniform equipment and experimental techniques, it seems clear that most interstitial waters are richer in silica than the overlying seawater. The median concentration of the nine-hundred or so determinations available to the author is close to 25 ppm, with geographic variations ranging from a 19 ppm median for the Atlantic to 60 ppm for interstitial waters from the Gulf of California and Bering Sea diatomaceous oozes.

Because the waters analysed so far do not represent a systematic sampling of deep-sea sediments (the Indian and Southern Oceans are inadequately represented, for example), and the extraction pressures and temperatures, and analytical techniques vary from study to study, it would be unwise to place too much faith in the figures quoted above (see, for example, Fanning and Pilson (1971) for a discussion of the excessively high values that can result if interstitial waters are extracted above *in situ* temperatures). Nevertheless, the existence of a concentration gradient across the sediment-water interface, which must force upward diffusion of dissolved silica, as well as the physical expulsion of interstitial water during the consolidation of sediments must inevitably add dissolved silica to the oceans. The question is, how much?

For the simple situation where reservoirs of interstitial and bottom waters differ in silica content by dS gm/cm^3, the flux of silica across the interface (Fs) is given by Fs = $-k_s$ dS/dz. Here, k_s is an effective diffusion coefficient for dissolved silica which we will allow to cover molecular and eddy diffusion and minor advection (minor, because sedimentation rates in the pelagic realm are slow relative to diffusion rates), and dz is the thickness of the layer separating the two reservoirs. Schink (1968) reports a value of 4 cm for dz, which does not conflict with other data although the vertical spacing of most interstitial water samples has been too large to permit a good estimate of this parameter. The value of k_s in the sediments of interest is unknown, but a range of (1.5 to 3) $\times 10^{-6}$ cm^2/sec appears conservative (see Bender (1971) and Wollast and Garrels (1971) for a discussion of this parameter). Similarly, a value of 10 ppm (10^{-5} gm/cm^3) appears conservative for dS.

If we use these estimates, the flux of dissolved silica from deep sea sediments to the ocean is:

$$(1.5 \text{ to } 3) \times 10^{-6} \times 3.2 \times 10^{18} \times 10^{-5} \times \tfrac{1}{4} \times 3.16 \times 10^7$$
$$= (3.8 \text{ to } 7.6) \times 10^{14} \text{ gms/yr}$$

or as much as twice the annual influx from rivers. Although the numbers used in the calculation of silica entering the oceans from below are far from adequately determined, it appears very unlikely that new data can reduce the range of (3.8 to 7.6) $\times 10^{14}$ gm/yr to the point where its influence on the silica cycle can be ignored. The author suspects that the value may well be substantially increased as our understanding of deep-sea geochemistry improves. For example, the calculation made here ignores any dissolution within the diffusion zone, a simplification clearly at variance with observations of the degradation of siliceous tests in the upper few centimeters of cores from areas of slow sedimentation such as the red clay zones of the North and South Pacific.

II. Transformation of Silica within the Ocean

Biological fixation.—Several taxa of marine organisms extract silica from seawater and use it to construct opaline tests. Two of the taxa, the diatoms (Bacillariophyta) and silicoflagellates (Chrysophyta) are primary producers whereas radiolaria and sponges, the remaining important users, occupy higher trophic levels and, consequently, display more complex distribution patterns. Diatoms are the dominant silica users in the ocean, and extract at least an order of magnitude more opal per year than the radiolaria. Vinberg (in Lisitzyn and others, 1967) estimates that diatoms are responsible for 70 percent of the phytoplankton productivity in the oceans. Recently, however, experiments by Watt (1971), using rates of uptake of radiocarbon, suggest that the role of nannophytoplankton (dinoflagellates, etc.) may have been underestimated because of failure to recognize that their rapid metabolic rates compensate for their small biomass in most samples. Further experimental work, particularly at a number of latitudes in open ocean areas of high productivity, is needed.

The net primary productivity of the world's oceans is probably in the range 1.5 to 2 $\times$ 10^{16} gm carbon/yr (Ryther, 1959; Vinberg, in Lisitzyn and others, 1967). Numerous analyses of plankton by Russian workers (Lisitzyn and others, 1967) show a mean silica : organic carbon ratio of 2.3 : 1 in diatoms. If the analytical ratio reflects relative rates of fixation of the two components, then for the case where diatom productivity is 50 to 70 percent of total primary productivity, the mass of silica extracted per year is:

$$\frac{(1.5 \text{ to } 2) \times 10^{16}}{1} \times \frac{2.3}{1} \times \frac{(50 \text{ to } 70)}{100}$$
$$= (1.7 \text{ to } 3.2) \times 10^{16} \text{ gm/yr}$$

or 40 to 75 times the annual river influx. This range, which lies between the earlier estimates of 0.77 $\times$ 10^{16} gm/yr of Harriss (1966) and 8 to 16.1 $\times$ 10^{16} gm/yr of Lisitzyn and others (1967), must remain tentative until the relative rates of fixation of carbon and silica are better understood. Nevertheless, there can be little doubt that the rate of transformation of silica within the ocean greatly exceeds the rate of influx or removal (assuming a steady state in the system). Figure 8, modified from Lisitzyn and others (1967), shows the rate of biologic uptake of silica in the surface waters of the oceans. This figure emphasizes once again the prime role played by oceanographic factors (in this case, upwelling) in controlling the behavior of silica in the marine environment.

Oxidative regeneration.—Most of the opaline frustules constructed by diatoms during their growth phase are extremely fragile and rapidly disintegrate once their protective organic covering disappears. Gilbert and Allen (1943) recorded decreases of up to 400 times in the concentrations of diatoms at 200 m relative to overlying surface values in the Gulf of California (fig. 9). Chumakov (in Lisitzyn and others, 1967) and Kozlova (1961) report similar decreases with depth in near-surface samples from the Southern Ocean. Because fragile species are much more susceptible to destruction than species with robust frustules (Calvert, 1966), the mass fraction of biogenic silica redissolved in the upper few hundred meters of the water column is less than the cell counts would suggest. Nevertheless, it appears that at least 90 percent of the opaline tests formed in the ocean will never be preserved in the geologic record, regardless of how ideal the depositional conditions.

This rapid post-mortem dissolution of fragile siliceous tests is here referred to as oxidative regeneration because it seems to be controlled primarily by the oxidation of protoplasm enclosing the tests. Figure 10 (after Berger, 1970) shows that the increase of dissolved silica with depth in the ocean is partly correlated with dissolved phosphate (a direct product of the oxidation of organic matter), and partly independent of this nutrient. The correlation is largely restricted to the upper kilometer of the water column. Dissolution of silica at depth appears independent of other reactions in the ocean.

The quantitative importance of oxidative regeneration of silica cannot be directly estimated at present because of inadequate knowledge of the "age" of waters directly below the photic zone. Without this time parameter, the concentration information from vertical profiles, such as figure 10, cannot be converted to rate information. From our estimates of the other components of the silica cycle, and assuming no net loss or gain of dissolved silica (i.e. steady state conditions), it appears that (1.2 to 2.8) $\times$ 10^{16} gm/yr of silica redissolve during oxidative regeneration.

Non-oxidative dissolution.—As mentioned in the introductory section of this paper, the silica content of deep ocean waters rises steadily with time as long as the waters remain below the photic zone. The source of this silica is largely the dissolution of opaline tests falling through the water column or resting on the sea floor. The deep waters are everywhere undersaturated relative to opal, so that dissolution must be rate limited, rather than governed by chemical equilibrium. Experiments by Berger (1968) and Bogoyavlenskiy (1967) suggest that the rate of dissolution depends on the turbulence of the water (see also Edmond, 1970), and is unaffected by the variations in concentration of dissolved silica found in the oceans. Bogoyavlenskiy (1967) suggests that the solution rate depends only on the concentration of suspended opaline silica. His evidence for such a simple relation is meager and largely derived from laboratory experiments. Intuitively, one suspects that the surface area of the solid phase and the agitation of the water (necessary to maintain maximum concentration gradients against silica particles) are also key factors. There is no evidence that either the rate of dissolution or concentration of dissolved silica in the oceans is influenced by observed variations in pH.

In his study of the influence of deep-sea circulation on the distribution of biogenic sediments, Berger (1970) used phosphate-silica plots like figure 10 to estimate the non-oxidative silica content of deep waters of the various oceans. These data, in combination with estimated "ages" or residence times of the deep-

waters allowed him to calculate a rate of about 4.3×10^{15} gm/yr for non-oxidative addition of silica to the oceans. Berger's "ages" are based on C^{14} dating of dissolved carbonate extracted from deep water samples. Craig (1969) has pointed out that such ages ignore vertical advection of the C^{14} in particulate matter, and must be considered questionable. In the absence of better estimates, however, we will use Berger's rates and simply emphasize that this is one area where new data are needed.

Berger (1970) considered that his 4.3×10^{15} gm/yr represented non-oxidative dissolution of biogenic silica in the water column or at the sea floor. In our model it is clear that this figure includes, in addition, halmyrolysis of non-biogenic silicates, escape of interstitial dissolved silica, and influx of silica of volcanic origin (b, c, d, and g of fig. 7). Using the values estimated in preceding sections we can calculate that the rate of non-oxidative dissolution of biogenic silica in the water column and on the

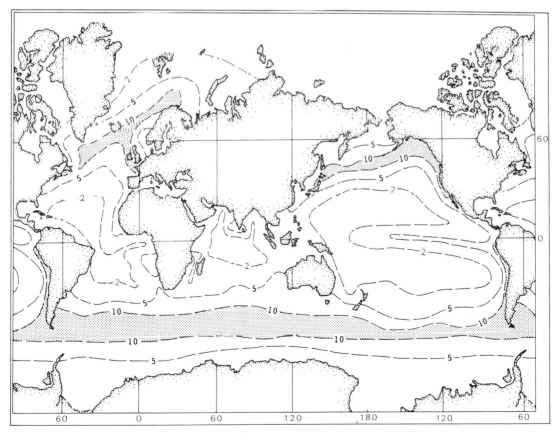

Fig. 8.—Rate of uptake of dissolved silica (gm/cm²/1000 yrs) by siliceous microplankton in the surface waters of the oceans. Modified after Lisitzyn and others (1967).

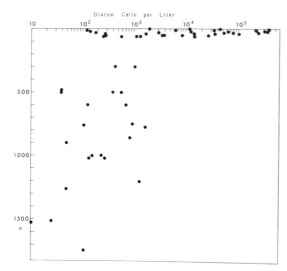

FIG. 9.—Concentration of diatom cells as a function of depth in the central Gulf of California. Data from Gilbert and Allen (1943).

sea floor prior to burial is:

Berger's value−volcanic input−vertical flux of dissolved interstitial silica−halmyrolytic input, or:

$$4.3 \times 10^{15} - 5.4 \times 10^{12} - (3.8 \text{ to } 7.6) \times 10^{14} - 8.1 \times 10^{13}$$
$$= (3.5 \text{ to } 3.8) \times 10^{15}$$

A number of independent sources of evidence suggest that fine detritus, including opal, settles through the oceans much faster than would be predicted for individual particles by Stoke's Law. The identification of fine radioactive debris at depths of several kilometers a few weeks after nuclear tests (Gross, 1967), and the virtual coincidence of boundaries between microfossil assemblages in surface waters and underlying sediments (Ruddiman, 1968) point to rapid deposition of fine particles, probably as fecal pellets of planktonic herbivores and carnivores. In view of the slow rate at which opaline silica dissolves, it appears that most of the dissolution occurs at the sea floor, rather than in the water column.

III. Sinks for Dissolved Silica

Deposition of biogenous opal.—Modern authors are almost unanimous in accepting that the input of dissolved silica to the oceans is largely balanced by the deposition of biogenous opaline tests. Only Harriss (1966), who suggests that the oceans are being stripped of silica, and Mackenzie, Garrels, and co-workers (Mackenzie and others, 1967; *see also* Burton and Liss, 1968) who favor inorganic reactions

between phyllosilicates and dissolved silica disagree with the concept of a biologically maintained steady state. Calvert (1968) has recently reviewed the alternatives and has emphatically reaffirmed the key role of siliceous microfossils in the silica system.

Direct determinations of the rate of deposition of biogenous opal in the deep ocean basins are still few and far between. In part, this lack of data is being overcome by large numbers of new determinations of deep-sea sedimentation rates by paleomagnetic-biostratigraphic and to a lesser extent radiometric dating techniques. However, the paucity of accurate opal determinations on dated cores, and the huge areas still to be studied suggest that reasonable quantitative estimates of global distribution patterns are still several years away. At this stage we can only balance input against removal to arrive at a deposition rate (excluding dissolution prior to burial) of:

River influx+volcanic influx+halmyrolysis+flux of interstitial silica−inorganic adsorption (next section) or:

$$4.27 \times 10^{14} + 5.4 \times 10^{12} + 8.1 \times 10^{13}$$
$$+ (3.7 \text{ to } 7.6) \times 10^{14} - 4.3 \times 10^{13}$$
$$= (0.85 \text{ to } 1.2) \times 10^{15} \text{ gm/yr.}$$

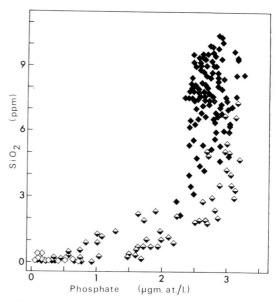

FIG. 10.—Relation of dissolved silica to dissolved phosphate in water samples from the central Pacific. Open diamonds—samples from the photic zone (less than 100 m) that are largely stripped of silica; half shaded diamonds—samples from 100–1000 m, where silica correlates with phosphate due to oxidative regeneration of biogenous matter; solid diamonds, samples below 1000 m from the region of non-oxidative dissolution. After Berger (1970).

Clearly, the "deposition rate" is strongly dependent on an arbitrary decision as to when an opal particle leaves the internal transformation portion of the silica cycle and becomes "sediment." The definition used here, that once buried a particle is effectively "deposited" seems reasonable to the author, but other definitions are possible and are considered in a later section.

Inorganic adsorption by detrital particles.—In a classic paper Bien and others (1959) showed that part of the dissolved silica load of the Mississippi is lost by reaction with particulate matter as the river enters the Gulf of Mexico. In a comprehensive laboratory study, they showed that the process required both suspended matter and electrolytes.

Sterilization of the reactants did not inhibit the reaction. Bien and others (1959) claimed that this inorganic reaction was responsible for a major portion of the loss of soluble silica observed at the mouth of the Mississippi. However, careful examination of their data suggests that such a conclusion is not warranted. Figure 11 shows the silica loss as a function of percentage of seawater in the system (1) observed in the field, (2) observed in the laboratory, and (3) the difference between (1) and (2) representing the loss that is not observed in a sterile system. Clearly, when curves (2) and (3) sum to 100 percent (at about 85% seawater) no further silica can be lost. Process (3) is probably biogenic uptake, and removes 50 percent of the silica even if the inorganic process is independent of the concentration of dissolved silica. In fact, the inorganic uptake (process 2) probably decreases as the silica concentration drops below the laboratory values, so that process (3) actually strips most of the dissolved silica from Mississippi waters. Schink (1967) has suggested that the field results of Bien and others (1959) are erroneous because they used an excessively high value for the salinity of Gulf of Mexico waters. This criticism is not substantiated by convincing data, and is opposed by the laboratory data.

Since the Mississippi study, Liss and Spencer (1970) have reported a 10–20% abiotic loss of dissolved silica from the River Conway in Wales, whereas Stefánsson and Richards (1963) have proved the absence of a similar loss off the Columbia River. Negative findings have also been reported by Burton and others (1970), Kobayashi (1967) and Maéda (1952). The inconsistency of the various studies probably results from differences in the mineralogy of suspended matter in the rivers studied. This must remain pure conjecture, however, until a

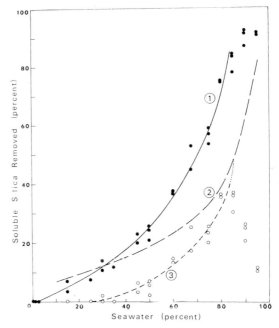

Fig. 11.—Loss of silica in excess of simple dilution from Mississippi River water entering the Gulf of Mexico, after Bien and others (1959). Solid circles and curve (1)—field data; curve (2)—laboratory data for sterile solutions; open circles and curve (3)—field data less curve (2). Curve (3) represents the minimum silica that must be removed by processes other than the inorganic adsorption described by Bien and others.

definitive comparative study is made or the actual mechanism by which the silica is removed is better understood.

For the purposes of our model, an arbitrary loss of 4.3×10^{13} gm/yr of dissolved silica is attributed to inorganic adsorption. This value, about 10 percent of the total river influx, is probably within a factor of two of the correct value, and in any case is not a dominant component of the silica cycle.

DISCUSSION

The estimated values of various components of the silica cycle are summarized in table II. For the sake of argument, one third of the non-oxidative dissolution is assumed to occur in the water (g) and two thirds at the sea floor (c2). The figures in the last column of table II are constrained in the following ways (letters refer also to fig. 7):

1. A steady state is assumed, that is to say supply = removal, or
   $a + b + c1 + d = h + i$
2. The biogenic subcycle must balance
   $e = f + g + h + c2$

TABLE 2.—APPROXIMATE MAGNITUDES OF COMPONENTS OF THE SILICA CYCLE OF THE OCEANS IN UNITS OF 10^{13} GM/YR. LETTERS REFER TO FIGURE 7. THE NUMBER OF SIGNIFICANT FIGURES RESULTS FROM MATERIAL BALANCE CALCULATIONS AND NOT FROM REAL PRECISION OF THE DATA

Components	From preceding sections	Used in discussion section
(a) River influx	42.7	42.7
(b) Deuteric/hydrothermal influx	0.004–0.54	0.54
(c) Halmyrolysis of basalt (c1)	8.1	8.1
Dissolution of tests on the sea floor (c2)	230–250	240
(d) Escape of interstitial silica	38–76	57
(e) Biologic fixation	1700–3200	2500
(f) Oxidative regeneration	1200–2800	2030
(g) Non-oxidative dissolution	120–130	125
(h) Deposition and burial of opaline tests	85–123	104
(i) Inorganic adsorption	4.3	4.3

3. Berger's (1970) value for the non-oxidative supply of silica to deep waters must be conserved:

$$b + c + d + g = 430 \times 10^{13} \text{ gm/yr.}$$

It need hardly be emphasized that these constraints only ensure that the model is internally consistent—they cannot control its relation to reality. If the final column of table II is accepted as a first approximation of the silica cycle, the values shown can be used to derive a number of secondary parameters.

RESIDENCE TIME

The residence time of a transient component in any reservoir (assuming a steady state) is given by: $\tau = A/(dA/dt)$, where A is the mass of the component in the reservoir and dA/dt is the rate of supply or removal of the component. For dissolved silica in the ocean, A is $(5.4 \text{ to } 8.1) \times 10^{18}$ gm (assuming an average concentration of 4 to 6 ppm) and dA/dt depends on the definition of "removal" or "supply." The following alternatives are of interest geochemically:

1. $\dfrac{dA}{dt}$ = biologic uptake (e)

$$\tau = \frac{(5.4 \text{ to } 8.1) \times 10^{18}}{2.5 \times 10^{16}} = 220 \text{ to } 320 \text{ years}$$

2. $\dfrac{dA}{dt} = \dfrac{\text{rate of deposition of silica on the sea floor}}{(h+i+c2)}$

$$\tau = \frac{(5.4 \text{ to } 8.1) \times 10^{18}}{(104 + 4.3 + 240) \times 10^{13}} = 1600 \text{ to } 2300 \text{ years}$$

3. $\dfrac{dA}{dt}$ = rate of burial of solid silica at the sea floor (h+i)

$$\tau = \frac{(5.4 \text{ to } 8.1) \times 10^{18}}{(85 \text{ to } 125) \times 10^{13}} = 4300 \text{ to } 9500 \text{ years}$$

4. $\dfrac{dA}{dt} = \dfrac{\text{rate of addition of silica to the geologic record}}{(h+i-d)}$

$$\tau = \frac{(5.4 \text{ to } 8.1) \times 10^{18}}{51 \times 10^{13}} = 11{,}000 \text{ to } 16{,}000 \text{ years}$$

Clearly, on a geologic time scale, the silica content of the oceans is not large enough to suppress the effects of changes in the supply or removal of silica due to variations in tectonic, climatic, or oceanographic conditions. In particular, the rate of biologic uptake of silica will react virtually instantaneously to changes in the system.

SEDIMENTATION RATES

As with the residence time, the sedimentation rate of silica depends on the definition of "sedimentation." Using options 2, 3 and 4 of the preceding section, a dry bulk density of 0.2 gm/cm³ for siliceous ooze, and deposition over 50% of the deep sea floor (1.6×10^{18} cm²), the values are:

1. For the rate of arrival of opal at the sea floor (h+i+c2):

$$\frac{3.5 \times 10^{15} \times 10^3}{1.6 \times 10^{18}} = 2.2 \text{ gm/cm}^2/1000 \text{ years}$$

$$= 10.9 \text{ cm}/1000 \text{ years}$$

2. For the rate of burial of solid silica (h+i):

$$\frac{1.1 \times 10^{15} \times 10^3}{1.6 \times 10^{18}} = 0.68 \text{ gm/cm}^2/1000 \text{ years}$$

$$= 3.4 \text{ cm}/1000 \text{ years}$$

3. For the rate of addition of solid silica to the geologic record (h+i-d):

$$\frac{5.1 \times 10^{14} \times 10^3}{1.6 \times 10^{18}} = 0.32 \text{ gm/cm}^2/1000 \text{ years}$$

$$= 1.6 \text{ cm}/1000 \text{ years}$$

The rate of deposition of diatomaceous oozes around Antarctica during the Brunhes normal magnetic epoch (0–700,000 years) locally exceeds 2.2 cm/1000 years (0.44 gm/cm²/1000 years) and has a median value of 0.74 cm/1000 years (0.15 gm/cm²/1000 years; Goodell and Watkins, 1968). Radiolarian oozes in the equatorial Pacific accumulate at about 0.4 cm/1000 years (0.08 gm/cm²/1000 years). The sedimentation rate averaged over 50% of the deep-sea floor is probably 0.2 to 0.3 cm/1000 years (0.04 to 0.06 gm/cm²/1000 years).

Clearly, the model rate, even after allowing for all the suggested dissolution possibilities, is still 5 to 8 times greater than the observed accumulation rate. This discrepancy may be explained in two ways: 1) values used in the model have a cumulative error of almost an order of magnitude; or 2) much of the biogenous silica is not accumulating in the deep-sea.

The first suggestion cannot be disproved using presently available data. Nevertheless, a serious discrepancy exists even if one ignores all silica sources except the relatively well-known river influx. Thus, either the second alternative applies, or there is an additional silica sink in the oceans.

Calvert (1966) has demonstrated that the Gulf of California is a global sink for dissolved silica, in that the diatomite basins in the Gulf collect about 50 gm opal/cm²/1000 years. A similar situation prevails in the Sea of Okhotsk (Bezrukov, 1955). In addition to these special environments where pure siliceous deposits accumulate, it appears that much silica is also deposited in bays, estuaries and other nearshore areas where its presence is masked by rapidly accumulating terrigenous debris. This suggestion, made by K. Turekian (personal communication, 1970) is confirmed by recent determinations in our laboratory of opal in Cascadia Basin sediments, off central Oregon. The opal is accumulating at 50 gm/cm²/1000 years now, and accumulated at more than 100 gm/cm²/1000 years during the late Pleistocene in this area of strong upwelling and high biological productivity. As a result of rapid terrigenous sedimentation, however, opal concentrations are less than 5 percent in most samples.

If the rates deduced from the model do approximate reality, it seems that 85–90 percent of the opaline silica entering the geologic record is laid down in estuaries and nearshore restricted basins where it is overlooked due to dilution by detrital particles.

TEMPORAL CHANGES IN THE SILICA CYCLE

The attempt to evaluate components of the silica cycle in the preceding sections has pinpointed numerous areas where additional observational data are needed. Because improved knowledge of the poorly known components does not require significant technical advances, we may assume that the cycle will be refined as additional manpower and resources are applied to its study. If we accept that the model presented here can be quantified to any degree we care to pay for, the question still remains as to its relevance to the geologic past.

Perhaps the most important aspect of today's silica cycle is that the deposition of opal is an oceanographically rather than a geochemically controlled phenomenon. Regardless of where dissolved silica is injected into the system, it is deposited in identifiable masses only beneath areas of upwelling where nutrient-rich deep waters enter the photic zone. As long as siliceous micro-organisms have thrived in the oceans, a similar pattern must have prevailed. Thus, from at least the Cretaceous, diatoms have deposited silica beneath areas of high biologic productivity. From the Cambrian until the middle or late Mesozoic, radiolaria probably dominated the siliceous microplankton. Unfortunately, almost nothing is known of the environmental versus genetic control of silica-uptake by radiolarians. Thus, we cannot assert with any confidence that sudden changes in the rate of input of dissolved silica to the oceans, in the absence of changes in other constituents, would change the rate of opal secretion in a simple way.

If, however, massive amounts of silica were injected into the oceans, dissolution of siliceous tests at the sea floor and escape of interstitial silica must have been inhibited due to lower concentration gradients at the sediment-water interface. Thus, even if the productivity of the radiolaria did not vary, changes in silica input due to volcanism, emergence and submergence of land masses, or other causes, would still have led to enhanced opal deposition beneath biologically productive areas. The pattern would differ slightly from the case of enhanced extraction (as practiced by diatoms) in that silica rich bottom waters would preserve siliceous deposits below less productive areas, as well as allowing the accumulation of thicker deposits in areas where silica would ordinarily be preserved.

This discussion inevitably leads to the perplexing association of siliceous sediments (cherts) and the products of volcanism. The arguments of the preceding paragraphs suggest that massive injections of volcanic silica (which would have to be at least two orders of magnitude greater than today's input to become a major component of the silica cycle) should lead to thicker siliceous deposits (and ultimately cherts) beneath biologically productive areas rather than near the volcanic sources. Yet a geographic relation between ancient volcanically active regions and cherts does exist.

Fortunately, Calvert's (1966) work on the siliceous deposits of the Gulf of California appears to have resolved this paradox. In the Gulf, tectonism which is associated with divergence and transform faulting along lithospheric plate boundaries has produced an oceanographic situation that is very conducive to silica-secretion by diatoms. It has also generated a series of closed basins, most of which are shielded from coarse terrigenous debris (van Andel, 1964). Finally, it is associated with late Cenozic volcanism. Clearly, the oceanographic and bathymetric features that are responsible for the diatom-rich sediments (the future cherts) are only indirectly related to the volcanism, despite the intimate association of the two rock types.

Geologically and oceanographically, there is nothing unique about the situation in the Gulf of California. It is easy to imagine that all the alpine-type chert-volcanic rock associations reflect a similar set of environmental conditions.

Finally, we must consider the possibility of inorganic precipitation of silica from a supersaturated ocean. This possibility permeates the geologic literature, yet has never been proved conclusively. Given the propensity of diatoms to extract as much silica from solution as is available (Lewin, 1962) it is hard to imagine that any part of the ocean has approached saturation since the Cretaceous, at the latest. Prior to the appearance of diatoms, the situation is much less clear. If the radiolarians have adjusted their silica uptake in the way diatoms do, so as to extract all that has been available, the concentration has probably been kept well below saturation since the Cambrian. If not, the oceans may have approached and even exceeded saturation relative to amorphous silica during the Phanerozoic.

Calcite is presently supersaturated in surface ocean waters. Because its solubility decreases with increasing temperature and decreasing pressure, calcium carbonate tends to precipitate in warm shallow areas (for example, the Bahama Banks). Silica, on the other hand, becomes less soluble with decreasing temperature and, to a slight extent with decreasing pressure. Thus, if the oceans were ever saturated with silica, precipitation should have taken place in cool, shallow areas. The Ordovician cherts of Ellesmere Island (Trettin, 1970) may reflect such an environment. Presumably, deep-sea cherts could precipitate if the effect of decrease in temperature with depth exceeded the effect of pressure increase. Since a negative temperature gradient of $\frac{1}{2}°C$ per kilometer cancels out the solubility increase due to rising pressure it would not be surprising to find inorganically precipitated, geologically ancient deep-sea cherts.

DIAGENESIS

Despite the enormous areas of deep-sea chert revealed by the drilling program of the "Glomar Challenger," remarkably little has been learned during the past decade of the diagenetic behav-

iour of silica in pelagic sediments. Riedel (1959) comments that pyroclastic material appears to help preserve siliceous skeletons from dissolution after burial. He suggests that this is due to liberation of silica by weathering of the volcanic material. Riedel's observations have been repeatedly confirmed by other workers, but his suggested mechanism is not supported by experimental data. Jones (pers. comm., see also fig. 6) finds that volcanic ash, regardless of composition, is much less soluble in seawater, and dissolves much more slowly than opaline silica. Conceivably, cations released by the altering ash reduce the solubility of amorphous silica (Krauskopf, 1959). Alternatively, the pyroclastic deposits may lack the clay minerals which otherwise act as a sink for dissolved interstitial silica (Mackenzie and others, 1967). Clearly, only further experimental work can confirm or refute such hypotheses.

Interstitial waters of siliceous oozes are commonly at or near saturation with respect to amorphous silica (see references cited under "Release of interstitial water from deep-sea sediments"), but diagenetic reprecipitation of silica is minimal in young, thinly covered deposits. Minor cementation of clay fillings of siliceous tests by opaline silica has been reported in near surface sediments (Heath, 1969), but true chert formation seems to require several hundred meters of overburden (and resultant elevated temperatures?) or long periods of time (tens of millions of years). The deep-sea cherts collected by the "Challenger" are described in the Initial Reports of the Deep Sea Drilling Project. In virtually all cases, it appears that biogenous opaline silica has dissolved and migrated within the sediments to form cristobalitic chert and porcellanite masses. Subsequently, the cristobalite has tended to invert to quartz, either via a solution step or by direct solid-solid transformation (Heath and Moberly, 1971). Unfortunately, despite the large number of samples recovered, the environmental factors responsible for the initiation, location and rates of the solution and inversion steps, and for the diverse textural features observed in the cherts are still virtually unknown.

CONCLUSIONS

1) The cycle of dissolved silica in the oceans is dominated by biologic extraction and oxidative dissolution of opaline tests in the upper kilometer of the water column. Each year these processes turn over an order of magnitude more silica than is supplied to or removed from the oceanic reservoir.

2) Processes supplying dissolved silica to the

oceans, in decreasing order of importance, are the escape of silica from the interstitial waters of pelagic sediments, river influx, submarine weathering of basalt, and volcanic influx. Of these, the first two supply about 90 percent of the soluble silica.

3) Deposition of opaline tests of siliceous microplankton must remove as much silica as enters the oceans each year to maintain a steady state in which the ocean is markedly undersaturated with respect to amorphous silica. The rate of dissolution of siliceous oozes relative to the turnover time of the oceans is too slow to saturate the bottom waters with silica.

4) Siliceous oozes that ultimately become chert are deposited beneath biologically productive areas, regardless of where the silica enters the oceans. The association of volcanic rocks and cherts in the geologic record apparently results from the production of suitable oceanographic and bathymetric conditions by the same tectonic processes that are responsible for the volcanism.

5) The residence time of dissolved silica in the oceans ranges from 2–300 years for biologic utilization to 11–16,000 years for incorporation of extracted silica into the geologic record. Thus, from a geologic viewpoint, changes in the rate of supply of silica to the oceans will be reflected virtually instantaneously in the rates of uptake and deposition. Such changes should not greatly affect the distribution patterns of siliceous deposits.

6) The diatom and radiolarian oozes of pelagic regions are the most conspicuous sinks for dissolved silica. However, as much as 85–90 percent of the siliceous remains may be deposited in nearshore or estuarine environments where they are masked by terrigenous debris.

7) Because of the dominant influence of biologic processes on the marine silica cycle, supersaturation and consequent inorganic precipitation of amorphous silica appears improbable since the Cambrian and virtually impossible since the Cretaceous. The final word on this subject awaits ecological studies of radiolarian uptake of silica.

ACKNOWLEDGMENTS

It is impossible to acknowledge by name all the people with whom I have discussed and argued the material presented in this review. To those not mentioned here, my sincere thanks. I am particularly grateful to T. C. Moore, Jr., and Tj. H. van Andel for penetrating comments and for reviewing the manuscript. In addition, I have been greatly assisted by discussions with W. H. Berger, J. L. Bischoff, S. E. Calvert, J. R. Corliss, J. P. Dauphin, J. R. Dymond, J. M. Edmond, J. D. Hays, M. M. Jones, A. P. Lisitzyn, H. Tappan Loeblich, F. T. Mackenzie, R. M. Pytkowicz, W. R. Riedel and K. K. Turekian. Needless to say, accountability for the ideas expressed here is mine.

REFERENCES

BENDER, M. L., 1971, Does upward diffusion supply the excess manganese in pelagic sediments?: Jour. Geophys. Research, v. 76, p. 4212–4215.
BERGER, W. H., 1968, Radiolarian skeletons: solution at depths: Science, v. 159, p. 1237–1238.
———, 1970, Biogenous deep sea sediments: fractionation by deep-sea circulation: Geol. Soc. America Bull., v. 81, p. 1385–1401.
BEZRUKOV, P. L., 1955, Distribution and rate of sedimentation of silica silts in the Sea of Okhotsk: Akad. Nauk. SSSR Dokl., v. 103, p. 473–476.
BIEN, G. S., CONTOIS, D. E., AND THOMAS, W. H., 1959, The removal of soluble silica from fresh water entering the sea, *in* IRELAND, H. A. (ed.), Silica in sediments: Soc. Econ. Paleontologists and Mineralogists Special Pub. 7, p. 20–35.
BISCHOFF, J. L., AND KU, T. L., 1970, Pore fluids of recent marine sediments: I. Oxidizing sediments of 20°N, continental rise to Mid-Atlantic Ridge: Jour. Sed. Petrology, v. 40, p. 960–972.
———, AND ———, 1971, Pore fluids of recent marine sediments: II. Anoxic sediments of 35° to 45°N Gibraltar to Mid-Atlantic: *ibid.*, v. 41, p. 1008–1017.
BOGOYAVLENSKIY, A. N., 1967, Distribution and migration of dissolved silica in oceans: Internat. Geol. Rev., v. 9, p. 133–153.
BRUYEVICH, S. W., 1966, The Pacific Ocean. Vol. 3, Chemistry of the Pacific Ocean: Akad. Nauk. SSSR, 351 p. (Translated by Office Naval Research, Clearinghouse for Federal Sci. and Tech. Inf. Ref. AD651498).
BURTON, J. D., AND LISS, P. S., 1968, Oceanic budget of dissolved silicon: Nature, v. 220, p. 905–906.
BURTON, J. D., LISS, P. S., AND VENUGOPALAN, V. K., 1970, The behavior of dissolved silicon during estuarine mixing. I. Investigations in Southampton Water: Jour. Cons., Cons. Int. Expl. Mer, v. 33, p. 134–140.
CALVERT, S. E., 1966, Accumulation of diatomaceous silica in the sediments of the Gulf of California: Geol. Soc. America Bull., v. 77, p. 569–596.
———, 1968, Silica balance in the ocean and diagenesis: Nature, v. 219, p. 919–920.
CORLISS, J. B., 1970, Mid-ocean ridge basalts: I—The origin of sub-marine hydrothermal solutions. II—Regional diversity along the Mid-Atlantic Ridge (Ph.D. dissertation): San Diego, Univ. California, 147 p.

CRAIG, H., 1969, Abyssal carbon and radiocarbon in the Pacific: Jour. Geophys. Research, v. 74, p. 5491–5506.

EDMOND, J. M., 1970, The carbonic acid system in sea water (Ph.D. dissertation): San Diego, Univ. California, 174 p.

———, AND ANDERSON, G. C., 1971, On the structure of the North Atlantic deep water: Deep-Sea Research, v. 18, p. 127–133.

FANNING, K. A., AND PILSON, M. E. Q., 1971, Interstitial silica and pH in marine sediments: some effects of sampling procedures: Science, v. 173, p. 1228–1231.

FANNING, K. A., AND SCHINK, D. R., 1969, Interaction of marine sediments with dissolved silica: Limnology and Oceanography, v. 14, p. 59–68.

FOURNIER, R. O., AND ROWE, J. J., 1962, The solubility of cristobalite along the three-phase curve, gas plus liquid plus cristobalite: Am. Mineralogist, v. 47, p. 897–902.

GARRELS, R. M., 1965, Silica: role in the buffering of natural waters: Science, v. 148, p. 69.

GIBBS, R. J., 1967, Amazon River: environmental factors that control its dissolved and suspended load: ibid., v. 156, p. 1734–1737.

GILBERT, J. Y., AND ALLEN, W. E., 1943, The phytoplankton of the Gulf of California obtained by the "E. W. Scripps" in 1939 and 1940: Jour. Marine Research, v. 5, p. 89–110.

GOODELL, H. G., AND WATKINS, N. D., 1968, The paleomagnetic stratigraphy of the Southern Ocean: 20° west to 160° east longitude: Deep-Sea Research, v. 15, p. 89–112.

GRANT, A. B., 1968, Atlas of oceanographic sections, Davis Strait-Labrador Basin-Denmark Strait-Newfoundland Basin, 1965–1967: Atlantic Ocean Lab., Bedford Inst., Rept. AOL 68-5, 80 p.

GROSS, M. G., 1967, Sinking rates of radioactive fallout particles in the northeast Pacific Ocean, 1961–62: Nature, v. 216, p. 670–672.

HARRISS, R. C., 1966, Biological buffering of oceanic silica: ibid., v. 212, p. 275–276.

———, AND PILKEY, O. H., 1966, Interstitial waters of some deep marine carbonate sedimens: Deep-Sea Research, v. 13, p. 967–969.

HART, R., 1970, Chemical exchange between sea water and deep ocean basalts: Earth and Planet. Sci. Letters, v. 9, p. 269–279.

HEATH, G. R., 1969, Mineralogy of Cenozoic deep-sea sediments from the equatorial Pacific Ocean: Geol. Soc. America Bull., v. 80, p. 1997–2018.

HEATH, G. R., AND MOBERLY, JR., R., 1971, Cherts from the western Pacific: Leg VII, Deep Sea Drilling Project, in WINTERER, E. L., AND OTHERS, Initial reports of the Deep Sea Drilling Project: Washington, D.C., U.S. Govt. Printing Office, v. 7, p. 991–1007.

ISAEVA, A. B., 1958, On the methods of silica determination in sea water: Akad. Nauk. SSSR, Inst. Okeanol., Trudy, v. 26, p. 234–242.

JONES, M. M., AND PYTKOWICZ, R. M., 1973, Solubility of silica in seawater at high pressures: Soc. Royale des Sciences de Liege, v. 42, p. 125–127.

KAPLAN, I. R., AND PRESLEY, B. J., 1970, Interstitial water chemistry; Deep Sea Drilling Project, Leg 2, in PETERSON, M. N. A., AND OTHERS, Initial reports of the Deep Sea Drilling Project: Washington, D.C., U.S. Govt. Printing Office, v. 2, p. 373.

KELLER, W. D., BALGORD, W. D., AND REESMAN, A. L., 1963, Dissolved products of artificially pulverized silicate minerals and rocks. Pt. I: Jour. Sed. Petrology, v. 33, p. 191–204.

KOBAYASHI, J., 1967, Silica in fresh water and estuaries, in GOLTERMAN, H. L., AND CLYMO, R. S. (eds.), Chemical environment in the aquatic habitat: Amsterdam, Uitgevers Maatschappij, p. 41–55.

KOZLOVA, O. G., 1961, Quantitative content of diatoms in the waters of the Indian sector of Antarctica: Akad. Nauk. SSSR, Dokl., v. 138, p. 207–210.

KRAUSKOPF, K. B., 1959, The geochemistry of silica in sedimentary environments, in IRELAND, H. A. (ed.), Silica in sediments: Soc. Econ. Paleontologists and Mineralogists Special Pub. 7, p. 4–19.

LEWIN, J. C., 1962, Silicification, in LEWIN, R. A. (ed.), Physiology and Biochemistry of Algae: New York, Academic Press, p. 445–455.

LISITZYN, A. P., 1967, Basic relationships in distribution of modern siliceous sediments and their connection with climatic zonation: Internat. Geol. Rev., v. 9, p. 631–652.

———, 1972, Sedimentation in the world ocean: Soc. Econ. Paleontologists and Mineralogists Special Pub., 17, 218 p.

———, BELAYAYEV, Y. I., BOGDANOV, Y. A., AND BOGOYAVLENSKIY, A. N., 1967, Distribution relationships and forms of silicon suspended in waters of the waters of the world ocean: Internat. Geol. Rev., v. 9, p. 604–623.

LISS, P. S., AND SPENCER, C. P., 1970, Abiological processes in the removal of silicate from sea water: Geochimica et Cosmochimica Acta, v. 34, p. 1073–1088.

LIVINGSTONE, D. A., 1963, Chemical composition of rivers and lakes: U.S. Geol. Survey Prof. Paper 440-G, 64 p.

MACKENZIE, F. T., AND GARRELS, R. M., 1965, Silicates: reactivity with sea water: Science, v. 150, p. 57–58.

———, AND ———, 1966a, Chemical mass balance between rivers and oceans: Am. Jour. Sci., v. 264, p. 507–525.

———, AND ———, 1966b, Silica-bicarbonate balance in the ocean and early diagenesis: Jour. Sed. Petrology, v. 36, p. 1075–1084.

———, BRICKER, O. P., AND BICKLEY, F., 1967, Silica in sea water: control by silica minerals: Science, v. 155, p. 1404–1405.

MAÉDA, H., 1952, The relation between chlorinity and silicate concentration of water observed in some estuaries: Seto Mar. Biol. Lab. Pubs., v. 2, p. 249–255.

MANHEIM, F. T., CHAN, K. M., AND SAYLES, F. L., 1970, Interstitial water studies on small core samples, Deep Sea Drilling Project, Leg. 5, in McMANUS, D. A., AND OTHERS, Initial reports of the Deep Sea Drilling Project: Washington, D.C., U.S. Govt. Printing Office, v. 5, p. 501–511.

MANHEIM, F. T., AND SAYLES, E. L., 1971, Interstitial water studies on small core samples, Deep Sea Drilling Project, Leg. 6, *in* FISCHER, A. G., AND OTHERS, Initial reports of the Deep Sea Drilling Project: *ibid.*, v. 6, p. 811–821.

METCALF, W. G., 1969, Dissolved silicate in the deep North Atlantic: Deep-Sea Research, v. 16 (suppl.), p. 139–145.

MOREY, G. W., FOURNIER, R. O., AND ROWE, J. J., 1962, The solubility of quartz in water in the temperature interval from 25° to 300°C: Geochimica et Cosmochimica Acta, v. 26, p. 1029–1043.

——, ——, AND ——, 1964, The solubility of amorphous silica at 25°C: Jour. Geophys. Research, v. 69, p. 1995–2002.

PETERSON, M. N. A., AND GOLDBERG, E. D., 1962, Feldspar distributions in South Pacific pelagic sediments: *ibid.*, v. 67, p. 3477–3492.

PRESLEY, B. J., GOLDHABER, M. B., AND KAPLAN, R. I., 1970, Interstitial water chemistry: Deep Sea Drilling Project, Leg. 5, *in* McMANUS, D. A., AND OTHERS, Initial reports of the Deep Sea Drilling Project: Washington, D.C., U.S. Govt. Printing Office, v. 5, p. 513–522.

——, AND KAPLAN, I. R., 1970, Interstitial water chemistry: Deep Sea Drilling Project, Leg. 4, *in* BADER, R. G., AND OTHERS, Initial Reports of the Deep Sea Drilling Project: *ibid.*, v. 4, p. 823–828.

——, AND ——, 1971, Interstitial water chemistry; Deep Sea Drilling Project, Leg 6, *in* FISCHER, A. G., AND OTHERS, Initial reports of the Deep Sea Drilling Project: *ibid.*, v. 6, p. 823–828.

——, AND ——, 1972, Interstitial water chemistry: Deep Sea Drilling Project, Leg 9, *in* HAYS, J. D., AND OTHERS, Initial reports of the Deep Sea Drilling Project: *ibid.*, v. 9, p. 841–844.

PYTKOWICZ, R. M., 1967, Carbonate cycle and the buffer mechanism of recent oceans: Geochimica et Cosmochimica Acta, v. 31, p. 63–73.

REID, J. L., JR., 1965, Intermediate waters of the Pacific Ocean: Baltimore, Maryland, Johns Hopkins Univ., 85 p.

RIEDEL, W. R., 1959, Siliceous organic remains in pelagic sediments, *in* IRELAND, H. A. (ed.), Silica in sediments: Soc. Econ. Paleontologists and Mineralogists Special Pub. 7, p. 80–91.

RILEY, J. P., 1965, Analytical chemistry of sea water, *in* RILEY, J. P., AND SKIRROW, G. (eds.), Chemical oceanography: London, Academic Press, v. 2, p. 295–424.

RUDDIMAN, W. F., 1968, Historical stability of the Gulf Stream meander belt: foraminiferal evidence. Deep-Sea Research, v. 15, p. 137–148.

RYTHER, J. H., 1959, Potential productivity of the sea: Science, v. 130, p. 602–608.

SAYLES, F. L., MANHEIM, F. T., AND CHAN, K. M., 1970, Interstitial water studies on small core samples, Leg 4, *in* BADER, R. G., AND OTHERS, Initial reports of the Deep Sea Drilling Project: Washington, D.C., U.S. Govt. Printing Office, v. 4, p. 401–414.

——, WATERMAN, L. S., AND MANHEIM, F. T., 1972, Interstitial water studies on small core samples, Leg 9, *in* HAYS, J. D., AND OTHERS, Initial reports of the Deep Sea Drilling Project: *ibid.*, v. 9, p. 845–855.

SCHINK, D. R., 1967, Budget for dissolved silica in the Mediterranean Sea: Geochimica et Cosmochimica Acta, v. 31, p. 897–999.

——, 1968, Observations relating to the flux of silica across the sea floor interface: Am. Geophys. Union Trans., v. 49, p. 335.

SCHUTZ, D. F., AND TUREKIAN, K. K., 1965, The investigation of the geographical and vertical distribution of several trace elements in sea water using neutron activation analysis: Geochimica et Cosmochimica Acta, v. 29, p. 259–313.

SCRIPPS INSTITUTION OF OCEANOGRAPHY, 1969, Physical and chemical data from the Scorpio Expedition, U.S.N.S. Eltanin Cruises 28 and 29: S.I.O. Ref. 69–15, 89 p.

——, 1970, Physical, chemical and biological data, Zetes Expedition, Leg 1: S.I.O. Ref. 70–5. 67 p.

SIEVER, R., 1968a, Establishment of equilibrium between clays and sea water: Earth and Planet. Sci. Letters, v. 5, p. 106–110.

——, 1968b, Sedimentological consequences of a steady-state ocean-atmosphere: Sedimentology, v. 11, p. 5–29.

——, BECK, K. C., AND BERNER, R. A., 1965, Composition of interstitial waters of modern sediments: Jour. Geology, v. 73, p. 39–73.

SILLÉN, L. G., 1961, The physical chemistry of sea water, *in* SEARS, M. (ed.), Oceanography: Am. Assoc. Adv. Sci. Pub. 67, p. 549–581.

STEFÁNSSON, U., AND RICHARDS, F. A., 1963, Processes contributing to the nutrient distributions off the Columbia River and Strait of Juan de Fuca: Limnology and Oceanography, v. 8, p. 394–410.

TRETTIN, H. P., 1970, Ordovician-Silurian flysch sedimentation in the axial trough of the Franklinian Geosyncline, northeastern Ellesmere Island, Arctic, Canada: Geol. Assoc. Canada Special Paper 7, p. 13–35.

VAN ANDEL, TJ. H., 1964, Recent marine sediments of Gulf of California, *in* VAN ANDEL, TJ. H., AND SHOR, G. G., JR. (eds.), Marine geology of the Gulf of California—A symposium: Am. Assoc. Petroleum Geologists Mem. 3, p. 216–310.

WARNKE, D. A., 1970, Glacial erosion, ice rafting, and glacial-marine sediments: Antarctica and the Southern Ocean: Am. Jour. Sci., v. 269, p. 276–294.

WATT, W. D., 1971, Measuring the primary production rates of individual phytoplankton species in natural mixed populations: Deep-Sea Research, v. 18, p. 329–339.

WOLLAST, R., AND GARRELS, R. M., 1971, Diffusion coefficient of silica in sea water: Nature, v. 229, p. 94.

THE CRETACEOUS-TERTIARY BOUNDARY EVENT IN THE OCEAN

THOMAS WORSLEY

University of Washington, Seattle

ABSTRACT

All DSDP pelagic sediment cores penetrating the Cretaceous-Tertiary boundary exhibit a major unconformity between the Cretaceous and Tertiary. The hiatuses in these cores are greater than in most marine shelf sections, although all are paleontologically unconformable. Furthermore, calcareous nannofossil biostratigraphy indicates that the magnitude of the Cretaceous-Tertiary unconformity is nearly identical in many shelf sections. The lack of a paleontologically continuous section across the boundary prohibits direct measurement of the span of this missing interval. However, indirect measurements based on inferred sedimentation rates suggest a hiatus of 10^5–10^6 years for shelf sections, and more for pelagic ones.

It appears likely that high carbonate production in the Maastrichtian, coupled with near base-levelling of the continents produced a nutrient-and-carbonate poor ocean, having a shallow CCD along with an oxygen-rich, cloud-free atmosphere characterized by sub-arid conditions and strongly differentiated climatic belts. The mass extinctions ending Cretaceous time would have occurred during the inferred 10^5–10^6 year interval when severe nutrient and carbonate depletion would have caused the CCD to approach the photic zone, thereby leaving only a thin layer of non-calareous deposits to record this spectacular event in the earth's history. The observed magnitude of the unconformity, as indicated by calcareous fossils would seem to be a function of paleobathymetry with pelagic sections having been below compensation depth longer than shelf sections and consequently exhibiting greater hiatuses.

INTRODUCTION

Numerous examples of mass extinctions exist in the fossil record. Among the better documented of these are the events which occurred at the terminations of the Permian and Cretaceous. A major decline in the number of species characterized the end of the Devonian but the extinctions appear not to be as synchronous as at the end of the Permian and Cretaceous. Newell (1962) showed that there are major differences between the crises at the end of the Permian and at the end of the Cretaceous. The Permian ended at a time of major orogenic movement with maximum emergence of the continents whereas the Cretaceous ended at a moment of relative tectonic quiescence during the Laramide Revolution, while the continents were still extensively flooded by shallow seas. The Devonian also ended during a major marine transgression and conditions at this time in many ways resemble those at the close of the Cretaceous. Calcareous plankton, however, had not yet evolved and in this case the sediments recording the extinctions are black shales rather than chalks.

Many *ad hoc* models seeking to explain the peculiar lack of paleontologic transition across the Cretaceous-Tertiary boundary rely on spectacular cataclysmic events, such as collision of the earth and a comet, or a sudden burst of radiation from the sun, for which there is no direct evidence. Cataclysms characteristically should be geologically instantaneous (i.e. beyond the limits of stratigraphic resolution), and should occur without warning. Therefore any evidence of foreshadowing would tend to preclude the Cretaceous-Tertiary boundary being a result of a cataclysm.

In the last two decades, several uniformitarian models not requiring cataclysmic agents have been proposed to explain the Cretaceous-Tertiary discontinuity but none conforms to all known evidence. Newell (1962), Tappan (1968), and Lipps (1970) present an extensive review of these and only the more significant ones will be discussed later in this paper. Tappan (1968) presented an especially significant "Phytoplankton Periodicity Model" which attempted to show that the productivity of marine phytoplankton has controlled the Oxygen-Carbon Dioxide balance of the atmosphere and oceans since the late Precambrian. This model is particularly attractive for explaining mass extinctions because it suggests they would occur among the phytoplankton (primary marine producers) as a result of changes in the environment. Diminution of the phytoplankton would in turn affect all dependent organisms in the marine food chain. In addition, the model suggested that a carbonate compensation depth (CCD), a horizon below which calcium carbonate dissolves, developed in the oceanic depths in the late Cretaceous and subsequently expanded to near the surface. Thus a record across the Cretaceous-Tertiary boundary should not be expected in the resulting calcareous deep ocean sediments. A more complete record should be available for the shallowest portions of the shelves still favorable to the growth and preservation of oceanic phytoplankton. Recent evidence from fossil calcareous phytoplankton sequences recovered by Deep Sea Drilling Project (DSDP) cruises support this hypothesis.

It is evident that an occurrence so unique in the geologic record should produce many consequences. It is the purpose of this paper to demonstrate that a short-lived expansion of the CCD into the photic zone did occur, suggest its cause, explore its consequences, and finally present a model which explains the abrupt extinction of a large number of taxa at the end of the Cretaceous as a consequence of this unusual change in CCD. In pursuing this goal, Maastrichtian-Danian physical stratigraphy will be outlined and the occurrences of calcareous nannofossils in this interval documented. The resulting biostratigraphic correlations will be used to demonstrate the worldwide synchroniety of the highest preserved Maastrichtian strata, above which the massive extinctions occurred, i.e. that there was a worldwide event. Other evidence will then be used to furnish a detailed account of the event which abruptly terminated the Cretaceous Period.

PHYSICAL ENVIRONMENT OF THE MAASTRICHTIAN-PALEOCENE INTERVAL

In many sections, basal Paleocene overlies a phosphate-glauconite layer or hardground capping the Maastrichtian with little or no angular discordance (Tappan, 1968). Attempts at measuring paleotemperatures across the Cretaceous-Tertiary boundary have thus far been frustrated by the extensive recrystallization occurring near the hardgrounds (Hay, personal communication), leaving only the more subjective paleoecological methods available for estimating these temperatures. The peculiarity of rock types associated with the boundary may appear to be unimportant compared to the massive and abrupt extinctions of organisms at the end of the Cretaceous but there is good reason to believe that the lithologic record of the event reflects the physical changes which caused the extinctions and may offer significant clues about the nature of the event.

Stratigraphy

Inasmuch as calcareous marine Maastrichtian-Danian sequences present similar lithologies throughout the world, physical description of these will be limited to the nannofossil-rich

beds of the United States to serve as a generalization for all. Berggren (1964) compiled an excellent lithologic summary of the type areas of Europe and detailed descriptions of oceanic drilled cores from this interval may be found in the Initial Reports of Deep Sea Drilling Project.

In the United States, marine Maastrichtian and Danian crop out in a narrow belt from the New Jersey Coastal Plain along the Atlantic Coast through Mexico on the Gulf Coast. Other important outcrops occur in the western interior although many of these lack nannofossils. A summary of stratigraphic relations is presented in figure 1.

New Jersey.—Physical stratigraphy of the New Jersey Coastal Plain has been reviewed by Olsson (1960, 1964). In this area, Upper Cretaceous and Paleocene strata consist of micaceous to lignitic calcareous greensand, generally leached in outcrop. These rocks are collectively referred to as the New Egypt Formation in the subsurface of central New Jersey. The New Egypt Formation is a facies equivalent of the Lower Maastrichtian Navesink, Upper Maastrichtian Redbank and Tinton, and Paleocene Hornerstown Formations which crop out in northeast New Jersey. Olsson (1960) suggested that there may be a paleontologically continuous section across the Cretaceous-Tertiary boundary in New Jersey, but subsequent nannofossil studies on cores do not corroborate this idea.

Between New Jersey and Alabama, sediments of this age are mostly of brackish or non-marine origin. The Peedee Formation, which consists of gray to greenish black calcareous glauconitic clayey silt, is marine and is the only unit in the southern portion of the Atlantic Coastal Plain which might yield well-preserved nannofossils. No samples, however, were available for study.

Alabama.—The Cretaceous-early Paleocene strata of Alabama have been discussed by La-Moreaux and Toulmin (1959), Copeland (1968), and Čepek and others (1968). In Central Alabama, the Maastrichtian-Danian section is much more calcareous than in the Atlantic Coastal Plain, consisting of (in ascending order): The Ripley Formation, the Prairie Bluff Chalk, and the Pine Barren Member of the Clayton Formation. The Ripley Formation in Lowndes, Dallas, and Wilcox Counties is generally a slightly glauconitic calcareous sandstone or sandy limestone containing an abundant macrofauna. The contact with the overlying Prairie Bluff Chalk is unconformable in this area and is easily recognized in the field by a thick (1–1.5 m.) phosphatic bed containing

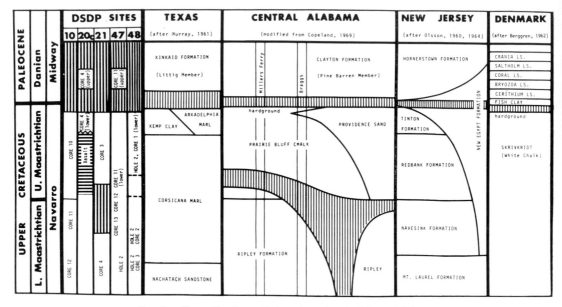

Fig. 1.—Generalized correlation chart for the Maastrichtian.

abundant *Ostrea subspatulata* Forbes. Nannofossil data indicate that this hiatus is of considerable magnitude. The Prairie Bluff Chalk is 10–15 feet (3–4 m.) thick in Wilcox County but thickens to 125 feet (37 m.) in Lowndes County. To the west, it is a gray-green glauconitic, clayey, silty and sandy chalk. The sand and silt content increases toward the east where it becomes a chalky silty clay and finally a calcareous sand called the Providence Sand. The Prairie Bluff Chalk is overlain by the early Paleocene Pine Barren Member of the Clayton Formation. A sharp paleontologic break at the Cretaceous-Tertiary boundary separates the two formations but no striking lithologic change exists at the contact. In fact, the boundary can only be located in the field by the abrupt extinction level of such characteristic Cretaceous megafossils as *Exogyra* and *Gryphaea*. Close inspection reveals that a thin (about one foot) phosphatic layer containing borings coincides with the main paleontologic break, but there are many other phosphatic layers within 4–5 m. of this level which do not accompany paleontologic discontinuities. The Pine Barren Member of the Clayton Formation is a dark, gray-green, calcareous, silty, micaceous clay with irregularly indurated layers of sandstone, siltstone and limestone, and does not differ significantly from the Ripley Formation or Prairie Bluff Chalk except in fossil content.

Western Gulf Coast.—Physical stratigraphic relationships of the late Maastrichtian formations of the western Gulf Coastal Plain are known but biostratigraphic relationships remain obscure. The boundary between the Lower and Upper Maastrichtian lies within the Corsicana Marl (Pessagno, 1967; Gartner, 1968). The Kemp Clay and Arkadelphia Marl are probably facies equivalents and are thought to overlie the Corsicana Marl (Gartner, 1968) and may even be, in part, the same age as the Corsicana Marl. The Littig Member of the Kinkaid Formation represents the basal Paleocene in this area.

The formations in Texas lithologically resemble those of Alabama, but nannofossil preservation ranges from poor to excellent in Texas whereas it is invariably excellent in Alabama (Čepek and Hay, 1969).

Generalized Depositional Environment

Available evidence suggests that the late Maastrichtian was a time of general worldwide decrease in temperature with climatic belts becoming more sharply differentiated. That evidence is summarized below for both terrestrial and marine strata.

Terrestrial sections.—In most sections of terrestrially-deposited strata, it is difficult to determine the exact level of the Cretaceous-Tertiary boundary. The main biostratigraphic indicators for terrestrial sections are vertebrates and flora, including spores and pollen, both of which have relatively poorly known fossil records. Axelrod (1952, 1966) has demonstrated that there was a general replacement of cycads and other thermophilic forms by deciduous hardwoods and conifers in middle latitudes during the late Cretaceous-early Paleocene interval indicating a drop in temperature for these regions. Megaphyta were generally thought to have been only slightly affected by the Cretaceous-Tertiary event, but Hall and Norton (1967) described a palynologically significant floristic change across the Cretaceous-Tertiary boundary in the North-Central United States in which the number of species declined abruptly from the Cretaceous to the Tertiary along with replacement of dicots by gymnosperms at the boundary (fig. 2). The Cretaceous-Tertiary boundary in this area is defined according to R. Brown's "formula" (1952) by the first persistent lignite seam above the highest occurrence of dinosaur remains. The section in Montana described by Hall and Norton (1967) is strikingly similar to a section in South Dakota described by Stanley (1965) suggesting that uniform conditions prevailed over extensive areas at the time of dinosaur extinction. There is no apparent sedimentary break between the Cretaceous Hell Creek Beds and the overlying Paleocene Fort Union Group but lignite accumulations near the boundary suggest changing depositional conditions.

The area is especially significant because the lignite in which the Cretaceous-Tertiary boundary is preserved is laterally equivalent to the lignite just below the base of the fossiliferous marine Cannonball Formation of North Dakota, where a nearly continuous Cretaceous-Tertiary sequence exists (Jeletsky, 1960; Fox and Ross, 1942). Although calcareous nannofossils are virtually absent in the Cannonball, attesting to its restricted marine environment, rare planktonic foraminifers document its early Danian age (Fox and Olsson, 1969). These relationships are illustrated on figure 3.

The continents apparently had very low relief in the Maastrichtian-Paleocene interval although many of the Upper Cretaceous epeiric seas had drained by that time (Brinkman, 1959; Termier and Termier, 1960). In such diverse areas as France, Senegal, and the southeastern United States, bauxite deposits and laterite occur in the Maastrichtian-Danian interval (Tappan, 1968). Paleontological evidence is not sufficiently precise for exact dating of these, but they indicate heavy leaching of terrain which had been reduced to near base level by the late Cretaceous. The only major orogeny progressing at that time was the Laramide Revolution. This provided the detritus in which the excellent Maastrichtian-Danian vertebrate and floral sequences of the Western Interior of the United States are preserved but the sediment apparently never reached marine environments ex-

MESOZOIC	CENOZOIC
Hell Creek	Tullock
47% DICOTS	30%
12% GYMNO.	30%

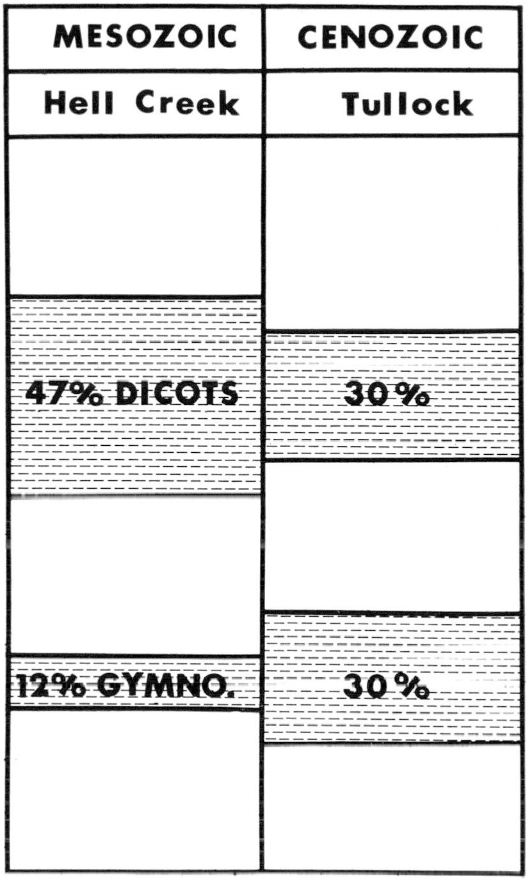

FIG. 2. Floristic change across the Cretaceous-Tertiary boundary in the western interior of the United States (after Hall and Norton, 1967).

cept in the restricted interior sea in which the Lance Group was deposited. For this reason, it seems likely that the Laramide Revolution was not a significant contributor of nutrients to the world's oceans (Bramlette, 1965).

Marine shelf sections.—Calcareous marine shelf sections in which rocks of latest Maastrichtian age are known, present similar lithologies throughout the world. The strata are always rich in glauconite and contain significant amounts of phosphate, both indicators of slow deposition. Most of these Upper Maastrichtian beds contain little detritus. Many are rich in planktonic foraminifers and nannofossils, an indication that the water column above them was neither hypersaline or brackish as is the case of the upper layers of sea water along some of the shelves today. Hardgrounds or phosphatic-glauconitic seams containing borings cap Maastrichtian strata in most areas.

Surface water temperatures for Late Cre-

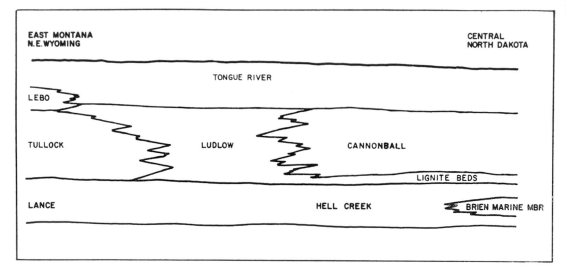

Fig. 3.—Correlation chart for Maastrichtian-Paleocene of the western interior of the United States (after Fox and Olsson, 1969).

taceous seas have been inferred from several lines of evidence. The most direct evidence of Late Cretaceous paleotemperatures are from O^{16}/O^{18} data. Lowenstam (1963) reviewed the available measurements for the Late Cretaceous. These indicate a decrease in oceanic surface water temperatures from the Campanian through the Maastrichtian. Data are not yet precise enough to delineate Late Maastrichtian trends but Early Maastrichtian measurements indicate a temperature variation from about 20°C at 30°N to about 10°C at 75°N. Reliable data are not yet available for the equatorial regions as most measurements have been made on belemnite rostra and these organisms were restricted to sub-tropical to polar latitudes in post-Cenomanian time (Jeletsky, 1951). Direct measurements for the Early Paleocene are inconclusive, but seemingly suggest lower temperatures than in the Late Maastrichtian. The more indirect paleoecologic evidence substantiates these measurements and will be treated in detail later.

Pelagic sections.—Available data for pelagic cores indicate the same general trends existed as in shelf sections for the Maastrichtian-Paleocene interval except that the record across the Mesozoic-Cenozoic boundary is not as complete. This phenomenon will receive considerable attention throughout this paper.

BIOSTRATIGRAPHIC FRAMEWORK OF THE MAASTRICHTIAN-DANIAN INTERVAL

Calcareous phytoplankton are ideally suited to the study of the Cretaceous-Tertiary bound-

ary because they offer the potential for high resolution biostratigraphic chronology of sediments near the boundary and also because they record changes in CCD through time. The living organisms are calcite secreting members of the golden brown algae. These unicellular, motile organisms constitute much of today's phytoplankton, which in turn control the O_2–CO_2 budget of the oceans and atmosphere. Fossil representatives of this group consist mostly of the disaggregated plates (coccoliths), usually between 2 and 15 μ in diameter, which once covered the living cell. In addition to coccoliths, bizarre calcite objects occur which are not comparable to those produced by any living species. They are included in the group because of their mineralogical and size similarity plus their universal occurrence with coccoliths. All these fossils are collectively referred to as nannofossils.

The Maastrichtian-Danian interval contains abundant well-preserved calcareous nannofossils in many areas of the world and are extremely useful for high resolution biostratigraphy provided paleoclimatic considerations are taken into account, as will be demonstrated later. These nannofossil-rich sequences should hold the answer to the question of the nature of the extinction of phytoplankton and the higher dependent invertebrate groups such as the planktonic foraminifers, belemnites, and ammonites at the end of the Cretaceous.

Inasmuch as no new species are described in this paper, micrographs and systematics are dispensed with. Excellent light and electron micrographs of the nannofossils discussed here may be found in Bramlette and Martini (1964), Hay and Mohler (1967), Gartner (1968), and Bukry (1969).

Previous Studies

Many papers have mentioned or described early Tertiary and late Cretaceous calcareous nannofossils, but few have dealt with the remarkable change in nannoplankton across the Cretaceous-Tertiary boundary. Čepek and Hay (1969) presented a chart summarizing published work on the Upper Cretaceous calcareous nannoplankton and Hay and others (1967) provided a similar chart for Tertiary calcareous nannofossils. The abrupt change in nannofossil populations at the Cretaceous-Tertiary contact was first documented by Bramlette and Martini (1964) who noted massive extinctions of many taxa at the boundary. Bramlette (1965) pointed out the relation between nannofossil extinctions and those of many other dependent taxa. Edwards (1966) described the change at the boundary in New Zealand and Perch-Nielsen (1969) has described in detail the extraordinary change across the boundary in Denmark. A discussion of physical conditions at the boundary and an account of the rise of early Tertiary floras was presented by Hay and Mohler (1967).

Previous Nannofossil Subdivision

Stradner (1963) termed the late Cretaceous nannofossil assemblages "Cymbiformis associations." This is an accurate indication of the nature of the late Cretaceous nannofloras because these are almost invariably dominated by the distinctive species *Arkhangelskiella cymbiformis* Vekshina. Bukry (1969) proposed four zones within the Upper Cretaceous but did not suggest a formal zone for Maastrichtian strata. Čepek and Hay (1969) have defined twelve zones within the Cenomanian-Maastrichtian interval, the lower limit of each being the first evolutionary occurrence of its name species. In this study, the upper three of these zones, in ascending order the *Chiastozygus initialis, Lithraphidites quadratus,* and *Nephrolithus frequens* Zones, were encountered. Martini (1969) has suggested the term *Tetralithus murus* Zone for the uppermost Cretaceous. Bukry and Bramlette (1970) used four zones (in ascending order), the *Eiffellithus augustus, Tetralithus nitidus trifidus, Lithraphidites quadratus,* and *Tetralithus murus* Zone. The base of Bukry's *Eiffellithus augustus* Zone was stated to be marked by the lowest occurrence of Broinsonia [=Arkhangelskiella] *parca* and its top by the highest occurrence of *E. augustus*. His *T. nitidus tri-*

fidus Zone was defined by the range of its name species and the base of his *L. quadratus* Zone was defined by the lowest occurrence of its name species. For these definitions to be unambiguous, the lowest specimens of *T. nitidus trifidus* must occur at precisely the level of the highest specimens of *E. augustus* (=E. eximius, see below) and a similar situation holds true for the lowest specimens of *L. quadratus* and the highest specimens of *T. nitidus trifidus*. As it can be demonstrated that these fossils do not have common datum levels (for example see Figure 8), this zonation is ambiguously defined and therefore not useable. Furthermore, recent studies by Worsley and Martini (1970) demonstrate that occurrences of *Nephrolithus frequens* and *Tetralithus murus* are almost mutually exclusive, as they are known to occur together at only two localities. It is apparent that the effects of provincialism among pelagic groups has led to considerable confusion in Maastrichtian correlation.

Calcareous nannofossil zonations of the 11 million year Paleocene interval have been reviewed by Hay and others (1967). A new zonation of the Lower Paleocene was proposed by Hay and Mohler (1967) who recognized five nannofossil zones within this interval. The base of each zone is defined by the lowest occurrence of the name species. The lowest two of Hay and Mohler's units, the *Markalius astroporus* Zone and the *Cruciplacolithus tenuis* Zone have been investigated in this study. Perch-Nielsen (1969) revised the definition of the base of the *M. astroporus* Zone, noting that the first occurrence of the name species is in assemblages of Maastrichtian age. She suggested using the lowest occurrence of *Biantholithus sparsus* to mark the base of this unit. Čepek and Hay (1969) also noted that the base of the *M. astroporus* Zone needed to be redefined. They did not suggest which species should serve as the marker, but tentatively defined the boundary as the level of extinction of most Cretaceous species.

Martini (1970) has reviewed and refined Paleogene nannofossil biostratigraphy and has subdivided the Paleocene into nine zones, a resolution of about one million years. This subdivision is sufficiently refined for the purposes of this paper and will not need modification. Figure 4 shows the relationships between the various Maastrichtian-Paleocene zonations.

Effects of Fossil Provincialism on Biostratigraphy

Although the Upper Cretaceous is widely thought to have had a remarkably uniform climate over tropical, temperate, and perhaps even

				STRADNER (1964)	CEPEK & HAY (1969)	HAY & MOHLER (1967)	MARTINI (1970)
TERTIARY	Paleocene	Upper		Helis Associations		D. multir. Zone	NP 9 D. multiradiatus Zone
						H. riedeli Zone	NP 8 H. riedeli Zone
		Middle				D. gemmeus Zone	NP 7 D. gemmeus Zone
						H. kleinpelli Zone	NP 6 H. kleinpelli Zone
						F. tympanif. Zone	NP 5 F. tympaniformis Zone
		Lower					NP 4 E. macellus Zone
							NP 3 C. danicus Zone
						C. tenuis Zone	NP 2 C. tenuis Zone
						M. astroporus Zone	NP 1 M. astroporus Zone
CRETACEOUS	Maastrichtian	Upper		Cymbiformis Associations	N. frequens Zone / L. quadratus Zone		T. murus Zone
					C. initialis Zone		

FIG. 4.—Biostratigraphic subdivision schemes for the Maastrichtian-Paleocene.

polar regions, there is evidence of climatic belts. The Maastrichtian index species *Belemnitella americana* is abundant in the New Jersey and Alabama Coastal Plains but the absence of the diagnostic Upper Maastrichtian species of Scandinavia and Northern Europe, *Belemnella casimirovensis*, has led some workers to speculate that strata of latest Maastrichtian age were absent in these areas. Jeletsky (1951) has since demonstrated that *Belemnitella* inhabited warm water whereas *Belemnella* was a cold water genus. Lowenstam (1963) has corroborated Jeletsky's findings with isotopic paleotemperature measurements derived from rostra of these two genera. More recently, absence of the diagnostic Upper Maastrichtian planktonic foraminifera *Abathomphalus mayaroensis* and *Racemiguembelina fructicosa* was used to support the contention that Upper Maastrichtian strata are absent in the Eastern Gulf and Atlantic Coastal Plains. However, Pessagno (1967) demonstrated that these fossils are restricted to the tropics; *A. mayaroensis* occurs only as far north as the Tampico Embayment of Mexico and *R. fructicosa* ranges as far as the Kemp Clay of Texas. This has revived controversy about the actual age of the highest Cretaceous strata in the Atlantic and eastern Gulf Coastal Plains.

Bramlette and Martini (1964) reported a single occurrence of the Upper Maastrichtian index nannofossil *Tetralithus murus* from the Arkadelphia Marl of Hempstead County, Arkansas. Čepek and others found *Nephrolithus fre-*

quens, another Upper Maastrichtian index nannofossil, in the upper few feet of the Prairie Bluff Chalk of Alabama and Worsley and Martini (1970) reported it from the New Jersey area. Worsley and Martini (1970) have demonstrated that *T. murus* and *N. frequens* were also latitudinally restricted. A revised plot of their known occurrences is shown in figure 5. It is highly significant that although both are essentially restricted to the Upper Maastrichtian, the lowest occurrence surface of *N. frequens* seems to be diachronous, being youngest near the limits of its province. In southwest France, where both occur together, their known concurrent stratigraphic range is approximately ten meters (Worsley and Martini, 1970). In this paper, the two are reported together in a single sample from the United States (Texas 715–720) and although their stratigraphic ranges in this area are not known, they are probably very short. In Alabama, *N. frequens* is restricted to the uppermost two meters of the Maastrichtian at the Braggs sections and specimens closely allied to *T. murus* have been identified from near the base of the Prairie Bluff Chalk at this section. It appears that *T. murus* began its evolution in the Lower Maastrichtian but only developed into *T. murus* in Upper Maastrichtian tropical climates.

In addition to *T. murus* and *N. frequens*, several other nannofossil species were also provincial in the Maastrichtian. The Upper Maastrichtian guide fossil *Ceratolithoides kamptneri* is restricted to low latitudes and *Cylindralithus gallicus* is essentially tropical also, having been found in only two high-latitude samples. Among the longer-ranging species, *Actinozygus splendens, Thoracosphaera operculata,* and *T. imperforata* are tropical, whereas *Markalius astroporus* preferred higher latitudes. Other restrictions are more subtle. *Lucianorhabdus cayeuxi* is essentially restricted to the Lower Maastrichtian in the tropics but ranges well up into the Upper Maastrichtian in high latitudes. *Tetralithus obscurus* does almost the opposite, becoming extinct within the Upper Maastrichtian in the tropics and in the lower Maastrichtian near the poles. Another interesting restriction occurs between *Tranolithus manifestus* and *Microrhabdulus decoratus* in that their occurrences are virtually mutually exclusive in the Maastrichtian. Most of these relationships are illustrated on figure 8.

High Resolution Biostratigraphic Subdivision of the Maastrichtian

Although lower Paleocene biostratigraphic resolution is sufficient for accurately outlining the configuration of the Cretaceous-Tertiary boundary on a worldwide basis, Maastrichtian resolution is not, as may be seen from figure 4. The voluminous nannofloral sequence of the approximately seven million year Maastrichtian interval has only been divided into two zones and part of a third (Čepek and Hay, 1969). Other fossil groups offer little improvement in this respect. Bramlette and Martini (1964), in their documentation of the drastic nannofossil change across the Cretaceous-Tertiary boundary, noted that very few species evolve or become extinct in the Maastrichtian, making zonation difficult.

In attempting to increase biostratigraphic resolution for the Maastrichtian, the underlying assumption was made that evolution is random so that the probability of two datum surfaces (highest or lowest occurrences of species) exactly coinciding is virtually zero (For a further discussion of this, see Shaw, 1964, Čepek and Hay, 1969). If two (or more) fossils are found to have a common datum at a locality: 1) the section is not continuous; 2) the sampling interval for the section is too large; 3) a facies change has occurred in the section as a

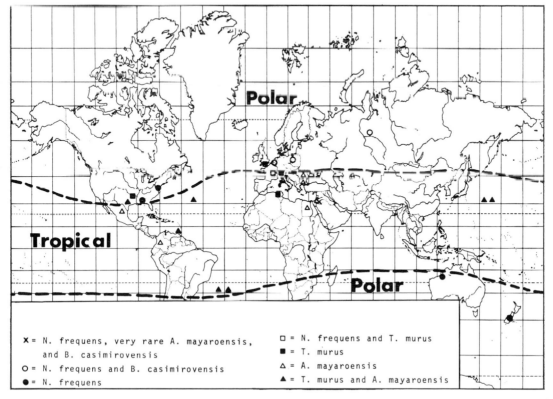

X = N. frequens, very rare A. mayaroensis, and B. casimirovensis

O = N. frequens and B. casimirovensis

● = N. frequens

□ = N. frequens and T. murus

■ = T. murus

△ = A. mayaroensis

▲ = T. murus and A. mayaroensis

FIG. 5.—Distribution of provincial pelagic fossils in the upper Maastrichtian (after Worsley and Martini, 1970).

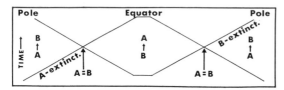

FIG. 6.—Schematic representation of climatic fossil provincialism.

result of a sudden shift in environment; 4) the two fossils are environmentally restricted in such a manner that the biostratigraphic order of their respective datum surfaces is a function of their preferred environments, being reversed between these environments. Localities along the common border of such environmental provinces will show the fossils as having identical highest and/or lowest levels of occurrence.

The first three of these considerations can be easily overcome by more continuous sampling or by sampling another locality. The fourth is where major biostratigraphic problems are encountered. For example: In figure 6, if fossil A became extinct before fossil B at the North and South Poles but B became extinct before A at the equator, their extinction data would be diachronous and their extinction sequence would be a function of latitude, being AB at the poles and BA at the equator. The time increment represented by either sequence AB or BA would be a function of latitude and would be equal to zero at some intermediate latitude where both became extinct at precisely the same time. Obviously, such fossils cannot be used for correlation normal to latitude but are extremely useful for correlation parallel to latitude. The Maastrichtian biostratigraphic subdivision proposed below appears to be strongly influenced by latitude in the manner described above and data were treated accordingly.

In their 1964 study of Maastrichtian nannofossils, Bramlette and Martini were not able to place suites of samples from around the world in stratigraphic order within the Lower or Upper Maastrichtian. Figure 7 reproduces their distribution chart for species which have been found to be stratigraphically or climatologically important in this paper. Note the incoherent distribution of most species on this chart. Worsley and Martini (1970) demonstrated that nanno-floral polar and equatorial provinces existed in the Maastrichtian which complicate biostratigraphic subdivision. Figure 8 is a reorganization of Bramlette and Martini's data modified to fit the Worsley and Martini findings in that samples are classified as either "tropical" or

"polar" and placed in such an order that each species has the most continuous sequence of occurrences. Subsequently, other Maastrichtian samples from around the world were examined by the author and fitted into this sequence by the technique outlined by Hay (1972). Figure 9 shows the most probable stratigraphic order of 32 of the best preserved tropical-subtropical samples. The highest occurrence of *Arkhangelskiella parca* was chosen as the contact surface between Lower and Upper Maastrichtian because it is the datum which does not seem subject to major ecologic control and which most nearly conforms to the definition of this boundary in the type area of Northern Europe. Although it has not yet been possible to stratigraphically order the samples between adjacent horizontal lines, this still leaves ten increments into which the tropical Maastrichtian may be divided, a resolution of roughly one million years. It is not suggested that formal zones be erected on the basis of this sequence but rather that additional samples be studied within this framework to determine which among these are the most reliable. However, these increments will serve to approximately subdivide the Maastrichtian for the purposes of this paper.

Figure 10 shows the most probable sequence for 19 cool-temperate to polar samples and is a considerably more subjective interpretation. Only one Maastrichtian species group (*Nephrolithus frequens et aff.*) has a bipolar distribution but its vertical range is greatly influenced by latitude, rendering it a rather poor datum indicator (Worsley and Martini, 1970). *Cylindralithus gallicus* is the only other essentially Upper Maastrichtian species found at high latitudes but this predominantly tropical species is too rare to be of consistent use. The Upper Maastrichtian extinction datums in the cool temperate-polar sequence may be subject to strong climatic control so that biostratigraphic resolution for this interval is probably not as good as figure 10 would suggest. The Lower Maastrichtian, was subdivided into six increments, most of which are not comparable to those found at low latitude, furnishing strong evidence that Maastrichtian climate was strongly differentiated according to latitude.

These results indicate that climate deteriorated throughout the Maastrichtian. The occurrence of *N. frequens* in the upper few meters of the New Jersey and Alabama Maastrichtian and its occurrence in a single sample (Texas 715–720) from Texas indicates that it was able to migrate to temperate and subtropical regions as subtropical climate cooled just prior to the Cretaceous-Tertiary event. Additionally, these results suggest that the highest preserved Maastrichtian of all marine shelf sections in the world topped by hardgrounds (solutional unconformities) appear to be nearly the same age, at least as correlated parallel to latitude, lending strong support to the idea that a worldwide episode of short duration ended Cretaceous time. This is in accord with the hypothesis advanced by Hay (1960), who did not have the benefit of such detailed stratigraphic and paleoclimatic information.

Maastrichtian-Paleocene DSDP Cores

Most DSDP cores penetrating the Mesozoic either contain major unconformities between Cretaceous and Tertiary or have large sampling gaps within that interval. The only cores directly examined or considered here are those either sampling the Cretaceous-Tertiary boundary, the Upper Maastrichtian, or Lower Paleocene. However, it should be noted that each deep-sea core penetrating the Mesozoic where a major unconformity exists lends further support to the idea of a large upward movement of carbonate compensation depth rather than a sedimentary bypassing or erosional unconformity because it is not possible to have worldwide erosion simultaneously throughout the world without concurrent deposition.

Cores containing the Cretaceous-Tertiary

(*) sample examined by writer	Arkhangelskiella parca	Reinhardtites anthophorus	Actinozygus splendens	Markalius inversus	Nephrolithus frequens et al	Tranolithus manifestus**	Thoracosphaera imperforata	Thoracosphaera operculata	Ceratolithoides kamptneri	Corollithion exiguum	Cylindralithus gallicus	Cylindralithus serratus	Lithraphidites quadratus	Lucianorhabdus cayeuxi	Marthasterites inconspicuus	Microrhabdulus decoratus	Microrhabdulus stradneri	Tetralithus murus	Tetralithus obscurus	STAGE
Bellocq*		X	X	X		X		X	X	X	X	X				X	X			Upper MAASTRICHTIAN
USGS		X	X			X	X	X	X	X	X					X	X			Upper MAASTRICHTIAN
Oued 641*		X						X	X		X					X	X			Upper MAASTRICHTIAN
Oued 633*		X						X	X	X	X	X			X	X	X			Upper MAASTRICHTIAN
Enci 16			X			X					X	X				X				Upper MAASTRICHTIAN
Enci 12					X							X				X				Upper MAASTRICHTIAN
Enci 10*			X								X	X				X				Upper MAASTRICHTIAN
Alabama 1*		X	X	X				X	X	X	X	X		X		X				Upper MAASTRICHTIAN
Alabama 18	X	X	X					X	X	X	X	X		X		X				Upper MAASTRICHTIAN
Stevns Kl. 1			X	X																Upper MAASTRICHTIAN
Stevns Kl. 7				X								X								Upper MAASTRICHTIAN
KG 7*			X	X								X								Upper MAASTRICHTIAN
KG 6*			X	X							X	X	X	X		X				Lower MAASTRICHTIAN
Alabama 30	X	X	X		X	X	X				X	X	X	X		X			X	Lower MAASTRICHTIAN
Oued 629	X	X			X						X	X	X			X			X	Lower MAASTRICHTIAN
Eperheide 5	X	X			X						X		X			X			X	Lower MAASTRICHTIAN

Fig. 7.—Distribution chart for Maastrichtian nannofossils (after Bramlette and Martini, 1964). (** = *Glaukolithus diplogrammus*)

(*) sample examined by writer / (+) species not originally found but identified by writer / (-) species not found in samp. within prop. seq.	Microrhabdulus decoratus	Lucianorhabdus cayeuxi	Tranolithus manifestus**	Cylindralithus serratus	Reinhardtites anthophorus	Tetralithus obscurus	Arkhangelskiella parca	Marthasterites inconspicuus	Microrhabdulus stradneri	Lithraphidites quadratus	Cylindralithus gallicus	Ceratolithoides kamptneri	Tetralithus murus	Corollithion exiguum	Actinozygus splendens	Thoracosphaera imperforata	Thoracosphaera operculata	Markalius inversus	Nephrolithus frequens et al	STAGE	CLIMATE
Bellocq*		X						+	X	X	X	X	X	X	X	-	X	X	X	Upper MAASTRICHTIAN	SUBTROPICAL-TROPICAL
Oued 641*								+	X	X	X	X	X	-	X	-	X	-	-	Upper MAASTRICHTIAN	SUBTROPICAL-TROPICAL
USGS									X	X	X	X	X	X	X	X	X	X	-	Upper MAASTRICHTIAN	SUBTROPICAL-TROPICAL
Alabama 1*						X	X	X			X	X		X	X	X	X	X		Upper MAASTRICHTIAN	SUBTROPICAL-TROPICAL
Alabama 18							X	X	X	X	X	X		X	X	X	X			Upper MAASTRICHTIAN	SUBTROPICAL-TROPICAL
Oued 633*					+	+	+	X	X	X	X	X		X	X	X	-			Upper MAASTRICHTIAN	SUBTROPICAL-TROPICAL
Alabama 30	X	X	X	X		X	X	X	X	X		X				X	X			L MAASTRICHTIAN	SUBTROPICAL-TROPICAL
Oued 629	X	X	X	X	X	X	X	+		X										L MAASTRICHTIAN	SUBTROPICAL-TROPICAL
Stevns Kl 7											X						X			Upper MAASTRICHTIAN	COOL TEMPERATE-POLAR
Enci 10*	X	X	-	X				X	X		X								-	Upper MAASTRICHTIAN	COOL TEMPERATE-POLAR
Enci 11*	X	X	-	X				X	X										-	Upper MAASTRICHTIAN	COOL TEMPERATE-POLAR
Kazmierz*	X	X	-	X				X	X	X									X	Upper MAASTRICHTIAN	COOL TEMPERATE-POLAR
KG 7*	X	X	-	X				X	-	X									X	Upper MAASTRICHTIAN	COOL TEMPERATE-POLAR
KG 6*	+	X		X		X	X	X	X		X					X	X			L MAASTRICHTIAN	COOL TEMPERATE-POLAR
Eperheide 5*	X	X	X	X	X	X	X	+ cf.												L MAASTRICHTIAN	COOL TEMPERATE-POLAR

FIG. 8.—Figure 7 reorganized into tropical and polar provinces.
(** = *Glaukolithus diplogrammus*)

boundary taken by Leg 3 of the Deep Sea Drilling Project were studied. These were obtained in the South Atlantic and consist of nannofossil chalk oozes with moderately well preserved nannofossils. However, nearly all the samples examined by the writer contain species stratigraphically downworked by drilling, rendering biostratigraphic age determination difficult in that only extinction datums can be relied on for such cases. There is apparently a sharp paleontologic discontinuity within the Maastrichtian between cores 3 and 4 in hole 21 although there is no recorded sampling gap for this interval. The bottom of core 3 contains *Tetralithus nitidus, Microrhabdulus decoratus,* and *Reinhardtites anthophorus.* The top of core 4 contains these in addition to *Corollithion sig-*num, *Eiffelithus eximius* (Stover) n. comb. [=*Clinorhabdus eximius* Stover, 1966, p. 138, pl. 2, fig. 15; =*Eiffelithus augustus* Bukry, 1969, p. 51, pl. 28, fig. 10], *Tetralithus aculeus, Cylindralithus serratus, Lucianorhabdus cayeuxi, Tranolithus manifestus,* and *Arkhangelskiella parca.* The simultaneous extinction of these seven species indicates a major unconformity rather than a small sampling gap. An idea of its magnitude may be obtained by noting that six of these species became sequentially extinct in the tropical composite shelf section (figure 9), indicating that most or all of the lower Maastrichtian is missing at this site. It would be interesting to know whether a similar hiatus exists in other deep water Maastrichtian sections for it would furnish strong evidence

(*) sample examined by writer (-) species not found in sample within proposed sequence	Eiffellithus eximus	Corollithion signum	Tetralithus nitidus	Cylindralithus serratus	Tranolithus manifestus	Reinhardtites anthophorus	Arkhangelskiella parca	Microrhabdulus decoratus	Microrhabdulus stradneri	Marthasterites inconspicuus	Lithraphidites quadratus	Cylindralithus gallicus	Ceratolithoides kamptneri	Tetralithus murus	STAGE
Bellocq*									X	X	X	X	X	X	UPPER MAASTRICHTIAN
Type A. mayaro.*									X	-	-	X	X	X	UPPER MAASTRICHTIAN
Qoed 641*									X	X	X	X	X	X	UPPER MAASTRICHTIAN
Trinidad*								X	X	X	X	X	X	X	UPPER MAASTRICHTIAN
Alabama 1									X	X	X	X	X	-	UPPER MAASTRICHTIAN
Braggs 112*									X	X	X	X	X	-	UPPER MAASTRICHTIAN
Texas 715-720*									-	-	-	X	X	X	UPPER MAASTRICHTIAN
Qoed 637*									X	X	X	X	X	X	UPPER MAASTRICHTIAN
USGS									X	?	X	X	X	X	UPPER MAASTRICHTIAN
TRC 599*									X	X	X	X	X		UPPER MAASTRICHTIAN
L 700*									X	X	X	X	X		UPPER MAASTRICHTIAN
Qoed 634*									X	X	X	X	X		UPPER MAASTRICHTIAN
L 710*									-	X	X	X	X		UPPER MAASTRICHTIAN
Braggs 34*									X	X	X	X	X		UPPER MAASTRICHTIAN
L 720*									X	X	X	X	X		UPPER MAASTRICHTIAN
Braggs 22*									X	X	X	X	X		UPPER MAASTRICHTIAN
TRC 623*									X	X	X	X	X		UPPER MAASTRICHTIAN
L 730*									X	X	X	X	X		UPPER MAASTRICHTIAN
CCL*								X	X	X	X	X	X		UPPER MAASTRICHTIAN
Braggs 18*								X	X	X	X	X	X		UPPER MAASTRICHTIAN
Braggs 14*								X	X	X	X	X	X		UPPER MAASTRICHTIAN
Alabama 18							X	-	X	X	X	X	X		UPPER MAASTRICHTIAN
Qoed 633*						X	X	-	X	X	X	X	X		UPPER MAASTRICHTIAN
Alabama 30				X	X	X	X	-	X	X	X				LOWER MAASTRICHTIAN
Oued 629				X	X	X	X	X	X	X	X				LOWER MAASTRICHTIAN
L 740				X	X	X	X	X	X	X					LOWER MAASTRICHTIAN
Qoed 623*			X	X	X	X	X	X	X	X					LOWER MAASTRICHTIAN
Braggs 2*		X	X	X	X	X	X	X	X	X					LOWER MAASTRICHTIAN
TRC 668*		X	X	X	X	X	X	X	X	-					LOWER MAASTRICHTIAN
TRC 691*	X	X	X	X	X	X	X		X	X					LOWER MAASTRICHTIAN
ONCR*	X	X	X	X	X	X	X	X	X						LOWER MAASTRICHTIAN
Qoed 621*	X	X	X	X	X	X	X	X	X						LOWER MAASTRICHTIAN

FIG. 9.—Suggested subdivision of tropical Maastrichtian shelf sections.

(-) species not found in sample within proposed sequence. All samples were examined by the writer	Corollithion signum	Cylindralithus serratus	Tetralithus obscurus	Arkhangelskiella parca	Reinhardtites anthophorus	Lucianorhabdus cayeuxi	Microrhabdulus decoratus	Tranolithus manifestus	Marthasterites inconspicuus	Microrhabdulus stradneri	Lithraphidites quadratus	Nephrolithus frequens et. al.	Cylindralithus gallicus	STAGE
New Zealand												X	-	UPPER MAASTRICHTIAN
Dania 3						cf.			X	-	X	X	-	
Stevns Klint						cf.			X	X	X	X	-	
Mercemierz						X	-	X	X	-	X	X	-	
Kazmierz					X	X	X	-	X	X	X	X	-	
Dania 2					X	X	X	-	X	X	X	X	-	
Enci 10					X	X	X	-	-	X	X	-	X	
Enci 11					X	X	X	-	-	X	X	-	-	
KG 7					X	X	X	-	X	-	X	X	-	
KG 6				X	X	X	X	-	X	-	X	X	X	LOWER MAASTRICHTIAN
Don 66-69				X	X	X	-	X	X	X	X	-		
Don 81-84				X	X	X	X	X	X	X	X	-		
KG 4.5	X	X	X	X	X	X	X	X	X	X	X	X		
Dania 1	X	X	X	X	X	X	-	X	X	X	X			
KG 4.2	X	X	X	X	X	X	-	X	X	X	X			
Don 102-106	-	X	X	X	X	X	X	X	X					
Eperheide 5	X	X	X	X	X	X	X	X	cf.					
Don 388-394	X	X	-	X	X	-	X	X						
Eperheide 4	X	X	X	X	X	X	X	X	X					

FIG. 10.—Suggested subdivision of polar Maastrichtian shelf sections.

for a rather large-scale upward migration of CCD at this time, analogous to the one which closed the Cretaceous although not as drastic. Biostratigraphic resolution is now available for testing this on other Maastrichtian deep-sea cores.

The Cretaceous-Tertiary boundary as expressed in DSDP cores from Site 21 is represented by an unconformity in which NP 1 (*Markalius astroporus* Zone) is probably missing, although NP 2 (*Cruciplacolithus tenuis* Zone) appears to be present. This remains uncertain because of the downhole contamination. However, above this, almost the entire Paleocene interval is absent, the next highest zone encountered being NP 9 (*Discoaster multira-*

diatus Zone). This suggests that the site was below CCD for much of the Paleocene, an expectable occurrence if CCD did migrate into the photic zone at the end of the Cretaceous and slowly downward through the Paleocene. The recent data of Ramsay in this volume confirm this.

More recently, the Cretaceous-Tertiary boundary was cored at four localities in the Venezuelan Basin by Leg 15 of the DSDP. As expected, hiatuses between Mesozoic and Cenozoic were encountered at all four sites. Samples were not available for study by the writer but published preliminary information suggests that these are the most significant Cretaceous-Tertiary boundary cores recovered by the DSDP. Following is a summary of these cores (after reports in Geotimes and post-cruise information circulars):

Site 146—Water depth 3942 m.
 450 m. (subbottom) NP 9
 450–475 m.—siliceous clay, no calcareous fossils (Below CCD)
 475 m.—20 cm. of fossiliferous limestone representing the *Globigerina eugubina* Zone of lowest Tertiary age but containing no nannofossils.
 Below 475 m.—Corroded specimens of *Micula* grading downward into calcareous ooze representing the *Abathomphalus mayaroensis* Zone. Nannofossil preservation is poor.
Site 151   Water depth 2029 m.
 340–360 m.—NP 12
 360–376 m.—*Globotruncana concavata* Zone (Lower Santonian)
Site 152—Water depth 3889 m.
 230 m.—NP 4–5
 230–250 m.—siliceous clay, no calcareous fossils (below CCD)
 250 m.—*Globotruncana gansseri* Zone (mid-Maastrichtian)
Site 153—Water depth 3932 m.
 590–605 m.—NP 3–5
 610 m.—*Globotruncana tricarinata* Zone (Lower to Middle Maastrichtian)

Sites 146 and 152 are especially significant because they are the only DSDP sites from which a seemingly continuous though non-calcareous Mesozoic-Cenozoic sequence has been cored. If the siliceous clay at sites 146 and 152 represents continuous non-calcareous pelagic deposition across the Cretaceous-Tertiary boundary, sedimentation rates of about 2m/my and 1m/my respectively can be calculated for these sites using Berggren's (1970) time scale. This rate is acceptable for siliceous clays having a low terrigenous component and strongly sug-

gests that the sites were below carbonate compensation depth throughout the interval. Unfortunately, these cores, like other deep-sea cores, are not particularly useful for estimating the duration of the Cretaceous-Tertiary event because one has no way of determining where in this non-calcareous sequence it occurred. The answer to this question must be sought from shelf sections which should have remained above carbonate compensation depth for a longer period of time.

Maastrichtian Chronology

Few reliable radiometric dates exist for Maastrichtian strata but Maxwell and others (1970) suggest that the interval represents approximately seven million years based on indirect measurements such as pelagic sedimentation rates. Little data is available for estimating the duration of the Upper Maastrichtian but such an estimate must be attempted if a reasonable suggestion of the amount of time missing in the stratigraphic record across the Cretaceous-Tertiary boundary is to be made using extrapolations of trends determined by quantitative paleoecologic methods.

In the two Upper Maastrichtian DSDP cores (10-10 and 21-3) available to the writer, the range of *L. quadratus* is 30 feet (9 m.) and is identical to that of *T. murus*, *C. kamptneri*, and *C. gallicus*, an indication that much of the lower portion of their ranges is missing in these sections. If a pelagic sedimentation rate of 20 m/my is assumed, the Upper Maastrichtian of these cores represents about 0.5 my, less for a higher sedimentation rate. The interval contains predominantly slowly evolving, long-ranging species, almost all of which abruptly become extinct at its top in all sections of the world so far studied. Figure 11 shows the ranges of these species which occur throughout the Maastrichtian (Upper Ripley and Prairie Bluff Formations) to become extinct at its top. The ranges of these species are not of great biostratigraphic value in this part of the section, but the abruptness of their extinctions suggests how catastrophic the event which ended the Cretaceous was.

Most of the extinctions occur within an interval of eight feet (2.6 m.) at the Braggs section. Abundant glauconite and phosphate at this level in the section indicates that biogenous accumulation during this interval might have been considerably slower, but this is probably offset by the relatively high rate of clastic influx at the Braggs section as compared to pelagic sections. To the writer's knowledge, it is the most nearly transitional section across the Creta-

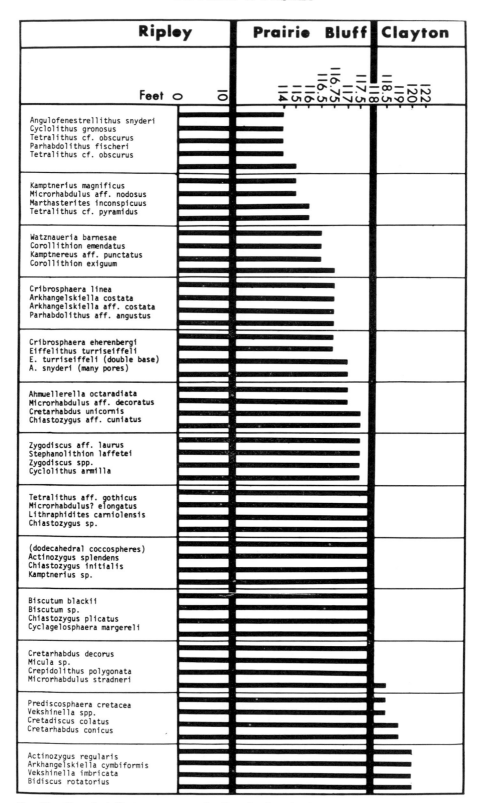

Fig. 11.—Terminal Cretaceous nannofossil extinctions in the Braggs section of Alabama.

ceous-Tertiary boundary in the world. The entire 105 feet of the Prairie Bluff Chalk at Braggs, Alabama, is within the range of *Lithraphidites quadratus* but the major unconformity at the base of the formation precludes a reliable estimate of the duration of the entire Late Maastrichtian here. *L. quadratus* is found in the subjacent Ripley Formation at Millers Ferry, Alabama, without the Upper Maastrichtian guide fossils *Ceratolithoides kamptneri* and *Cylindralithus gallicus* which always seem to occur simultaneously at the base of the Prairie Bluff in Alabama, so that there is no precise way of estimating the duration of the Ripley-Prairie Bluff unconformity. The many extinctions occurring at this unconformity suggest that a large part of the Upper Maastrichtian and/or Lower Maastrichtian are missing here (figure 12).

At Oued El Abiod, Tunisia, Maastrichtian strata are 200 m. thick. However this abnormally great thickness is expectable because these strata form the south limb of a major geosynclinal basin (Bramlette and Martini, 1964). Of this total, 70–80 m. belong to the Upper Maastrichtian (above the highest *Arkhangelskiella parca*). If these strata represent the same interval as other sections, the calculated sedimentation rate is about 150 m/my. If the section is assumed to be continuous for the entire Maastrichtian, a sedimentation rate of about 30 m/my can be calculated for the entire Maastrichtian of Oued El Abiod. If this rate were uniform, the calculated duration of the Upper Maastrichtian at this section would be 2–2.5 my, based on a seven million year Maastrichtian.

The above suggests that the Upper and Lower Maastrichtian greatly differ in duration, the former representing only about 0.5–2.5 million years of the approximately seven million year Maastrichtian interval. Averaging these yields a crude figure of one million years for the duration of the Upper Maastrichtian. This figure will be used in calculating the duration of the terminal Cretaceous event in the hope that it is not off by more than a factor of two or three.

The Duration of the Terminal Cretaceous Event

According to the above calculations, the eight-foot extinction interval at the top of the Prairie Bluff Chalk represents a minimum of about 100,000 years. As this is the only section with a

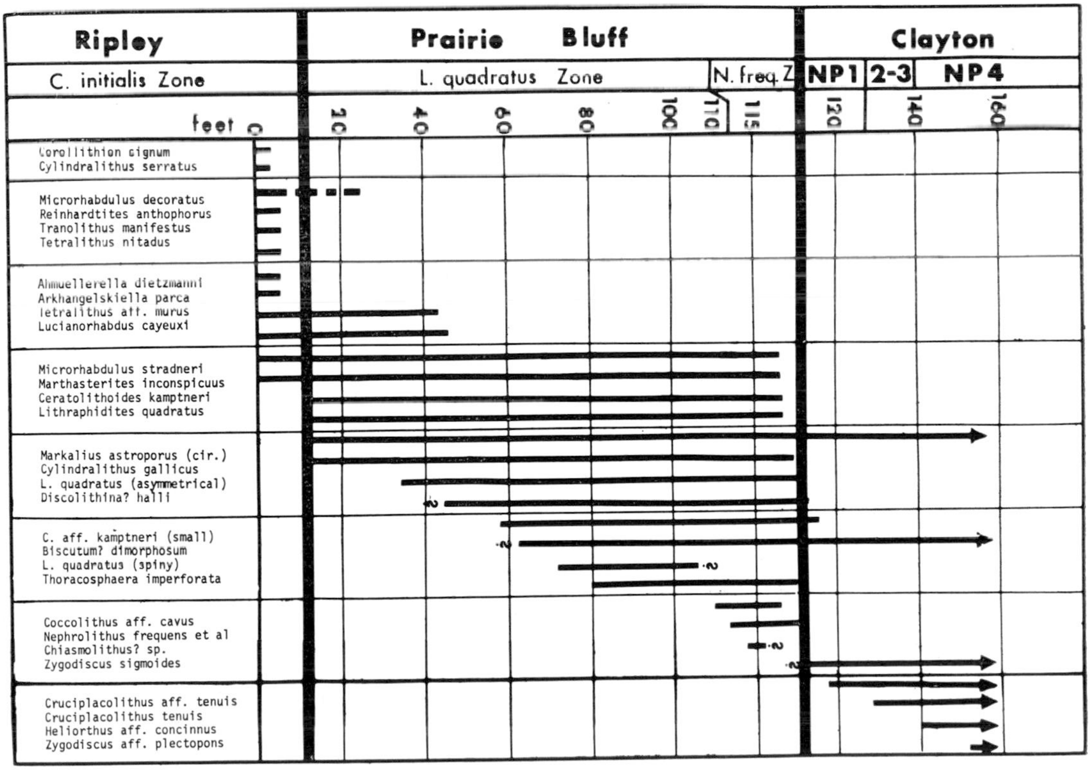

Fig. 12.—Stratigraphically useful nannofossils in the Braggs section of Alabama.

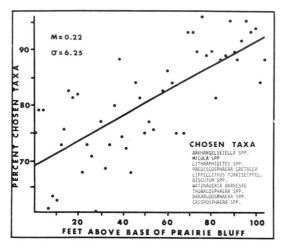

FIG. 13.—Nannofossil population trends in the upper Maastrichtian of Alabama (for explanation, see text and Appendix III).

transitional extinction record known to the writer, comparison with other sections is not now possible. Fortunately, another method exists for estimating the interval missing at the top of the Maastrichtian. It requires closely spaced, uncontaminated samples, however, and the only such section available to the writer was the Braggs section of Alabama. The mechanics of the technique are outlined in Appendix 3. The technique consists essentially of point counting selected nannofossil taxa at many levels in a section and plotting the relative percentage of each to the total nannofossil population for each stratigraphic level. A straight line is then fitted to a plot of the relative percentage of a species vs. stratigraphic level. Those taxa found to increase in relative abundance toward the top of the section are presumed to have become extinct last. The one having the steepest slope should be the last one to become extinct: i.e. it will eventually comprise 100 percent of the nannoflora at the end of the Cretaceous, just prior to its own extinction. In reality, the 100 percent figure was never reached for any species. Figure 13 shows the composite of ten long-ranging Upper Cretaceous taxa. At the top of the section, these comprise about 93 per cent of the nannoflora. Extrapolation of the straight line fit to the 100 percent level indicates that about 30 feet (9 m.) of section is missing. This represents 3×10^5 years if the preserved Prairie Bluff interval is 10^6 years long. Figure 14 shows that almost the entire slope of figure 13 can be accounted for by an increase in the proportion of *Micula*, so that it might be more reasonable to use this

single fossil to estimate the duration of the terminal Cretaceous event. According to such calculations, 2×10^6 years are missing between Cretaceous and Tertiary. These figures are a first approximation and could be modified if the data are found to fit a second or higher order equation rather than a linear one. The writer apologizes for the crudeness of these estimates but they must suffice for the present because without radiometric dates or a continuous transitional section across the Cretaceous-Tertiary boundary, no other way of estimating the duration of the Cretaceous-Tertiary event is available. It is interesting to note parenthetically that these figures are of the same order of magnitude as those suggested by Ramsay elsewhere in this volume for short duration Tertiary fluctuations in carbonate compensation depth.

CONSTRUCTION OF A MODEL TO EXPLAIN THE TERMINAL CRETACEOUS EVENT

The premise on which the subsequently presented model of the terminal Cretaceous event is based is the assumption that the carbonate compensation depth (CCD) ascended into the photic zone of the oceans at the end of the Cretaceous. If such is the case, there can be no record of that event preserved in calcareous sediments, as none were being deposited at that time. In the following, the factors controlling CCD are discussed with reference to their effects on the stratigraphic record.

Carbonate Compensation Depth, Biostratigraphy and the Terminal Cretaceous Event

A continuous calcareous biostratigraphic record can occur only in areas which have re-

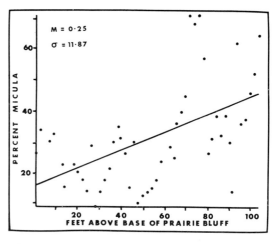

FIG. 14.—Proportion of *Micula* vs. stratigraphic level in the Braggs section of Alabama (Worsley and Cline averaged, see Appendix III).

mained below sea level but above carbonate compensation depth (CCD) throughout history. Therefore one could expect to find such a record in any of the shallower portions of the ocean basins if the CCD had remained static throughout geologic time. However, results of the Deep Sea Drilling Project demonstrate that such a record probably does not exist: 1) because of the relatively young age of much of the ocean crust according to the hypothesis of sea floor spreading and, 2) because the CCD has not remained at a constant level throughout geologic time.

According to Broecker (1970), rather than being a fixed depth of about 4 km. in the ocean which is governed by temperature and pressure, the level of the CCD is controlled by the rate of carbonate supply to and removal from the oceans. It is supplied from the continents, being derived from calcic igneous and metamorphic rocks as well as terrestrially exposed marine carbonate rocks. It is removed through biologic precipitation of calcite by both pelagic and benthonic organisms. This system presents two mechanisms by which CCD can vertically migrate: 1) A change in the rate of supply from the continents, which in turn is governed by the rate of orogenically controlled erosion of positive areas. This has been shown to be highly variable throughout the Mesozoic and Cenozoic. 2) A change in the rate which organisms precipitate calcite. At present, the rate of removal by organisms exceeds the supply from the continents, and balance is maintained by dissolution, resulting in a CCD. This has not always been the case.

There is little evidence for a Mesozoic CCD in the Atlantic Ocean although data from DSDP legs 6 and 7 indicate that a Late Cretaceous CCD was present in the Pacific. These results are not surprising because present CCD in the Pacific is higher than in the Atlantic owing to substantially lower stream influx yielding a proportionately lower $CaCO_3$ influx. Apparently, these conditions have not changed appreciably since the Late Mesozoic. However, the limited deep sea drilling data from both oceans offers no evidence that a CCD existed in the Early Cretaceous or Late Jurassic. It therefore seems that a CCD first appeared sometime in the Late Cretaceous in the Pacific and at the end of the Cretaceous in the Atlantic. The probable history of its development is as follows.

Before Jurassic time, carbonate-secreting pelagic organisms comprised a negligible proportion of the ocean's total carbonate-secreting biota. Therefore, practically all carbonate removed from the oceans was precipitated by benthonic organisms on the continental shelves where it could be recycled. The development of calcareous plankton in the Jurassic intiated a mechanism capable of permanently removing large quantities of carbonate as deposits in the deep ocean basins where it cannot be readily recycled. Steady carbonate removal progressed through the Late Mesozoic. When enough carbonate had been permanently removed from the reservoir, part of the ocean became undersaturated with $CaCO_3$ and a CCD developed, first in the Pacific and then in the Atlantic.

Recent DSDP results indicate that once it developed, the CCD did not remain at a constant level below the surface but has been subject to considerable vertical fluctuations throughout the Cenozoic (Hay, 1970; Ramsay, this volume). Furthermore, it has been demonstrated that calcareous nannofossils are more solution-resistant than planktonic foraminifera and consequently have had a lower CCD throughout the Cenozoic (and therefore a more complete biostratigraphic record in deep-sea sections). Figure 15 illustrates these relationships. Data are admittedly sparse but major trends are already discernible. Ramsay has taken into account the subsidence due to seafloor spreading and modified Hay's original estimate of 1.5 km. vertical migration of CCD in the Atlantic to about 1.0 km. Ramsay's more detailed data suggest that the fluctuations occur more rapidly than indicated on Hay's curve; in fact he suggests that they take place in less than 250,000 years, a remarkably rapid rate of change. The prominent spike on Hay's curve at the Cretaceous-Tertiary boundary, where CCD is postulated to have migrated up into the photic zone (Tappan, 1968, Worsley, 1970) is based on the fact that no calcareous sediments representing this interval have been discovered in the deep sea anywhere in the world. Furthermore, DSDP results indicate that the hiatus is greater in the ocean basins than on many shelf sections, an expectable result if CCD did indeed migrate upward into the photic zone and then back down again.

Figure 16 is an interpretative cross section showing the age relationships and present configuration of sediments draped over the southern part of the Mid-Atlantic Ridge at about latitude 30°S. The Cretaceous-Tertiary boundary was cored only at DSDP sites 20 and 21 in the South Atlantic so that the Cretaceous-Tertiary unconformity plotted is my own schematic lateral extrapolation of the drilling data. The data for the continent are also schematic in that they are not intended to represent

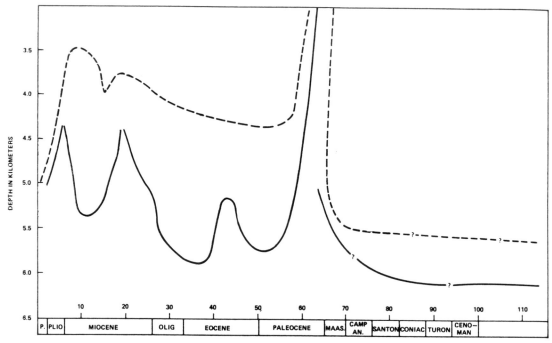

Fig. 15.—Cenozoic fluctuations of carbonate compensation depth (after Hay, 1970). Dashed line = lower limit of accumulation of planktonic foraminiferal tests; solid line = lower limit of accumulation of coccoliths.

South America alone, but rather a composite of shelf sections from all continents. If the meager data for the South Atlantic have been interpreted correctly, a similar cross section would hold true for all ocean basins that have experienced sea-floor spreading since the late Cretaceous.

Figure 17 shows that the more continuous deep-sea record of the Maastrichtian-Paleocene interval occurs on the Maastrichtian-Danian Mid-Atlantic Ridge. This is reasonable because the shallower ridge areas should have remained above the CCD for a longer period than the deep ocean basins, but not as long as the shallower marine shelves. Available data do not permit precise conclusions, but do suggest that the descent of the sea floor as it spread from the Mid-Atlantic Ridge outstripped the downward migration of the CCD after the Cretaceous-Tertiary event. DSDP Site 20, which was almost at the crest of the Ridge in the late Maastrichtian, experienced a pause in calcareous sedimentation as the CCD rapidly migrated toward the surface during the Cretaceous-Tertiary event. It again received calcareous sediment shortly after the event as CCD migrated below the ridge crest. The time during which CCD was above the ridge crest represents most of the Danian. DSDP Site 21, which also contains Early Maastrichtian calcareous sediments,

was apparently lower on the ridge flank and did not again receive calcareous sediment until the Late Paleocene, when the CCD finally descended low enough to permit calcareous sedimentation in the area of the Rio Grande Rise. The magnitude of the Cretaceous-Tertiary hiatus in the deep sea is a function of paleobathymetry with deeper water sections exhibiting a greater unconformity. Figure 18 schematically represents the sequence described above.

That such a dramatic paleo-oceanographic event should produce many consequences is evident. It is the purpose of the remainder of this paper to demonstrate that such an event did occur, suggest its cause, explore its consequences, review previous explanations of the extinctions, and finally present a model which explains the abrupt extinctions at the end of the Mesozoic as a consequence of this unusual change in CCD.

Previous Models of the Terminal Cretaceous Event

Within the last 20 years, a number of models have been offered to explain the abruptness of the extinctions in general, with particular reference to those at the end of the Cretaceous. Those which adhere closely to known facts and rely on uniformitarianism are reviewed and scrutinized below. A more complete review may

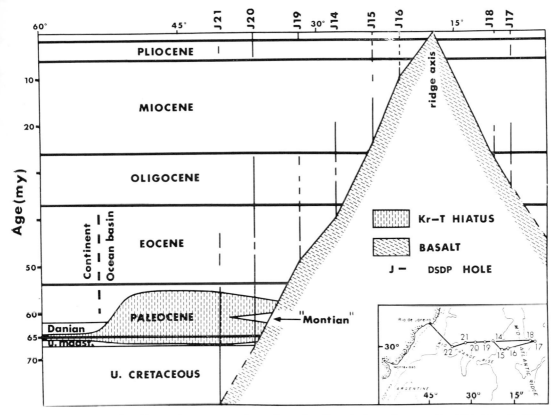

FIG. 16.—Age relationships and present configuration of sediments draped across the Mid-Atlantic Ridge at about latitude 30°S showing the magnitude of the Cretaceous-Tertiary unconformity (after Worsley, 1971).

be found in Newell (1962), Tappan (1968), and Lipps (1970).

Schatz (1957) suggested that the extinctions were caused by CO_2 depletion in the atmosphere resulting from adaptive radiation of the angiosperms during the late Cretaceous. He reasoned that the more efficient photosynthesis of the angiosperms removed CO_2, causing a lowering of global temperatures by reversal of the greenhouse effect drastically affecting the worldwide tropical fauna and flora of the Upper Creta-

ceous. There is little doubt that late Cretaceous climate deteriorated but the extinctions resulting from such a process should have been gradual rather than abrupt.

Hay (1960) believed that a short period of drastic cooling of the earth caused the mass extinctions of warmth-loving Upper Cretaceous organisms at the end of the Maastrichtian. He offered no specific mechanism by which the sudden temperature lowering could occur, but discussed several lines of evidence suggesting

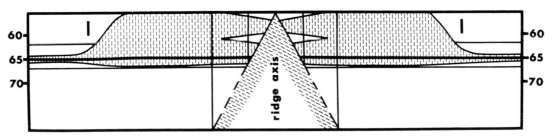

FIG. 17.—Palinspastic reconstruction of figure 16 (after Worsley, 1971).

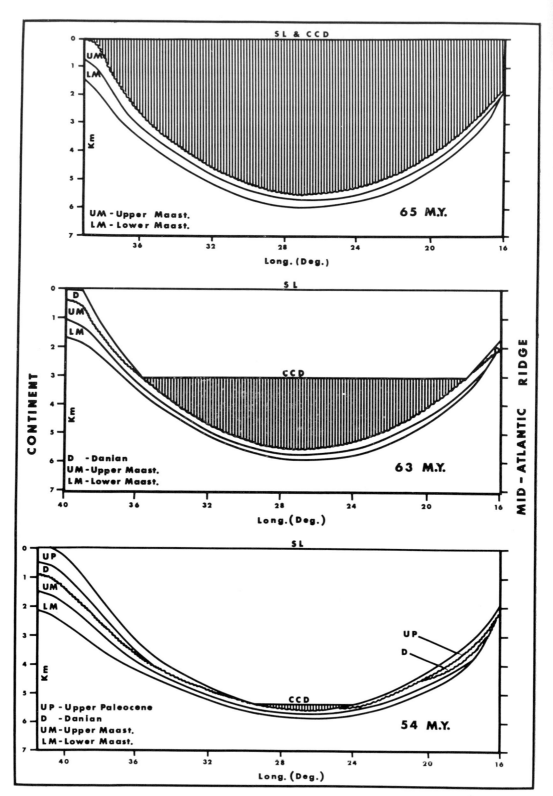

Fig. 18.—Schematic reconstruction of the Atlantic and adjacent continental mass at the time of the terminal Cretaceous event: top, at the Mesozoic-Cenozoic boundary; middle, within the Danian; bottom, within the upper Paleocene.

that worldwide temperature did become appreciably lower toward the end of the Maastrichtian. However, Lipps (1970) noted that climatic deterioration leads to environmental stress which in turn should lead to species diversification rather than diminution. Therefore climatic deterioration in itself cannot have been solely responsible for the abrupt terminal Cretaceous extinctions.

Newell (1962) favored the idea that fluctuations in the strandline of the oceans control the abundance of biota by altering climate. However late Cretaceous sea-level changes appear to have been gradual and could not have been the direct cause of the near-instantaneous extinctions at the end of the Cretaceous.

An excess of dissolved salts in the ocean at the end of the Permian was postulated to have caused massive extinctions by Cloud (1959), but there are no salt deposits associated with the Cretaceous-Tertiary boundary, nor are there other indications of hypersaline or even brackish conditions having existed at this time.

Schindewolf (1954) indicated that an increase in cosmic radiation at the end of the Cretaceous would have increased mutation rates and caused a burst of rapid evolution resulting in replacement of older forms by new ones. The mechanism is possible but there is no evidence that cosmic radiation rates fluctuate appreciably through geologic time. Furthermore, the astronomical number of phytoplankton individuals would indicate that an ample standing crop of mutants would always be available for exploiting new environments as they became available without need of increased radiation to induce additional mutations. Even if such a fluctuation occurred, marine organisms would have been better shielded by the sea water they inhabited than terrestrial animals and plants— yet the most striking extinctions are among the oceanic plankton (Bramlette, 1965).

Bramlette (1965) inferred that extinction of higher organisms in the marine food chain resulted from decimation of the phytoplankton, the primary producers. He attributed the extinctions within this group to progressive reduction of nutrient supplies resulting from orogenic stagnation. He tentatively suggested that rapid extinction could have occurred when nutrient supplies reached a critically low level, as happens in certain laboratory cultures of algae. The span of time this would encompass for a system as diverse as that found in the oceans would still be short enough to appear "geologically instantaneous." The mechanism is doubtful, but if it did occur, the non-depositional interval between Cretaceous and Tertiary would eliminate much of the record of dwindling, thereby making the extinctions seem "instantaneous." Calculations presented above suggest that the nondepositional interval is on the order of a few hundred thousand to a million or more years.

Simpson (1966) thought that a reversal of the earth's magnetic polarity at the close of the Cretaceous could have caused the massive extinctions by temporarily eliminating the earth's magnetic field. This would collapse the Van Allen Belts which supposedly shield the earth from intensive radiation. Even if a polarity reversal is shown to be contemporaneous with the Cretaceous-Tertiary event, and thus far this is not the case, the theory encounters the same difficulties as Schindewolf's (1954) cosmic radiation theory; the already large standing crop of mutants and the insulating effect of sea water. Furthermore, many documented polarity reversals do not seem to have had devastating effects upon flora and fauna (McElhinny, 1971).

Axelrod and Bailey (1968) suggested that a worldwide equability decrease at the end of the Cretaceous was the main cause of dinosaur extinctions. Their model is also applicable to the marine realm. They defined equability quantitatively as the amount of seasonal and diurnal departure of points on the earth's surface from the mean temperature (about 57°F.) of the earth's surface, noting that cold-blooded dinosaurs could have survived neither cold nor warm temperature extremes even if they were of relatively short duration. They suggested that the worldwide climatic deterioration (decreased equability) toward the end of the Cretaceous placed severe environmental stress on the cold-blooded dinosaurs, which had become highly adapted to the equable climates existing since the late Triassic. All known evidence is in accord with this hypothesis. Extinctions among the dinosaurs were gradual throughout the Late Cretaceous but culminated in sudden extinction of all remaining species immediately below the Cretaceous-Tertiary boundary. The abruptness of the extinctions is especially well documented in the Western Interior of the United States. Axelrod and Bailey also enumerated the reasons why the decreased equability would have a correspondingly severe effect on marine life but were not able to suggest why the extinctions were so abrupt, or why life is so diverse in today's oceans while worldwide climate is so strongly differentiated.

In 1968, Tappan presented a model of periodic phytoplankton productivity which sought to link the O_2/CO_2 balance of the atmosphere and oceans to the productivity of the phytoplankton throughout geologic time. Following is her summary of that model:

> Phytoplankton photosynthesis has controlled the atmospheric carbon dioxide-oxygen balance since the early Precambrian when algal abundance became sufficient to convert the reducing atmosphere to an oxygenic one. Later phytoplankton maxima indicated in the geologic record coincide with and are here suggested to have caused extensive biogenic calcareous deposition, and evolutionary diversification of the contemporaneous biota. In contrast, the onset of decreased productivity in the geologic past triggered a general biotic turnover on both land and sea.
>
> Times of phytoplankton extinctions coincide with similar periods affecting animal taxa rather than terrestrial plants. These periods of severely reduced microfloras and low productivity resulted in atmospheric oxygen depletion and increased pCO_2, ^{12}C enriched limestones, formation of ^{32}S enriched sulfates, and submarine dissolution of carbonates. Selective extinctions of animal taxa were due to quantitative variations in the interrelated processes of carbon fixation (the food source for the marine environment), and the photosynthetic consumption of carbon dioxide and production of oxygen.
>
> The phytoplankton abundance may have been controlled by contemporaneous continental physiography, through its effect on climate, atmospheric circulation and oceanic upwelling. Low continents, equable climates, little influx of land-derived materials and lessened effectiveness of upwelling allowed the sinking of nutrients to exceed their renewal, resulting in marked reduction of phytoplankton, with the attendant effects of the decreased productivity and oxygen depletion crossing ecologic and systematic boundaries.
>
> Continental rejuvenation with resultant climatic changes and increased oceanic circulation stimulated renewed phytoplankton diversification and growth, and allowed a renewed expansion of dependent animal taxa.

The high CO_2 levels postulated by Tappan for the end of the Cretaceous suggest higher temperatures caused by the greenhouse effect. Temperatures are thought to have been decreasing in the late Cretaceous so Tappan reasoned that increased CO_2 levels yield increased water vapor in the atmosphere leading to more cloudiness. She concluded from this that increased cloudiness would have resulted in greater albedo for the planet, negating the increase of temperature caused by the greenhouse effect. As this mechanism is a feedback response to increased temperature, it does not seem reasonable to invoke it for explaining a lowering of worldwide temperature. Furthermore, Axelrod and Bailey's (1968) compilation suggests that humid, cloudy climates, which facilitate heat transfer around the globe, are generally highly equable whereas arid ones are subject to greater temperature extremes because they are more dependent on direct insolation. This evidence is in direct contradiction to Tappan's suggestion that Upper Maastrichtian phytoplankton extinctions are related to highly equable climate. It is therefore simpler to accept the idea that free atmospheric CO_2 decreased during the Upper Cretaceous as temperatures decreased. At colder temperatures, the solubility of CO_2 increases in water so that equilibrium conditions between the oceans and atmosphere would naturally result in lower atmospheric and higher oceanic levels of CO_2. Holland (1965) suggested, and Mackenzie and Garrels (1966) demonstrated that detrital silicate minerals react very rapidly (faster than calcite) to changes in the pH of sea water and showed that they could constitute an effective buffer against large changes in the CO_2 pressure of the atmosphere and oceans. However Tappan noted that the orogenic stagnation which characterized the late Cretaceous resulted in a sharp decline in the supply of detrital silicates so that silicate buffering would have been much less effective during that time.

In its salient characteristics, the Tappan model effectively explains the massive terminal Cretaceous extinctions but does not offer a reason for their apparent abruptness. The model offered below avoids many of the difficulties of the Tappan model while retaining its strong points.

Proposed Model of the Terminal Cretaceous Event

The following model of the Cretaceous-Tertiary event was first presented in summarized form by Worsley (1971). In the following, a more detailed account is presented, followed by a discussion of the implications of this model for environmental geology and biostratigraphy.

Before Jurassic time, $CaCO_3$ eroded from the continents was precipitated on the continental shelves by benthonic organisms with only a very minor proportion being permanently lost to the deep ocean basins via pelagic organisms with calcareous skeletons. With the advent of calcareous plankton in the Jurassic, a mechanism originated for effectively removing carbonate from the orogenic cycle. The effects of this $CaCO_3$ depletion were first seriously felt during the late Cretaceous when it progressed without replacement from continents that were nearly base-leveled (Newell, 1962; Bramlette, 1965).

During the late Maastrichtian, pronounced climatic deterioration ensued. Among marine organisms, belemnites, several species of planktonic foraminifers, and several species of calcareous nannofossils became climatically restricted (Jeletsky, 1960; Worsley, 1970). Additionally, there was selective replacement of more rapidly-evolving nannofossil taxa by slowly evolving forms (Worsley, 1970). On the continents, cycads and other thermophilic floral elements were replaced by temperate conifers and hardwoods in middle latitudes, with a concurrent decline of reptiles (Axelrod and Bailey, 1968; Hall and Norton, 1967; Stanley, 1955). The most probable cause of the deterioration was a decrease of CO_2 in the atmosphere brought about primarily by the late Cretaceous phytoplankton bloom responsible for the worldwide deposition of chalk (Tappan, 1968). Secondary mechanisms for converting CO_2 to O_2 were due to the rise of the photosynthetically efficient angiosperms (Schindewolf, 1954) and perhaps removal of carbon from the atmospheric cycle by lignite formation (Schwartzbach, 1963). There is no method available for directly testing whether changes in CO_2 content in the atmosphere entail climatic changes, but Plass (1956), on the bais of theoretical considerations, calculated that present-day worldwide temperatures would drop about 4°C if the CO_2 content of the atmosphere were reduced by seven percent. This would also reduce cloudiness and tend to accentuate the effects of climatic deterioration by reducing effective means of heat transfer between poles and equator, making all areas of the globe more dependent upon direct isolation. Lower worldwide Maastrichtian temperatures and equability should have decreased precipitation and lowered terrestrial weathering and erosion rates, reducing the already critically low supply of nutrients and carbonate available to marine phytoplankton.

As climatic deterioration progressed in the Maastrichtian, polar cooling of sea water would have increased the horizontal and vertical oceanic thermal gradients (Lipps, 1970) and hence would increase the solubility of CO_2 in higher latitudes and deeper water. Ultimately, a CCD developed in the deep ocean basins and migrated to progressively shallower levels (Tappan, 1968; Hay, 1970). Absence of early Danian fossils in deep sea cores penetrating the Cretaceous-Tertiary boundary in calcareous sediments (with the exception of those shown to be on the Maastrichtian-Danian midoceanic ridge) is evidence of the process (Hay, 1970; Maxwell and others, 1970; Ewing and others, 1969; Peterson and others, 1970). Concurrent with CO_2 increase in the ocean, the lack of detritus reduced the effects of silicate buffering

during this time (Tappan, 1968), resulting in a slight lowering of pH in the oceans. Evidence of this is found in numerous deep-sea and shelf phosphate-glauconite layers and hardgrounds in this part of the column, which suggest submarine solution of carbonate. Upward migration of the CCD through the late Maastrichtian suggests that the most continuous biologic record across the Cretaceous-Tertiary boundary should be found on the shallowest portions of shelves favorable to growth of calcareous nannoplankton. This was shown to be the case in the section at Braggs, Alabama, discussed above. Eventually, the CCD approached the surface of the ocean, directly affecting planktonic organisms (Tappan, 1968; Hay, 1970). It was during this time that the massive extinctions that ended the Cretaceous occurred. In the marine realm, sharp phytoplankton reduction would ensure the concomitant extinctions of dependent marine taxa throughout the pelagic food chain. It is interesting to note parenthetically that the sparse nannoflora surviving the terminal Cretaceous event were dominated by *Braarudosphaera* and *Thoracosphaera,* both of which are known to tolerate and even prefer conditions adverse for the growth of other calcareous nannoplankton in today's oceans (Hay and Mohler, 1967).

On land, the increased latitudinal thermal gradient plus the sharper seasonal and probably diurnal temperature differential, caused the relatively abrupt extinction of the last surviving species of dinosaurs (Axelrod and Bailey, 1968). The megaphyta apparently suffered few extinctions across the Cretaceous-Tertiary boundary, but dicots were abruptly shifted toward the equator in response to the chilling of middle latitudes (Hall and Norton, 1967; Stanley, 1965).

The mechanism by which recovery from the event ensued is inherent in the model. Removal of a major portion of the phytoplankton had severely curtailed photosynthetic CO_2 to O_2 conversion and carbonate precipitation in the oceans, finally releasing CO_2 from the oceans into the atmosphere. This increase of atmospheric CO_2 would lead to amelioration of climate and downward migration of the CCD. The oceans, however, would remain relatively sterile with a somewhat elevated CCD throughout the early Paleocene until the supply of nutrients and carbonate was replenished by orogeny (Tappan, 1968). Deep sea drilling results for the Paleocene interval support this idea.

Geologic and Environmental Implications

Should the above model be a true representation of the terminal Cretaceous event, several additional consequences can be inferred which could conceivably offer a test of the model. Furthermore, it is suggested that the equilibrium existing between carbonate compensation depth in the oceans and rate of calcium and nutrient supply from the continents is far more delicate than has previously been assumed in the past, so that the terminal Cretaceous event might offer a foreshadowing of the consequences of man's rapidly increasing rate of alteration of the world's oceans.

Solution extinctions.—If the CCD migrated upward at a relatively slow rate during the Maastrichtian, one would expect to find a record in which the terminal Cretaceous extinctions are a function of selective solution among Maastrichtian calcareous plankton species—i.e. a record of sequential extinctions of taxa in the relative order of their individual CCD's which would be traceable around the globe. However, the increments of this sequence would be homeotaxic rather than synchronous. The age of one of the increments at a particular locality would be a function of paleobathymetry, not evolution. It may be possible to construct nearly isochronous surfaces through such a solutional extinction sequence using the relatively few evolutionary datum surfaces occurring within the Maastrichtian and preserved in shelf deposits. Such a subdivision was suggested on figures 9 and 10. If the sequence changes as a function of paleobathymetry, a selective solution sequence is indicated. The thickness of the selective solution sequence at different paleodepths would offer a method for calculating the rate of upward migration of the CCD. Similar reasoning is applicable to the Cenozoic also, where chronostratigraphy is better understood and therefore would be the most likely place for initial detection of such a sequence.

Thus far, evidence for a solution extinction sequence at the end of the Cretaceous is limited to the 8-foot (2.6 m.) sequence at the Braggs section of Alabama and DSDP sites 146 and 152 in the Caribbean (Hay, personal communi-cation). A possibility for one exists in Trinidad where Bramlette and Martini (1964) noted a dearth of nannofossil species in an isolated sample within the *Tetralithus murus* Zone.

ACKNOWLEDGMENTS

This study was initiated as a Ph.D. dissertation under the direction of William W. Hay at the University of Illinois and many of the ideas contained in this paper are a direct outgrowth of informal discussions with Sherwood Wise and William Hay. Upon completion of the dissertation, the project was expanded to incorporate JOIDES (Joint Oceanographic Institutions Deep Earth Sampling) DSDP data.

Financial support for field work in Alabama was provided by summer grants from the University of Illinois Geology Department and the Society of the Sigma Xi. Funds for laboratory work during the latter stages of the project and manuscript preparation were supplied by the Quaternary Research Center at the University of Washington under Science Development Grant GU-2655.

Many individuals and organizations have contributed data, samples, ideas, and encouragement throughout the project and their support is gratefully acknowledged. Erlend Martini and Richard K. Olsson provided valuable samples and even more valuable advice. Several particularly significant samples from Texas were donated by Mrs. Gene Ross Kellough. Charles Copeland of the Alabama Geological Survey informed me of the unique suitability of the Alabama outcrops and the Survey provided valuable assistance in field collection. DSDP samples were supplied by the National Science Foundation.

I am indebted to Charles Cline for valuable technical assistance and aid in the preparation of the manuscript. My wife Helen gave technical assistance to the project but more importantly, without her understanding and moral support, it would never have been completed.

This is contribution no. 765 of the Department of Oceanography, University of Washington.

REFERENCES

Axelrod, D. I., 1952, A theory of angiosperm evolution: Evolution, v. 6, p. 29–60.
———, 1966, Origin of the deciduous and evergreen habits in temperate forests: *ibid.*, v. 20, p. 1–15.
———, and Bailey, H. P., 1968, Cretaceous dinosaur extinction: *ibid.*, v. 22, p. 595–611.
Berggren, W., 1964, The Maastrichtian, Danian and Montian Stages and the Cretaceous-Tertiary boundary: Stockholm Contr. Geol. II, p. 103–176.
Bramlette, M. N., 1965, Massive extinctions in biota at the end of Mesozoic time: Science, v. 148, p. 1696–1699.
———, and Martini, E., 1964, The great change in calcareous nannoplankton fossils between the Maastrichtian and Danian: Micropaleontology, v. 10, p. 291–322.
Brinkman, R., 1959, Abriss der Geologie, historische Geologie: Stuttgart, Ferdinand Enke Verlag, v. 2, 360 p.

BROECKER, W. S., 1971, Calcite accumulation rates and glacial to interglacial changes in oceanic mixing: *in* TUREKIAN, K. K. (ed.), The late Cenozoic glacial ages. New Haven, Connecticut, Yale Univ. Press, p. 239–265.

BROWN, R., 1952, Tertiary strata in eastern Montana and western North and South Dakota: Billings Geol. Soc. Guidebook 3, p. 89–92.

BUKRY, D., 1969, Upper Cretaceous coccoliths from Texas and Europe: Lawrence, Univ. Kansas Paleont. Contr., Art. 51 (Protista 2), 79 p.

ČEPEK, P., AND HAY, W. W., 1969, Calcareous nannoplankton and biostratigraphic subdivision of the Upper Cretaceous: Gulf Coast Assoc. Geol. Soc. Trans., v. 19, p. 323–336.

———, ———, MASTERS, B., AND WORSLEY, T. R., 1968, Calcareous plankton in the Upper Cretaceous of Alabama, *in* SCOTT, J. C., AND OTHERS, Facies changes in the Selma Group in central and eastern Alabama: Alabama Geol. Soc. 6th Ann. Fieldtrip Guidebook, p. 27–40.

CLOUD, JR., P. E., 1959, Paleoecology—retrospect and prospect: Jour. Paleontology, v. 33, p. 926–962.

COPELAND, C., 1968, Facies changes in the Selma Group in central and eastern Alabama, *in* SCOTT, J. C., AND OTHERS, Facies changes in the Selma Group in central and eastern Alabama: Alabama Geol. Soc. 6th Ann. Fieldtrip Guidebook, p. 2–26.

DENNISON, J. M., AND HAY, W. W., 1967, Estimating the needed sampling area for subaquatic ecologic studies: Jour. Paleontology, v. 41, p. 706–708.

———, AND SHEA, J. H., 1966, Reliability of visual estimates of grain abundance: Jour. Sed. Petrology, v. 36, p. 81–89.

EDWARDS, A. R., 1966, Calcareous nannoplankton from the uppermost Cretaceous and lowermost Tertiary of the mid-Waipara section South Island: New Zealand Jour. Geology and Geophysics, v. 9, p. 481–490.

EWING, M., AND OTHERS, 1969, Initial reports of the Deep Sea Drilling Project: Washington, D.C., U.S. Govt. Printing Office, v. 1, 672 p.

FOX, S. K., AND OLSSON, R. K., 1969, Danian planktonic foraminifera from Cannonball Formation, North Dakota: Am. Assoc. Petroleum Geologists Bull., v. 53, p. 718.

———, AND ROSS, JR., R. J., 1942, Foraminiferal evidence for the Midway (Paleocene) age of the Cannonball Formation in North Dakota: Jour. Paleontology, v. 16, p. 660–673.

GARTNER, S., 1968, Coccoliths and related calcareous nannofossils from Upper Cretaceous deposits of Texas and Arkansas: Lawrence, Univ. Kansas Paleont. Contr., Protista, Art. 1, p. 1–56.

GORKA, H., 1957, Coccolithophordae z gornego mastrychtu Polski srodkowej (Les Coccolithophorides du Maestrichtien supérieur du Pologne): Acta Paleontologia Polonica, v. 2, p. 235–284.

HALL, J. W., AND NORTON, J. J., 1967, Palynological evidence of floristic change across the Cretaceous-Tertiary boundary in eastern Montana: Palaeogeography, Palaeoclimatology and Palaeocology, v. 3, p. 121–131.

HAY, W. W., 1960, The Cretaceous-Tertiary boundary in the Tampico Embayment, Mexico: 21st Intnat. Geol. Cong. Proc., pt. 6, p. 70–77.

———, 1970, Calcium carbonate compensation: *in* BADER, R. G., AND OTHERS, Initial Reports of the Deep Sea Drilling Project: Washington, D.C., U.S. Govt. Printing Office, v. 4, p. 672.

———, 1972, Probabilistic stratigraphy: Eclogae Geol. Helvetiae, v. 65, p. 255–266.

———, AND MOHLER, H. P., 1967, Calcareous nannoplankton from early Tertiary rocks at Pont Labau, France, and Paleocene—early Eocene correlations: Jour. Paleontology, v. 41, p. 1505–1541.

———, ———, ROTH, P. H., SCHMIDT, R. R., AND BOUDREAUX, J. E., 1967, Calcareous nannoplankton zonation of the Cenozoic of the Gulf Coast and Caribbean-Antillean area, and transoceanic correlation: Gulf Coast Assoc. Geol. Soc. Trans., v. 17, p. 428–480.

HOLLAND, H. D., 1965, The history of ocean water and its effect on the chemistry of the atmosphere: U.S. Natl. Acad. Sci. Proc., v. 53, p. 1173–1183.

JELETSKY, J., 1951, Die Stratigraphie und Belemnitenfauna des Obercampan und Maastricht Westfalens, Nordwestdeutschlands und Dänemarks sowie einige allgemeine Gliederungs-Probleme der jungeren borealen Oberkreide Eurasiens: Geol. Jahrb. Beih. 1, 142 p.

———, 1960, Youngest marine rocks in western interior of North America and the age of the *Triceratops*— beds: with remarks on comparable dinosaur-bearing beds outside North America: Copenhagen, 21st Geol. Cong., pt. 5, p. 25–39.

LAMOREAUX, P. E., AND TOULMIN, L. D., 1959, Geology and ground-water resources of Wilcox County, Alabama: Alabama Geol. Survey County Rept. 4, 280 p.

LIPPS, J. H., 1970, Plankton evolution: Evolution, v. 24, p. 1–22.

LOWENSTAM, H., 1963, Paleotemperatures of the Permian and Cretaceous Periods, *in* NAIRN, A. E. M. (ed.), Problems in paleoclimatology: p. 227–247.

MACKENZIE, F. T., AND GARRELS, R. M., 1965, Silicates—reactivity with sea water: Science, v. 150, p. 57–58.

MARTINI, E., 1969, Nannoplankton aus dem Latdorf (locus Typicus) und weltweite Parallelisierungen im oberen Eozän und unteren Oligozän: Senck. Lethaia, v. 50, p. 117–159.

———, 1970, Standard Paleogene calcareous nannoplankton zonation: Nature, v. 226, p. 560–561.

MAXWELL, A., AND OTHERS, 1970, Initial reports of the Deep Sea Drilling Project: Washington, D.C., U.S. Govt. Printing Office, v. 3, 806 p.

MCELHINNY, M. W., 1971, Geomagnetic reversals during the Phanerozoic: Science, v. 172, p. 157–159.

NEWELL, N. D., 1962, Paleontological gaps and geochronology: Jour. Paleontology, v. 36, p. 592–610.

OLSSON, R. K., 1960, Foraminifera of latest Cretaceous and earliest Tertiary age in the New Jersey coastal plain: *ibid.*, v. 34, p. 1–58.

———, 1964, Latest Cretaceous and earliest Tertiary stratigraphy of New Jersey coastal plain: Am. Assoc. Petroleum Geologists Bull., v. 47, p. 643–665.

PERCH-NIELSEN, 1969, Die Coccolithen einiger Dänischer Maastrichtien- und Danienlokalitäten: Dansk Geol. For., Medd., v. 19, p. 51–69.

PESSAGNO, E. A., JR., 1967, Upper Cretaceous planktonic foraminifera from the western Gulf Coastal Plain: Paleont. Amer., v. 5, p. 245–445.

PETERSON, M., AND OTHERS, 1970, Initial reports of the Deep Sea Drilling Project: Washington, D.C., U.S. Govt. Printing Office, v. 2, 491 p.

PLASS, G. N., 1956, The carbon dioxide theory of climatic change: Tellus, 8 p. 140–154.

SCHATZ, A., 1957, Some biochemical and physiological considerations regarding the extinction of the dinosaurs: Pennsylvania Acad. Sci. Proc., v. 31, p. 26–36.

SCHINDEWOLF, O. H., 1954, Über die möglichen Ursachen der grossen erdgeschichtlichen Faunenschnitte: Neues Jahrb. Geologie u. Paleontologie, Monatsh., 10, p. 457–465.

SCHWARTZBACH, M., 1963, Climates of the past: Van Nostrand Co., New York, 328 p.

SHAW, A. B., 1964, Time in stratigraphy: New York, McGraw Hill, 365 p.

SIMPSON, J. F., 1966, Evolutionary pulsations and geomagnetic polarity: Geol. Soc. America Bull., v. 77, p. 197–203.

STANLEY, E. A., 1965, Upper Cretaceous and Paleocene plant microfossils and Paleocene dinoflagellates and hystrichosphaerids from northwestern South Dakota: Bull. Am. Paleontology, v. 49, p. 179–384.

STRADNER, H., 1963, New contributions to Mesozoic stratigraphy by means of nannofossils: 6th World Petroleum Cong. Proc., Sect. 1, Paper 4 (preprint), 16 p.

TAPPAN, H., 1968, Primary production, isotopes, extinctions and the atmosphere: Palaeogeography, Palaeoclimatology, and Palaeoecology, v. 4, p. 187–210.

WORSLEY, T. R., 1970, The nature of the terminal Cretaceous event as evidenced by calcareous nannoplankton extinctions in Alabama and other areas (Ph.D. thesis): Urbana, Univ. Illinois.

————, 1971, Terminal Cretaceous events: Nature, v. 230, p. 318–320.

————, AND MARTINI, E., 1970, Late Maastrichtian nannoplankton provinces: *ibid.,* v. 225, p. 1242–1243.

APPENDIX I

Sample Localities

The Alabama section.—The lithologies of Maastrichtian-Danian shelf sequences are similar in many parts of the world, differing chiefly in the magnitude of the Cretaceous-Tertiary hiatus and state of fossil preservation. It is therefore desirable that a representative subtropical-temperate sequence containing well preserved nannofossils be described for this interval, for the type sections of northern Europe lack many of the important upper Maastrichtian species restricted to low latitudes. Although Maastrichtian sections throughout the Gulf and Atlantic Coastal Plains of the United States contain diverse assemblages, most suffer from either poor preservation or incomplete sequences with the exception of those in Alabama. The sequence in the vicinity of Braggs, Lowndes County, Alabama, is chosen as the most representative example of a Maastrichtian-Danian sequence because its long continuous surface exposures contain diverse assemblages of well preserved nannofossils at all levels. Furthermore, this section contains both polar and tropical elements making it a valuable link between the two realms. Lower Tertiary species diversity is low and specimens are scarce although preservation remains good in the Braggs area.

Figure 19 shows the road cut localities near Braggs, Alabama. At each locality, samples were collected at two-foot intervals except close to the Cretaceous-Tertiary boundary where the interval was made progressively smaller. The number assigned to each represents the stratigraphic position in feet above sample number Braggs 0, which is in the upper portion of the

Ripley Formation, 12 feet below the Ripley-Prairie Bluff contact. It is the lowest stratigraphic level exposed on Alabama Highway 7, 2.1 miles southeast of Braggs. Figure 20 is a composite section indicating the locations and stratigraphic levels of samples studied. Physical correlations had been worked out previously by Phillip Reed and John Newton of the Alabama Geological Survey using the Alabama Department of Highways road profile. Measurements were made by odometer and altimeter. Errors between adjacent sections are not greater than ±2 ft. (0.6 m.) with a total error no greater than ±2 ft. (0.6 m.). Figure 21 shows the ranges of stratigraphically useful species for the Braggs section.

Other samples.—Symbols as follows: + = collected by writer; * = donated by E. Martini, Geol. Paleont. Inst. Frankfurt, Germany; # = donated by R. K. Olsson, Dept. Geology, Rutgers Univ., N.J.; ¢ = sample not available—literature only used.

*Alabama 1: Prairie Bluff Fm. (u. Maast.) about 1 m below top, on Highway 28, 4.8 miles southeast junction with Highway 5, Wilcox Co., Ala. (Bramlette and Martini, 1964).

¢ Alabama 18: Prairie Bluff Fm. (u. Maast.) 4.4 miles northwest Linden on Highway 28, Marengo Co., Ala. (Bramlette and Martini, 1964).

*Alabama 30: Ripley Fm. (l. Maast.) 6 miles north of Livingston, Sumter Co., Ala. (Bramlette and Martini, 1964).

*Bellocq 1: U. Maast., bank Gave de Pau River, Bellocq, southwest France (Bramlette and Martini, 1964).

Type *A. mayaro:* Type *Abathomphalus mayaroensis* Zone sample, Bolli (1957, p. 54).

CCL: Corsicana Clay (u. Maast.), Navarro Gr., from clay pit 2 miles south of Corsicana, Navarro Co., Tex. (donated by G. R. Kellough).

*Dania 1, 2, 3: U. Maast. sampled from glacial boulder Dania near Mariager' Jutland. 1 = 6–7 m

from ground surface; 2 = 16–17 m from ground surface; 3 = 23–24 m from ground surface.

*Donietz 66–69, 81–84, 102–106: Kupjanskapa—well (u. Maast.), Village of Podvysokoe, region of Charkov, U.S.S.R. Depths: 66–69 m below surface, 81–84 m below surface, 102–106 m below surface.

*Donietz 297–303, 388–394: U. Maast. Sinevsko-Zuravnenskapa well, Village of Berjosov, region of Sumsk, U.S.S.R. Depths: 297–303 m below surface, 388–394 m below surface.

*ENCI Quarry 11: U. Maast. sec. III about 7.5 m below top of Gulpen Chalk, Zone F, ENCI Quarry near St. Pietersberg, Holland (Bramlette and Martini, 1964).

*ENCI Quarry 10: U. Maast. sec. II about 1.5 m below top of Gulpen Chalk, Zone F, ENCI

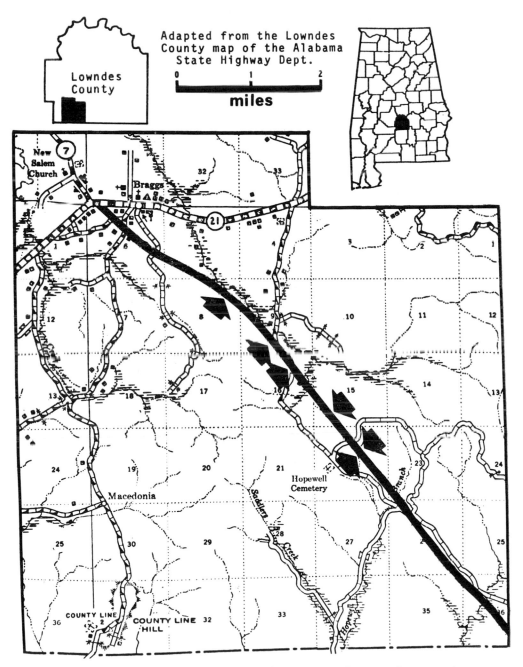

FIG. 19.—Road cuts along Alabama Highway 7 near Braggs, Lowndes County, Alabama.

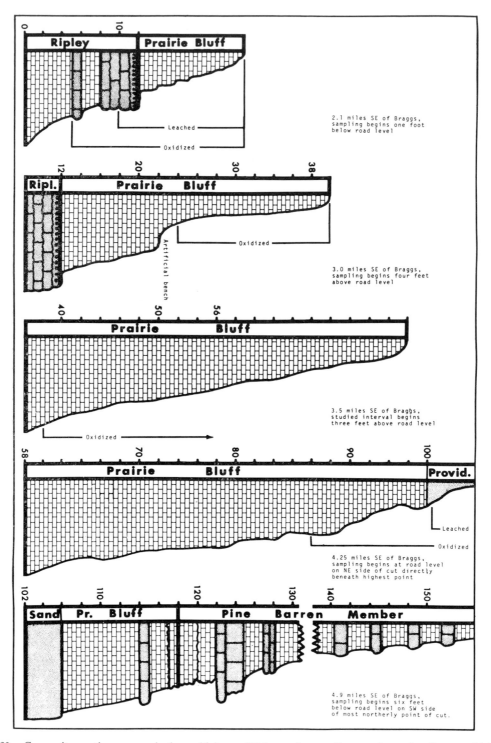

FIG. 20.—Composite section exposed along Alabama Highway 7 near Braggs, Lowndes County, Alabama.

Quarry near St. Pietersberg, Holland (Bramlette and Martini, 1964).

* Eperheide 5: Gulpen Chalk (l. Maast.), Zone B, Onderste Bos, Eperheide, Holland (Bramlette and Martini, 1964).

* Eperheide 4: Gulpen Chalk (u. Campanian), upper 5 m Zone A, Onderste Bos, Eperheide, Holland.

* Trinidad: Guayaguayare Fm. (Maast.), Trinidad, exact locality unknown.

* Kazimierz, Mecmierz: U. Maast., Poland (reference: H. Gorka, 1957).

* Kjolby Gaard 4.2: Maast., chalk below K. G. 4.5 Kjolby Gaard 12 km northeast of Tisted, Denmark.

* Kjolby Gaard 4.5: Maast., chalk below K. G. 6, 12 km northeast of Tisted, Denmark.

* Kjolby Gaard 6: L. Maast., white chalk 6.3 m below base of Danian, Kjolby Gaard, 12 km northeast of Tisted, Denmark (Bramlette and Martini, 1964).

\# L 700: U. Maast., E. I. Dupont test well 2 (Leggette Well), Willow Grove, N. J., Cumberland Co., 700 below ground level.

\# L 710: 10 ft below L 700, U. Maast.

\# L 720: 10 ft below L 710, U. Maast.

\# L 730: 10 ft below L 720, U. Maast.

\# L 740: 10 ft below L 730, U. Maast.

\# L 750: 10 ft below L 740, L. Maast.

* New Zealand N 1013: U. Maast. F 13804, N 141/508, (Edwards, 1966).

ONCR: Onion Creek (L. Maast.) upper Navarro Fm., undifferentiated at Onion Creek, Travis Co., Tex, (donated by G. R. Kellough).

* Oued el Abiod 641: Argiles d'El Haria (Maast), sec A, about 4 m below #642 A (Bramlette and Martini, 1964).

* Oued el Abiod 637: Argiles d'El Haria (Maast.), sec. A, about 60 m below #642 A (Bramlette and Martini, 1964).

* Oued el Abiod 634: Argiles d'El Haria (Maast.), sec. A, about 75 m below #642 A (Bramlette and Martini, 1964).

* Oued el Abiod 633: Argiles d'El Haria (Maast.), sec. A, about 85 m below #642 A (Bramlette and Martini, 1964).

¢ Oued el Abiod 629: Abiod Formation (Maast.), sec. A, about 165 m below #642 A (Bramlette and Martini, 1964).

* Oued el Abiod 623: Abiod Formation (Maast.), sec. A, about 210 m below #642 A (Bramlette and Martini, 1964).

* Oued el Abiod 621: Abiod Formation (Maast.), sec. A, about 230 m below #642 A (Bramlette and Martini, 1964).

* Stevns Klint: U. Maast. chalk east of Rodviga, Denmark, 5 m below Danian-Maast. boundary.

Texas 715–720: U. Maast., 5.5 miles south of Kerens on Highway 309 and 1 mile east of Alligator Cemetery Road intersection (well cuttings) (donated by G. R. Kellough).

\# TRC 599: U. Maast., Toms River Chemical Co. well #84 2.35 miles northwest State Highway 37, 200 ft east of railroad siding by company plant, Lakewood, Ocean Co., N.J., 599 ft below ground level.

\# TRC 623: 24 ft below TRC 599, U. Maast.

\# TRC 668: 45 ft below TRC 623, L. Maast.

\# TRC 691: 23 ft below TRC 668, L. Maast.

¢ USGS 16991: Arkadelphia Clay (u. Maast.), 4 miles north of Hope, Hempstead Co., Ark. (Bramlette and Martini, 1964).

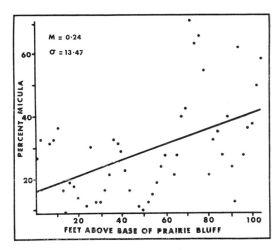

FIG. 21. Proportion of *Micula* vs. stratigraphic level in the Braggs section (counts per level by T. Worsley).

DSDP Leg 3: Samples supplied courtesy of the Natl. Sci. Found. through curator of samples for Deep Sea Drilling Project.

APPENDIX II

Stratigraphic Analysis of Samples

Biostratigraphic correlation relies ultimately upon the ability to accurately determine the absence or presence of species in samples. In the past, little use was made of information about the absence of species because of the difficulties encountered when species were not present due to ecological restrictions, and a general reluctance among biostratigraphers to accept negative evidence for correlation purposes. However, the virtually unlimited numbers of nannofossils in samples make statistical descriptions of populations a valid basis for biostratigraphic correlation based on probability and relying upon absences as well as occurrences. Such techniques have been thoroughly discussed by Shaw (1964), and Čepek and Hay (1969) have pointed out the unique suitability of calcareous nannofossils for this type of correlation. Following is a description of the technique used to determine absence or presence of species for the high resolution nannofossil biostratigraphy presented in this paper.

Inasmuch as many samples contain over 40 and sometimes over 60 nannofossil species, counts would have to be impractically high in order to reliably determine the absence or presence of rarer species. In order to be 95% confident of detecting a species constituting 1/1000 of the population, it would be necessary to count over 3,000 specimens. As it takes ap-

TABLE 1.—Criteria used for determining the abundance of nannofossil species on a slide

Approximate time required to find a given species	No. specimens per field of view at 1000×	Assigned $\log_{10}$ value per field of view	Assigned $\log_{10}$ maximum population proportion value
10 seconds	10	+1	0
1 minute	1–10	0	−1
5 minutes	1/10–1	−1	−2
15 minutes	1/100–1/10	−2	−3
30 minutes	1/1000–1/100	−3	−4

proximately 10–20 minutes to count 100 individuals, the total time required for each sample would be at least 16 hours. The difficulty is compounded by occurrences of broken or corroded specimens which cannot be identified with certainty. The more fragile or more easily dissolved species will certainly differ in abundance and this shifts the apparent proportion of all other species. Therefore counting is not practical if large numbers of specimens are to be analyzed. Fortunately, Dennison and Hay (1967) developed a graph which establishes reliable criteria for determining the absence or presence of a species in a sample as well as providing a means for reliably estimating its abundance in a population if it is present. The estimation technique described below is based on that graph.

When estimating true population proportions of nannofossil species within samples, it is necessary to use a smear slide or equivalent to avoid selective concentration or removal of species so that only observer bias needs to be taken into account. Table I lists the criteria used for deciding the abundance of species of nannofossils contained on a slide. For example: The abundance of a species represented by three or four (3 or 4 × 10^0) specimens per field of view would be denoted by a zero. A species which was detected only after having searched 50 fields of view (equivalent to 1/50 specimen per field of view) would be denoted by a −2. Conversely, if it were known that a given species occurred about once in 50 fields of view, the probability of finding it within 15 minutes would be about 0.50. Differences in recognizability between species and irregular efficiency of the operator cannot be standardized and this is why estimation was only used to determine relative abundance to within an order of magnitude.

To give an idea of the number of specimens involved in such estimations, consider the fact that the number of specimens in each field of

view in the light microscope is generally between ten and fifty. Selecting 20 specimens per field as a rough average would mean that 20 × 50 or 1,000 specimens were scanned in the 50 fields and a crude approximation of the population proportion of a species for which one specimen was found would be 0.001. A species with an assigned value of −3 would have a population proportion of around 0.0005 to 0.00005, or roughly 1/10,000.

The search for a species can be carried on indefinitely with an ever-increasing probability of detecting it. Therefore an assigned population proportion value of −4 was chosen as an arbitrary limit in searching for a species. Of course, hours of diligent searching, even though they might produce a "required" species, in no way guarantees that it is not stratigraphically reworked, or is not a contaminant in the population being searched. For this reason, increased searching time will probably not result in increased biostratigraphic resolution even though more species would be found.

Although the above technique is also applicable to scanning electron or transmission electron microscopy, searching for a species in the electron microscope (E M) is at least an order of magnitude slower than in the light microscope and preparation techniques are more complex. Therefore a conservative estimate of the time required to detect species at the 0.0001 population proportion level using E M would be five hours for each sample rather than the 30 minutes required with light microscope. This drawback may be offset by the more precise identification of small species in well-preserved samples, but this would prove small consolation if hundreds of samples had to be analyzed. Furthermore, poorly preserved samples are better analyzed by light microscopy because the diagnostic polarization figure of nannofossils remains unaltered long after their surface morphology is destroyed beyond recognition, rendering E M study almost useless. Of course E M is unsurpassed for taxonomic purposes using well-preserved samples and where rapidity of observation is not essential.

APPENDIX III

Quantitative Paleoecological Sample Analysis

Environmental reconstructions depend upon the availability of samples large enough to quantitatively determine the relative proportions of constituent species. Dennison and Shea (1966) demonstrated that visual estimation is not sufficiently precise for this purpose. Dennison and Hay (1967) showed that most quantitative paleoecological work has relied on samples far too small to adequately describe fossil populations. The latter suggested sample sizes required for reliable paleoecologic work.

For larger fossils, collection of adequately large samples would be impractical at many stratigraphic levels. Even if sufficient samples could be collected, processing would prove overwhelmingly tedious. Calcareous nannofossils offer a unique opportunity for paleoecologic study because virtually unlimited numbers of specimens are obtainable from small samples with little preparation. Furthermore, species diversity is large and the group has present-day representatives whose ecology is known. Unfortunately, previous attempts at nannofossil population counting have not yielded reproducible results. Bramlette and Martini (1964) and Gartner (1968) have discussed the difficulties inherent in applying quantitative techniques to the study of nannofosils. Because of the diverse preparation techniques in various laboratories and differences in taxonomic concepts, it is doubtful that two workers using splits of the same sample would record numerical abundance ratios of the nannofossil species with a sufficiently small standard deviation to permit an impartial observer to recognize them as being from the same original sample.

An attempt has been made to standardize techniques so that reproducible results can be attained for nannofossil population counts. Differential settling techniques were used to concentrate large, easily-identified taxa and eliminate the smaller, hard-to-identify ones. Even though these concentrates do not represent true population proportions of taxa in the sediment, their populations are always related to them and results are reproducible using the technique. The technique was designed specifically to test whether there was variation of relative population proportions of selected taxa within the late Maastrichtian which would lead to a clearer understanding of the nature of the Cretaceous-Tertiary event and was implemented as follows:

A small amount of sediment (2–3 mm³) was placed in a 2.3 cm. column of distilled water which was buffered to a pH of 9.4 with sodium bicarbonate. The sample was then agitated in an ultrasonic tank for one minute. After ultrasonic treatment, the suspension was allowed to settle for one minute. The supernatent liquid was then decanted and allowed to settle in a second vessel of the same size for ten minutes. The one-minute residue containing the sand and coarser silt was discarded. The supernatant liquid remaining after the ten-minute settling

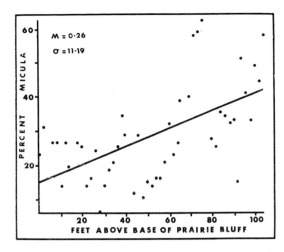

Fig. 22.—Proportion of *Micula* vs stratigraphic level in the Braggs section (100 counts per level by C. Cline).

was decanted and discarded, leaving a residue comparatively rich in nannofossils and relatively free of clay particles. The ten-minute residue was then resuspended in a 4.6 cm. column of distilled water and allowed to settle for 15 minutes. The supernatant liquid was discarded and the residue was used to prepare light microscope slides relatively free of sand and clay size material but greatly enriched in large, readily identified nannofossils. These slides were used for the counts of ten, arbitrarily chosen, easily-identified taxa known to range through the upper Ripley and the entire Prairie Bluff Formations (Maastrichtian). Their names are given on Figure 13.

The counting procedure and analytical technique are as follows: 100 nannofossils on a slide from each level of the Braggs section prepared by the technique described above were point-counted and the number of each of the above taxa was recorded. Figure 13 is a plot of the proportion of the sum of the ten taxa to the total population for each slide, and the regression line fitted to the data by computer. The proportion of each species was then plotted separately but only *Micula* produced a significant trend (Fig. 14). In fact *Micula's* trend is responsible for practically all of the variation of the ten taxa chosen. Counts of the proportion of *Micula* were repeated by another operator to test the validity of *Micula's* trend. Figure 21 (counts by the writer) and Figure 22 (counts by Mr. Charles Cline) demonstrate the reproducibility of results for *Micula*.

PALEOGEOGRAPHY, PALEOBIOGEOGRAPHY AND THE HISTORY OF CIRCULATION IN THE ATLANTIC OCEAN

W. A. BERGGREN AND C. D. HOLLISTER

Woods Hole Oceanographic Institution, Woods Hole, Massachusetts

ABSTRACT

The history of surface and bottom current circulation is delineated in the Atlantic and Tethys-Mediterranean Ocean over the past 200 million years within the framework of continental drift and sea-floor spreading.

An intimate relationship between changing paleogeography, paleobiogeography and paleo-circulation is demonstrated for the Mesozoic and Cenozoic. Major Mesozoic events include: a) initial opening of the North Atlantic Ocean about 180–190 my ago and the subsequent separation of Eurasia and Africa (about 160–170 my ago) allowing a Tethyan-North Atlantic faunal exchange; 2) separation of Africa and South America (about 95 my ago) allowing North-South Atlantic surface water mass and faunal exchange.

Distinct latitudinal control of the distribution of marine microfaunas in the North Atlantic Ocean began in the early part of the Tertiary (Paleogene) and is related to the opening of the seas in the North Atlantic about 50 my ago when the deep-water circulation pattern was probably first initiated in the Atlantic basins. At that time a boreal zoogeographic province was established in the Atlantic Ocean for the first time.

Seismic Horizon A is both a depositional and erosional feature of late early and middle Eocene age. In the central portion of the North Atlantic basin it correlates with beds of chert that were deposited when the ocean was unusually enriched with silica and its geographic distribution is a reflection of the subtropical North Atlantic gyre (Gulf Stream) and westward flowing North Equatorial Current which flowed into the Pacific Ocean along the paleoequator. Along the margin of the basins drilling has shown that the seismic horizon correlates with an unconformity or hiatus between mid-Cenozoic and early to middle Cretaceous sediments. Here Horizon A is related to the initiation of strong bottom circulation that followed the opening of the North Atlantic seas and the formation, for the first time, of cold North Atlantic bottom water.

Caribbean and Mediterranean benthonic foraminiferal faunas exhibit a marked degree of similarity during the early Tertiary. The gradual displacement of west-east current migration routes into higher latitudes and the compression of Spain against North Africa brought an end to this amphiatlantic distribution pattern about 15 my ago. The late Miocene evaporation of the western remnant of the once extensive Tethys Sea exacerbated this situation but in the early Pliocene, 5 my ago, normal marine connections were resumed with the Atlantic.

In the Pliocene two events occurred which significantly affected circulation in the Atlantic Ocean: 1) the elevation of the Isthmus of Panama about 3.5 my ago brought an end to a long history of Atlantic and Pacific marine faunal interchange and allowed the free passage of continental mammals between North and South America; 2) the initiation of glaciation in the Northern Hemisphere 3 my ago generated the Labrador Current which displaced the Gulf Stream southwards to its present position at about latitude 45°N. At this time the Polar Faunal Realm developed, thus effectively completing the process of biogeographic provincialization which began in the early Cenozoic, about 60 my ago.

The Western Boundary Undercurrent has played a major role in controlling fine-grained sediment deposition only since the early Tertiary. Data from piston coring and deep drilling in the Pacific and Indian oceans as well as the Atlantic Ocean suggests that during early to middle Tertiary times extensive unconformities and redistribution of sediment occurred, and it is proposed here that during this time vigorous deep and bottom circulation on a global scale was first initiated in response to the nearly synchronous opening of the circum-Antarctic and North Atlantic basins. Thus the deep cold circulation of the Circumpolar Current and Antarctic Bottom Current in the Pacific, Indian, and Atlantic oceans and the Western Boundary Undercurrent in the North Atlantic probably is no older than about 50–60 million years.

INTRODUCTION

In the introduction to the fifth edition of his brother Alfred's major work "The Origin of Continents and Oceans" (translated and published by Dover Publications, Inc., 1966) Kurt Wegener indicates that "this book was concerned with reestablishing the connection between geophysics on the one hand and geography and geology on the other, a connection which had been completely broken by specialist development of these branches of science." Although general interest in the implications of this book was initially great (it was translated into English, French, Spanish, Russian, and Swedish within a decade of its publication in 1915), it would be fair to state that by 1930

126

geologists, geophysicists and geographers, with paleontologists in the vanguard, had returned to their single-track approach to resolving basic problems in earth history. One has but to peruse the literature of the three decades between 1930–1960 to see that the balance of opinion among protagonists in the "continental drift argument" came down heavily on the side of stable continent-ocean relationships.

The past decade, on the other hand, has witnessed a resurgence of interest in continental drift through a theory of sea-floor expansion (Heezen, 1960). This theory was later modified to include convection currents and is called sea-floor spreading (Hess, 1962; Dietz, 1961). Paleontologists and geologists are reexamining their data in light of recent advances in the geophysical sciences and, although acceptance of Wegener's (1915) fundamental concepts of dynamic movements between oceans and continents (modified by more recent research) is still not universal, it would appear that more and more scientists are interpreting earth history in terms of the concept of "continental drift."

The present work is an attempt to delineate the history of surface and bottom-current circulation patterns in the Atlantic and Tethys-Mediterranean Ocean over the past 200 million years. The data come primarily from the fields of paleontology, paleobiogeography and sedimentology and involve an analysis of data from outcrop sections in land areas peripheral to the oceans as well as deep sea cores, particularly those obtained by the Deep Sea Drilling Project (DSDP). The conceptual framework in which our paleo-oceanographic reconstructions have been made is that of continental drift, as envisaged so beautifully by Alfred Wegener over 50 years ago.

Thus, in a manner somewhat analogous to the alternate fragmentation and amalgamation of continents suggested by various recent proponents of the drift hypothesis, it would appear that we are entering a period of "amalgamation of thought" in which continental drift is used as the conceptual framework for various reconstructions of earth history. We hope that this work will form a small link in this chain of thought.

PALEOGEOGRAPHY OF THE ATLANTIC

Examination of a tectonic map of the land areas on both sides of the Atlantic reveals that none of the Paleozoic orogenic belts extends across the edge of the continent to the deep ocean, but that they are truncated near the continental edge. On the other hand several Cenozoic features (such as fold belts in southern Spain) do appear to extend towards the deep ocean. The stratigraphic and structural similarities between the Paleozoic basins of Brazil and Argentina and those of southwestern Africa were indicated by Du Toit (1937). These various lines of evidence suggest that post-Paleozoic separation of continents has occurred and that the reconstructions of the various continents around the Atlantic made by various authors (Bullard, and others, 1965; Le Pichon, 1968; Funnell and Smith, 1968; Harland, 1967a, 1969; Kay, 1969; Dietz and Holden, 1970a,b; Berggren and Phillips, 1971) do indeed represent the approximate relative positions of the continents which were contiguous prior to their fragmentation in mid-Mesozoic time.

According to recent global tectonic models (Valentine and Moores, 1970; Dietz and Holden, 1970a,b) the present day geographic distribution of continents and oceans is but the most recent phase of a dynamic process of alternate fragmentation and amalgamation of continental units. The most recent phase involved the Triassic-early Jurassic extension of the Tethyan seaway situated between the two large continental masses of Gondwanaland in the south and Laurasia in the north. The subsequent fragmentation of the former into several smaller continental units and of the latter into Eurasia and North America occurred by the opening of the Atlantic Ocean and closing of the Tethyan seaway during mid-Mesozoic and Cenozoic. The Tethys is a large shear zone along which Laurasia and Gondwanaland have moved many thousands of kilometers relative to one another. Sea-floor spreading data suggest that significant dispersal of most of the original continent of Gondwanaland occurred during the Cenozoic and, by extrapolation, during the Cretaceous. Le Pichon (1968) suggested that Australia, New Zealand and Antarctica were a single unit until the early Cenozoic and that New Zealand separated from Antarctica in Paleocene time and Australia separated during the Late Eocene (anomaly 18). On the basis of geometric reconstruction (using the method of Bullard and others, 1965) Smith and Hallam (1970) indicated an earlier period of spreading and suggested the break-up of Gondwanaland in Jurassic and Early Cretaceous time. At least eight continental fragments were established as a result of the break-up of Gondwanaland—now separated by the South Atlantic, South Pacific, Indian Ocean and Tasman Sea. These fragments are: South America, Africa, Arabia,

Madagascar, India, Antarctica, Australia and New Zealand.

Recent geophysical/oceanographic data suggest that the North Atlantic and South Atlantic have had separate and distinct histories (Drake and Nafe, 1968a,b; Drake and others, 1968; Heirtzler and Hayes, 1967; Dickson, 1968; Maxwell and others, 1970; Berggren and Phillips, 1971). The oldest sediments recovered in the (western) Atlantic approximately 500 km from the edge of the continental slope to date are middle-late Jurassic (ca. 150 my old). These sediments were probably deposited in a relatively shallow early Atlantic on the outer shelf and upper slope (based on occurrence of nannoconids, coccoliths, radiolaria and epistominid foraminifers). Using apparently reliable values of rates of sea-floor spreading it appears reasonable to suggest that the Atlantic opened approximately 180–200 my ago and the temptation to seek a relationship between the upper Triassic-early Jurassic vulcanism and tensional faulting in eastern North America, West Africa and northeastern South America and the initial rifting of the North Atlantic is strong (May, 1971).

The North Atlantic may be considered to consist of portions of three crustal plates:

1. North America (including Greenland and the western Atlantic Ocean).
2. Eurasia (including the eastern Atlantic Ocean north of the Azores-Gibraltar Ridge.
3. Africa (including the eastern Atlantic Ocean, south of the Azores-Gibraltar Ridge). The North Atlantic was originally formed by the separation of the Eurasian and African plates from the North American plate, i.e., by sea-floor spreading away from the Mid-Atlantic Ridge. From an analysis of the magnetic anomaly patterns a history of sea-floor spreading in the North Atlantic has been compiled by Pitman and Talwani (1972). Their main conclusions were:

1. Prior to anomaly 31 (72 my) the North Atlantic Ocean (north of the Azores-Gibraltar Ridge) was, with the exception of parts of the Newfoundland and Iberian Basins, nearly closed. South of the Azores Ridge a wide North Atlantic, including what are now the deep basins, was in existence.
2. The initial phase of rifting in the North Atlantic occurred between 180–200 my (late Triassic—early Jurassic).
3. From late Triassic to late Cretaceous there was a large component of left lateral motion between North Africa and southwestern Europe. Counterclockwise motion of Iberia was probably completed by late Cretaceous time.

From the late Cretaceous to Oligocene relative motion was right lateral offering a means for possible clockwise rotation of Iberia.

4. With the Norwegian-Greenland Sea closed, Greenland separated from North America about 81 my ago as part of the Eurasian plate. Active spreading in the Norwegian-Greenland Sea began about 60 my ago. Greenland then moved independently northwards to its present position at about 47 my ago. Since then Greenland has been part of the North American plate; and its position relative to North America during this time has been the same as at present.

The Barents shelf between Greenland and Scandinavia is a continental structure and if a part of it were at least intermittently above sea-level it could have served as the land bridge by which early Cenozoic land mammals migrated between Europe and North America (Kurtén, 1966, 1967, 1969) and as an effective barrier to the interchange of Arctic and Atlantic waters.

5. In the Arctic region (northern Greenland to eastern Siberia and including Bering Sea region) the relative motion between Eurasia and North America has been compressional from late Cretaceous time to early Cenozoic time (ca. 63 my ago). Reconstruction of the Bering Sea area suggests that a land bridge could have existed since 60 my. (Hallam, 1967, concluded on paleozoogeographic grounds that the Bering Land was in existence—although not continuously—by Middle to Late Cretaceous time.)

6. Most of the drift between Europe and North America has occurred during the Cenozoic (i.e., over the past 60–65 my), although initial rifting may have occurred as early as the Jurassic.

7. About 60 percent of the drift between Africa and North America occurred between Late Triassic and Late Cretaceous.

8. During the early Cenozoic (ca. 63 my ago) relative motion between Eurasia and North America became extensional. With the separation of the Lomonosov Ridge from the Eurasian shelf by spreading at the Nansen (Mid-Arctic) Ridge, approximately half of the Arctic Ocean was formed during the Cenozoic (Pitman and Talwani, 1972, Fig. 9).

Emery (1966, 1967), Emery and others (1970) and Uchupi and Emery (1968) have summarized the geological history of the continental margin off North America and a synthesis of the conclusions presented in these papers follows:

1. Geomagnetic surveys indicate that North America could have separated from Europe and

Africa as early as the Permian Period. However, recent data (Hollister and others, 1972) suggest that the initial rifting occurred at a much later, mid-Mesozoic date.

2. Gravity and seismic information suggests that a relict structure of the initial rift is preserved in the form of a complex linear ridge of crystalline rocks bordered on both sides by linear trenches beneath the seaward part of the continental shelf, the continental slope, or the upper continental rise.

3. The general form of the continental margin off the Atlantic coast of North America was established during the early Mesozoic by diastrophic forces which continued into Cretaceous time.

4. The continental slope and adjoining Blake Plateau were probably formed by early faulting.

5. The ridge and associated trenches parallel to the coast served as sediment traps for terrigenous sediments during the Mesozoic. During this time pelagic oozes are the predominant lithology on the seaward side of these topographic barriers. Sediment thicknesses up to 9 km have accumulated in the marginal trenches.

6. The rise is thought to be a large prism of generally seaward dipping interbedded pelagic sediments and turbidites containing sediments displaced from higher on the rise and from the continental slope. However, recent data from the DSDP (Hollister and others, 1972) indicate that turbidite sedimentation was ineffective on the rise except during the Pleistocene and that southerly flowing bottom currents have been the principal depositional agent on the rise since the middle Eocene.

7. From late Cretaceous to middle Eocene time a broad, blanket-like deposit of deep-sea chert was formed (Horizon A) throughout the central portions of ocean basins.

8. Pleistocene sediments (averaging about 80 m on the open continental shelf) are virtually absent on the outer part of the continental shelf, but are present on the continental slope and rise. Most of the continental shelf is covered by "relict" sediments (*i.e.,* lacustrine and paludal sediments deposited on the shelf during and immediately following the latest glacial stage of the Pleistocene).

Stride and others (1969) have presented an account of the marine geology and geophysics of the Atlantic continental margin of Europe. Among the conclusions they reach pertinent to our discussion are the following:

1. Cretaceous sediments appear to be the oldest continental slope deposits on the eastern side of the North Atlantic.

2. An episode of erosion of the continental margin occurred during the late Cretaceous and early Cenozoic (Paleogene).

3. Cenozoic continental slope and shelf sediments are widespread. Shelf sediments encroached progressively up the continental block concomitant with its downwarping.

4. Cenozoic sediments are thickest west of the English Channel trough and the Aquitaine Basin (up to 4 km thick). In general, the amount of downwarping and the thickness of continental margin deposits is considerably less than that on the eastern continental margin of the United States (Drake and others, 1959; Uchupi and Emery, 1968).

5. Significant faulting, canyon cutting, and slumping occurred on the continental margin towards the end of the Cenozoic.

6. The present continental shelf may range from early Cenozoic (Paleogene) to late Cenozoic (Pleistocene) in age.

7. The episodic evolution of the European continental margin may indicate that the Atlantic Ocean was formed during two periods of continental drift (Mesozoic through late Cretaceous and Eocene to Miocene).

Pitman and Talwani (1972) suggested that most of the drift between Europe and North America occurred since the late Cretaceous. They indicated that separation occurred at a rate of about 2 cm/year from late Cretaceous until the end of the Eocene, followed by a major hiatus in opening from 38 my to 9 my ago, during which the rate of spreading was about 0.4 cm/year. Williams and McKenzie (1971) suggested a continuous spreading rate in the NE Atlantic since anomaly 32 (79 my). Results from Legs 2 and 11 of the DSDP and the data of Phillips and Luyendyk (1970) suggest that sea-floor spreading in the central North Atlantic was relatively constant—*ca.* 1-2 cm/year —over the past 150 my.

Extrapolation of sea-floor spreading rates (from DSDP data) of 2 cm/year in the South Atlantic suggests that the South Atlantic may have begun to open approximately 130 my ago (Maxwell and others, 1970). Paleomagnetic data suggest that initial opening occurred as a rotational movement of South America away from Africa prior to east-west separation (Tarling, 1971). Reyment (1969), using biostratigraphic evidence of ammonite faunas associated with oscillatory marine transgressions in West Africa and South America, has indicated that significant drift began in the Lower Turonian (~90 my ago) and that for a short (pre-rotational) moment in Late Albian time the North and South Atlantic may have been connected by a marine seaway.

The striking similarity between the Mesozoic sedimentary basins of Brazil and Gabon have been reviewed by Belmonte and others (1965) and Allard and Hurst (1969). Upper Jurassic and lower Cretaceous non-marine ostracod and fish faunas of Brazil and West Africa are essentially identical (Krömmelbein, 1962; Krömmelbein and Wenger, 1966; McKenzie and Hussainy, 1968) thus indicating continental connection between the two areas into Early Cretaceous time.

The data suggest the following sequence of events in the South Atlantic:

1. Late Jurassic-Early Cretaceous—continents of South America and Africa essentially contiguous, or separated by narrow, linear non-marine graben, which may have formed by initial rifting during the period 200–130 my ago.

2. Brief marine connection between North and South Atlantic during Late Albian time (ca. 110 my ago).

3. Cenomanian (~110 my)—rotation of South America relative to Africa.

4. Final separation in early Turonian (~90 my) of Africa and South America in the vicinity of western Nigeria and Ivory Coast/eastern Brazil after which at least a shallow marine connection between North and South Atlantic was established.

Reconstruction of the pre-drift Atlantic (Bullard and others, 1965) brings the extensive evaporite basins of northwest Africa contiguous to the shelf regions of the eastern Canadian continental margin (Grand Banks, Nova Scotian Shelf) where possible evaporite deposits (salt diapiric structures) have been seismically inferred (Watson and Johnson, 1970) and, in some cases, cored (Smith, 1971a,b). The salt is part of a widespread Upper Triassic (Keuper) unit (Smith, 1971b) and on the east side of the Atlantic it extends from Iceland and western England through western Germany, France, the Iberian Peninsula to the Maghreb (North Africa), Mauretania and Senegal (West Africa). On the west side this evaporite sequence extends through southern Florida, Cuba, the Gulf Coastal Region and eastern Mexico. Smith (1971b) concluded that the evaporite deposition was independent of and predated the opening of the proto-Atlantic.

Gradual subsidence of the oceanic crust coupled with lateral widening of the initial rift led to the formation of a normal marine sequence. Evidence from Leg 11 of the DSDP (Hollister and others, 1972) suggests that the early sedimentary and structural evolution of the proto-Atlantic resembles the history of the Red Sea up to the present time. The Red Sea

opened within the past 5 million years (Phillips, 1970) although it had existed as a tectonic feature for a considerable period of time prior to this.

Hallam (1971) suggested on independent grounds that the Atlantic Ocean "probably" did not exist during the Jurassic. He envisaged a single northern continent in the Jurassic with a single boreal inland sea with free oceanic connections (to the Tethys) but persistently kept at lower salinity to account for observed relationship betwen the biogeography of ammonite faunas and northern continental paleogeography. However, Hollister and others (1972) have reported the presence of bathyal sediments as old as late Jurassic in the western Atlantic.

THE HISTORY OF THE ATLANTIC OCEAN
AND TETHYS SEA

The following is a short outline of the geologic history of the Atlantic Ocean and Tethys Sea. It represents a compilation of views expressed by various authors and is not meant to be a definitive and critical statement. Rather this outline is presented as a guide to the various stages through which the Atlantic and Mediterranean regions have evolved. The sequence of events, as outlined, provides a framework for, and places constraints upon, the history of the Atlantic and Tethyan circulation outlined below. Other areas (India, Australia, etc.) are mentioned insofar as they pertain to the general evolution of the Atlantic-Tethyan region.

Triassic (~200 my ago).—The universal land mass Pangaea was surrounded by Panthalassa (ancestral Pacific Ocean). The Tethys Sea (ancestral Mediterranean) was a triangular embayment separating Africa and Eurasia (Dietz and Holden, 1970a,b). Land masses were generally located south and east of their present location relative to the North Atlantic plate; distribution was approximately equally balanced in northern and southern hemispheres (presently two-thirds of all land area lies north of the equator).

Late Triassic-Early Jurassic separation of Pangaea resulted in two major land masses, Laurasia and Gondwanaland. The initial separation of Laurasia and Gondwanaland (North American-Africa) occurred coincident with mid-Triassic (~190–200 my) intrusives of North America (Newark basalt series) and North Africa. Formation of extensive evaporite beds occurred in the shallow, narrow proto-Atlantic basin (Schneider and Johnson, 1970; Smith, 1971a, b) from the Gulf Coastal Region to the Grand Banks and Nova Scotian shelf regions of the eastern Canadian continental margin and from Ireland through France and western Germany to Iberia and through the Maghreb to Mauritania and Senegal in West Africa. Conditions were not unlike the modern Persian Gulf or Red Sea.

Jurassic (~190–~135 my).—During the Jurassic further fragmentation of Gondwanaland occurred: eastern Gondwanaland began to split in mid-Jurassic (Tarling, 1971) and marine transgressions spread along east coasts of India and Africa. India and Australia ruptured in late Jurassic or early Cretaceous time (Veevers and others, 1971). India began moving northwards towards Eurasia. Australia and Antarctica remained connected. Rotation of Eurasia began to close the eastern end of the Tethys Sea. North America continued to drift northwestwards with respect to South America. The active phase of spreading in the North Atlantic may have begun about 175 my ago and the North Atlantic continued to widen and deepen. Bathyal depths for late Jurassic marine sediments are indicated along the western margin of the North Atlantic (DSDP, Legs 1 and 11).

A shallow marine connection between Atlantic and Pacific was probably maintained throughout much of Jurassic between North and South America. The Bay of Biscay may have started to open during the Jurassic by counterclockwise rotation of Iberia away from France. This process continued essentially unabated until the late Mesozoic and may have continued into the early Cenozoic as well.

Cretaceous (~135–~65 my ago).—Dispersal of Gondwanaland fragments continued as India moved northward towards Eurasia. Africa drifted northward and continued its counterclockwise rotation as the Eurasian plate rotated slowly clockwise, further restricting the Tethys Sea in the East. Left lateral movement of Africa relative to Europe created an extensive, wide western Tethys Sea which opened into the Atlantic (Pitman and Talwani, 1972). The South Atlantic was initiated by late Jurassic or early Cretaceous rifting, resulting in a narrow, linear graben similar to the Red Sea. Rifting was probably completed by Aptian time but the Indian Ocean did not become linked to the North Atlantic until Early Turonian time (ca. 90 my ago) (Reyment, 1969). This accords well with evidence from DSDP Leg 3 (Maxwell and others, 1970) where a calculated age of 130 my (early Cretaceous) was derived from estimated rates of sea-floor spreading. This indicates that South Africa and Antarctica had separated by this time.

In the North Atlantic the Mid-Atlantic Ridge extended northwards and began splitting Greenland from North America to form the Labrador Sea. Although initial rifting in the Labrador Sea may have occurred as early as mid-Jurassic it is not likely that active sea-floor spreading began until mid-Cretaceous time (~100 my) or somewhat later. The North Atlantic remained closed to the Arctic around its northern perimeter. The Bay of Biscay continued to open by counterclockwise rotation and was, by late Cretaceous at least, a deep turbidite-filled abyssal plain (Laughton and others, 1972).

Cenozoic (~65 my–present).—Dispersal of the Gondwanaland fragments continued in the Cenozoic. Australia separated from Antarctica in the Eocene and India collided with Asia in the late Eocene (Veevers and others, 1971).

Northward movement and rotation of Africa continued to close the Tethys Sea in the east. In the west right lateral motion between Africa and Europe narrowed the western junction of the Tethys with the Atlantic between Spain and Morocco. In the North Atlantic the ocean floor continued to widen as North America moved westward. Active spreading of the Mid-Atlantic Ridge then shifted to the Reykjanes Ridge (ca. 60 my) and opened the Norwegian Sea between Greenland and Norway (Harland, 1969; Johnson and Heezen, 1967; Vine and Hess, 1971). Europe and North America were finally separated in the Middle Eocene (ca. 50 my ago) with the separation of Spitsbergen from Greenland (Pitman and Talwani, 1972). This established connection between the North Atlantic and the Arctic through a deep passage for the first time and resulted in the initiation of cold, deep water circulation.

During the early Cenozoic (ca. 60 my ago) relative motion between Eurasia and North America became extensional. The Lomonosov Ridge was separated from European shelf by the Nansen (Mid-Arctic) Ridge. Generation of about half of the Arctic Ocean occurred by continued spreading at Nansen Ridge throughout the Cenozoic.

A major hiatus in sea-floor spreading in the North Atlantic between Europe and North America may have occurred from late Eocene until late Miocene time (ca. 38–9 my; cf. Williams and McKenzie, 1971). Apparently no hiatus or marked slowdown in sea-floor spreading occurred between Africa and North America during this interval (Phillips and Luyendyk, 1970; Pitman and Talwani, 1972).

Continued compression between Africa and Eurasia resulted in a junction between Arabia and Asia in Early Miocene time (ca. 18 my ago; Van Couvering and Miller, 1971; Van Couvering, 1972; Berggren, 1972) separating the eastern and western Tethys Sea. The rotation of Iberia having ceased, compression and continued right lateral shear of Eurasia relative to Africa produced the so-called tectonic fabric known as the "Tethys Twist" (Van Hilten, 1964) characteristic of the Mediterranean and Middle East. At the same time the junction of Europe and Africa at Gibraltar occurred in Middle Miocene time (ca. 16–14 my ago) significantly altering the paleobiogeography of the marine benthos. At about the same time (mid-Miocene) India collided with Asia (Veevers and others, 1971).

During the late Miocene the western Tethys underwent extreme evaporation and sea-level change of several thousand feet (Ryan and others, 1970) causing the deposition of extensive evaporite beds. In the early Pliocene rapid transgression from the Atlantic Ocean reestablished marine connections and the Mediterranean Sea assumed its modern aspect.

The Isthmus of Panama was uplifted in early Pliocene (ca. 3.5–4 my ago), connecting North and South America and ending the interchange of Atlantic and Pacific waters.

By mid-Pliocene time (ca. 3.5 my ago) the Atlantic Ocean and Mediterranean Sea had attained their present day relationships to the surrounding and adjacent continents. Relative changes since that time between land and sea have been due to climate-induced glaciations at high latitudes.

CONCEPT OF FAUNAL PROVINCES AND THE TETHYS

Hazel (1970) has presented a thorough review of the historical development of usage pertaining to faunal provinces on the North American and European sides of the Atlantic Ocean. It is only necesary here to clarify our usage of two terms: Boreal and Tethys.

The term Boreal has been frequently used in geologic and biologic literature in the sense of a faunal province as well as a climatic zone. It has been used more frequently by European workers to delineate a North Atlantic faunal province (generally between latitude 50°–60°N to 70°N) characterized by faunas which are adapted to a relatively low average annual mean temperature. As Hazel (1970, p. 6) pointed out, "marine climate zones are not really based on temperature. Temperature is the underlying factor controlling the distribution of organisms, but it is the distribution of kinds of organisms that determines the province, and it is the boundaries between provinces upon which the climatic zone boundaries have been based."

With this in mind the term "Boreal" as used in this paper refers to a faunal province characterized by cold-temperate faunas, as distinct from warm-tropical faunas. The use of "Boreal" in the paleobiogeographic sense is based on analogy with living representatives of fossil faunas. We do not believe that a distinct North Atlantic Boreal Faunal Province existed in the Mesozoic but that it became established during the early-middle Cenozoic (Paleogene) as a result of opening of the North Atlantic to the polar regions and the consequent development of a stronger equatorial-polar thermal gradient. Late Mesozoic faunas of the North Atlantic contain a larger number of "Tethyan" elements than Cenozoic faunas in the North Atlantic [see also discussion by Ried (1967) summarized in the following section].

The paleobiogeography and paleoclimatology of the Tethys Sea was the subject of an international symposium in Leicester (Adams and Ager, eds., 1967). The following brief discussion of the nature of the Tethys Sea is presented here in order to clarify some misconceptions which exist regarding the "concept" of the Tethys and to define our own use of the term in the context of this paper.

In the early Mesozoic (Triassic) the Tethys was essentially a broad, triangular embayment —an extension of the ancestral Pacific (Panthalassa)—which separated eastern Gondwanaland (India and Africa) and Eurasia. In the mid-Mesozoic (Jurassic) this seaway extended in a broad belt connecting the Atlantic in the west and the Pacific in the east and separating Eurasia (in the north) from Gondwanaland (in the south). These relationships continued through the late Mesozoic (Cretaceous) and into the Cenozoic. In the mid-Cenozoic it was divided into an eastern and western region by the junction of Eurasia and Africa. The collision of India and Asia also served to define two oceans north of the equator. The continued rotation and compression of Africa relative to Eurasia caused constriction of the eastern Tethys and it evolved into the present Indian Ocean. The western Tethys, following the junction of Europe and Africa (at Gibraltar) evolved into an evaporite basin in the late Miocene. Following a transgression from the Atlantic Ocean in early Pliocene time it evolved into the Mediterranean Sea as we know it today.

The Tethys Sea has been the main agent responsible for the worldwide dispersal of certain marine faunas during the Mesozoic and Cenozoic. Indeed, the Holocene is a relatively unique moment in geologic history. The relatively recent modifications of the Tethys Sea which have occurred since mid-Miocene time have resulted in completely different circulation patterns in comparison to what had been typical prior to that time. Present day faunas, in many instances, owe their distribution to the former extent of the Tethys Sea.

Tropical conditions during the Cretaceous and into the Eocene extended as far north as the Paris Basin which, in the Paleogene, was situated at about lat. 35°N (vs. lat. 50°N today). Subtropical conditions continued into the late Eocene in Central Europe. There is evidence of a significant cooling trend within the latest Eocene-early Oligocene, followed by a gradual increase in temperature during the early Miocene. Since the middle Miocene the earth has experienced a gradual, but inexorable, decline in temperature, accentuated by severe cooling during the glacial phases of the Pleistocene Epoch. It was not until the late Miocene that the European fauna began to develop its present day character.

During the Paleogene the eastern Atlantic fauna was much more closely related to the Indo-Pacific fauna than it is today. This affinity disappeared for the most part in the Miocene-Pliocene with the closing of the Tethys Sea to the east in the mid-Miocene. At the same time (Paleogene) a closer relationship existed between the eastern and western parts of the Atlantic Ocean than at the present. This similarity in terms of the benthonic foraminiferal fauna has been discussed by Berggren (1969a) and elsewhere in this paper. During this interval (~65–23 my B.P.) the Atlantic Ocean between North America and Africa opened up from approximately 75% to 85% of its present size (Berggren and Phillips, 1971).

The tropical character of the former central Atlantic fauna changed considerably during the later part of the Cenozoic. This was due primarily to the gradual decrease in temperature (euphemistically referred to as "climatic deterioration"). In the Mediterranean region various tropical elements in the corals, echinoderm, molluscan, and fish faunas show a decrease in diversity. Northern elements of a temperate fauna immigrated into the Mediterranean region; especially during the Pliocene. Part of the fauna which withdrew from the Mediterranean sought refuge along the coast of West Africa. Some of these forms, no longer present in this region, probably fell victim to the cooler water conditions during the late Pleistocene glaciation. Similar conditions occurred on the western side of the Atlantic. Tropical marine faunas of Florida and vicinity were replaced by cooler-

water faunas in mid-late Miocene times. Some of these tropical forms reappeared in the Pliocene and a few more in the Pleistocene. The general picture, however, is one of lowered temperature in the Caribbean-Antilles region during late Cenozoic.

Both sides of the Atlantic were thus subjected to late Cenozoic climatic deterioration. In contrast to the Caribbean-Antilles area, however, the Mediterranean-West African region has not recovered its once rich and diversified tropical fauna.

In the Paleogene the Mediterranean region and eastern Tethys was a rather uniform zoogeographic province. The Indo-European elements occurred as far west as the Caribbean-Central American region. The climatic cooling in the Miocene and modification of the Tethys Sea to the east (cut off) and gradual closure to the west (by the compression between Africa and Spain) are the most significant events in the late Cenozoic history of the warm water faunas of the tropical regions.

Durham (1952) pointed out that Du Toit (1937) was of the opinion that during the Oligocene the Caribbean region and Europe and Africa were close enough for there to have been a "close relationship" between the marine invertebrate faunas of the West Indies and the Mediterranean (Tethys). Connection between the two areas was thought not to have been severed until perhaps late Miocene time. Data on sea floor spreading (Berggren and Phillips, 1971; Pitman and Talwani, 1972) indicate that the North Atlantic was open to over 80% of its present width at these latitudes. Faunal similarities between the two regions is, rather, a testimony to the ability of marine organisms to achieve widespread geographic distribution by active or passive means of transport. The interruption of faunal exchange in the Miocene is more likely a result of the junction of Africa and Europe at Gibraltar (Berggren and Phillips, 1971).

Du Toit (1937) also believed that the Tethys Sea extended to the Caribbean area of the Americas, that the Americas were relatively close to each other (compared to the present day situation) and that there were belts of orogenic movement where uplift occurred extending across the ancestral mid-Atlantic. Recent evidence from marine geology and geophysics indicates that, indeed, orogenic activity has occurred in the ancestral Atlantic but that it has been associated with the development and maintenance of a ridge system which is the locus of lateral translation of coupled sea-floor-continental plates.

The Tethys should be considered as the ancestral Mediterranean. It joined a widening Atlantic Ocean in the west. Westward currents which flowed across the Atlantic into the Caribbean region and on into the Pacific carried "Tethyan faunal elements" across the Atlantic (Fell, 1967; Adams, 1967, 1970; Berggren and Phillips, 1971; Benson and Sylvester-Bradley, 1971) but to apply the term "Tethys Sea" to the western side of the Atlantic is incorrect. Beyond its actual geographic limits, the adjective "Tethyan" should be used in a descriptive, zoogeographic sense, as denoting an area characterized by faunal elements having their maximum development within the Tethys region. Oceanic regions had been sufficiently differentiated during the Mesozoic to warrant the use of present geographic names in describing their characteristics. Inasmuch as there is not a strong similarity in marine invertebrate faunas on both sides of the Atlantic during the Eocene, Durham (1952) considered that continental drift (*sensu* Du Toit, Wegener) did not occur since the late Cretaceous. However, percentages alone cannot be used to determine whether continental drift has occurred. Modern geophysical data provide ample evidence of the reality of continental drift, although within a time and geodynamic framework quite different from that suggested by either Wegener (1915, 1924) or Du Toit (1937, 1944).

Introduction

An extensive body of literature now exists indicating that a major reorganization of marine invertebrates occurred at the Paleozoic-Mesozoic transition. Data dealing with this phenomenon have been admirably summarized and discussed by Newell (1952, 1963, 1967). In summarizing a study of radiation of reptiles in the Permian and Mesozoic and of mammals in the Cenozoic within the paleogeographic framework provided by continental drift, Kurtén (1967) essentially reached the same conclusions subsequently elucidated by Valentine (1969): namely, that the resultant taxonomic variety is related to the size of the area available for colonization and radiation, to its environmental variety and to the number of disjunct areas. Valentine (1969) and Valentine and Moores (1970) have presented a stimulating discussion in which late Paleozoic reduction in invertebrate taxonomic diversity is broadly correlated with a diminution in ecologic structure, resulting in a reduction of biospace. The initiation of the present phase of continental drift in the early Mesozoic would,

then, have provided gradually expanding ecologic structure (*i.e.* increased biospace) in which marine invertebrates could have rapidly rediversified. At the same time latitudinal provinciality due to cooling poles and an increase in longitudinal provinciality caused by fragmentation of various land masses in early Jurassic time is reflected in the fossil record (Newmayr, 1883; Uhlig, 1911; Arkell, 1956, Chap. 28; Stevens, 1963; Imlay, 1965; Hallam, 1969a; Gordon, 1970; Scheibnerova, 1971b). Biogeographic provincialization began on a worldwide scale in Bajocian time (160 my).

The relationship of paleogeography to paleobiogeography has been strikingly illustrated by Kurtén (1967) who discussed the influence of continental drift on the paleobiogeography of reptiles and mammals. The radiation of these two groups is strikingly different in paleogeographic setting. The radiation of the reptiles occurred during the Mesozoic while Eurasia and Gondwanaland were essentially contiguous; the mammalian radiation occurred in the Cenozoic, well after the fragmentation of these two land mases into several smaller units. The ratio of ordinal variety and time among mammals for the last 100 million years has been 1 : 3; for reptiles it is about 1 : 10 (1 : 5 if reptilian suborders are used). Kurtén (1967) suggested that taxonomic variety is correlated with the size of the area available, with its environmental variety and with the number of disjunct areas.

The Holarctic Realm includes Europe, Asia and North America and with few exceptions it is difficult to ascertain in which area a particular mammalian order originated. The role of amalgamation (by formation of continental migration routes), leading to elimination of ecologically overlapping forms, and the duplication of adaptive types in areas separated by large distances was stressed by Kurtén (1967).

Areas of origin for the following reptilian orders were suggested as follows:

Probable

Gondwanaland:	Laurasia:
Chelonia	Sauropterygia
Mesosauria	Therapsida
Eosuchia	Squamata
Rhynchocephalia	
Ornithischia	

Possible

| Ictidosauria | Pterosaura |

For the mammals Kurtén (1967) suggested the following tentative scheme:

Holarctic region:

Multituberculata
Insectivora
Deltatheridia
Dermoptera
Chiroptera
Primates
Dinocerata
Pholidota
Carnivora
Condylartha
Perissodactyla
Artiodactyla
Tillodontia
Taeniodontia
Amblypoda
?Edentata

North America:

Rodentia

South America:

Paucituberculata
Astrapotheria
Pyrotheria
Litopterna
?Notoungulata

Africa:

Hyrocoidea
Embrithopoda
Proboscidea
Sirenia
Pongidhominid group
(*Propliopithecus*)

Asia:

Lagomorpha

Australia:

Peramelina
Diprotodonta

Discussion

There is little substantial data on the regional distribution of marine Triassic microfaunas. The little that exists for invertebrate faunas suggests relatively cosmopolitan distribution. The data on terrestrial vertebrates, summarized by Hallam (1967) suggest that there was free communication between the northern and southern continents of the Old World during the Triassic. Relationships between Eurasia and North and South America are more controversial. The close similarity between tetrapod faunas of North America and Europe and the presence of cynodont reptiles in Brazil and South Africa exclusively, suggest that the Old and New World was a single land mass during the Triassic. Jurassic tetrapods suggest continued cosmopolitan development (Hallam, 1967).

Arkell (1956) recognized a Tethyan, Boreal and Pacific realm based on the distribution of Jurassic ammonites. Hallam (1969a) relegated the latter to a province of the Tethyan Realm. The Boreal Realm was said to occupy the northern part of the Northern Hemisphere with a gradational and oscillating (through time) southern boundary roughly coincident with the line of the Alpine fold belts. The area south of this belongs to the Tethyan Realm. Using foraminifers, Scheibnerova (1971b) recognized the following marine biogeoprovinces during the Mesozoic Tethyan (Mediterranean, tropical/subtropical); Boreal (temperate, cool, polar); and Austral (equivalent to the Boreal of the Northern Hemisphere) Mesozoic biogeo-

provinces and, during the Cretaceous an additional Transitional biogeoprovince, situated between the Tethyan and Boreal/Austral biogeoprovinces. The provinces recognized by Scheibnerova (1971b) were regarded as being circumglobal due to paleogeographic relationships between the continent and oceans. Subsequent to the break-up and dispersal of Gondwanaland and Laurasia, the various continental fragments became dispersed over large longitudinal distances rather than being latitudinally homogenous as they had been prior to the present phase of continental drift.

Unable to relate the distribution of Jurassic foraminifera to distinct faunal provinces, Gordon (1970) grouped the known Jurassic foraminiferal faunas of the world into five broad types of assemblage. Each of these types was said to retain its general characteristics throughout the Jurassic. Three of the assemblage types are typical of shelf regions (simple arenaceous foraminifers, including reophacids, simple lituolids, and textulariids; nodosariids, and certain calcareous forms such as epistominids, buliminids, or opthalmidiids); the other two kinds of assemblage are characteristic of the Tethys seaway and its margins (planktonic foraminifers, or arenaceous forms including pavonitids, discocyclinids and forms with complex internal structures, such as the Spirocyclinidae—see Banner, 1970, for a recent synopsis of this family).

Several generalizations regarding the biogeographic distribution, paleoecology and evolutionary patterns of early Mesozoic foraminifers can be made based upon the detailed analysis presented by Scheibnerova (1971b):

1. The Mesozoic is characterized by the origin and development of new groups of foraminifers which are probably derived from ancestral forms of the Endothyracea and constitute two main groups: Nodosariidae and Rotaliina (early forms include the Epistominidae, Discorbidae, Involutinidae; somewhat later the Orbitoidacea, Cassidulinacea, Robertinacea and the planktonic Globigerinacea). Agglutinated foraminifers also underwent expansion and diversification during the early Mesozoic.

2. The general character of Jurassic foraminiferal assemblages is very similar to that observed in the Triassic: Nodosariidae predominate; certain groups of the Rotaliina (Epistominidae, Trocholina) and primitive, agglutinated forms also occur.

3. In early Jurassic time (Lias) foraminiferal faunas of both the Tethys and epicontinental shelf seas to the north and south were cosmopolitan and relatively uniform as were

molluscan faunas (belemnites, ammonites and pelecypods).

4. The original environment of early Mesozoic foraminifera was probably temperate (cool rather than warm) and shallow (neritic). Deep water deposits of the Tethyan seaway rarely contain foraminifers; instead they are characterized by nannoplankton of various types: tintinnids, globochaetids, saccocomids, stromiosphaerids, nannoconids, and radiolarians. Globigerinid-like forms—which may represent the earliest calcareous planktonic foraminifers successfully adapted to a pelagic existence—occur in relatively shallow water facies in the Tethyan and epicontinental areas.

5. The Cretaceous is characterized by continued diversification of various calcareous and agglutinated benthonic foraminifers. Adaptation to a relatively deep environment can be seen in several groups, although the large majority remain adapted to life in a shelf environment. In mid-Cretaceous time the planktonic foraminifers underwent rapid expansion and diversification. With the advent of the globotruncanids, rotaliporids, hedbergellids, and related forms biogeographic provincialization can be delineated for the first time utilizing planktonic forms.

6. Temperature was the primary factor controlling the distribution of Mesozoic foraminifera. An efficient temperature control which affected the distribution of Mesozoic foraminifers was warm currents (such as the Gulf Stream).

Gordon (1970) noted that Bowen (1966, p. 144) had suggested a 15°–20°C equatorial-polar spread in mean annual temperature during the Jurassic. If this is the case, the influence of temperature as a significant biogeographic control may have been considerably less than today because of the greater climatic uniformity over the earth during that time. Gordon (1970) concluded that the five broad types of Jurassic foraminiferal assemblages are related partly to temperature control and partly to the broad geotectonic-sedimentary environment. Scheibnerova (1971) indicated that the latter did not play a primary role in the origin of Mesozoic or modern biogeoprovinces inasmuch as most of the foraminiferal species in the Australian and New Zealand Jurassic and Cretaceous are either strongly similar or identical to those in other parts of the Southern Hemisphere as well as to some faunal elements in the Boreal Province of the Northern Hemisphere. She considered the Tethyan region, and the shelf areas to the north and south of it, to be a special case because the Tethys coincided with the tropical

climatic belt. Hallam (1969) related the differences in composition and diversity of marine invertebrates in the Tethyan and Boreal Realms of the Jurassic to three sedimentary facies associations (terrigenous clastic, intermediate, and calcareous). He related the existence of the Boreal Realm to an extensive inland sea of slightly reduced salinity in the Northern Hemisphere which had free access to the Tethys and to the Pacific (Panthalassa) Ocean.

In the course of DSDP Leg 11 (Hollister and others, 1972) Upper Jurassic-Lower Cretaceous sediments were encountered north and east of San Salvador (Bahama Islands) and at the base of the continental rise (northern end of the Hatteras abyssal plain) about 600 km east of Cape Hatteras (Luterbacher, 1972). According to Luterbacher:

1. Sediments of Kimmeridgian to Oxfordian age contain "primitive" agglutinated foraminifers and lagenids, saccocomids (pelagic crinoids) and ammonite aptychi.

2. Tithonian to Kimmeridgian sediments contain ammonite aptychi (*Lamellaptychus*, i. al.), saccocomids and *Brotzenia* spp. (benthonic foraminifers).

3. Valanginan to Tithonian sediments are characterized by irregular occurrences of lenticulinids and vaginulinids (foraminifers), tintinnids (*Tintinnopsella, Calpionella* and *Remaniella*) nannoconids and radiolarians.

4. Hauterivian to Upper Valanginian sediments contain the benthonic foraminiferal genus *Lenticulina* and ammonite aptychei referable to *Lamellaptychus*.

5. Sediments of late Albian-early Cenomanian age contained planktonic foraminifers belonging to *Rotalipora, Praeglobotruncana* and *Hedbergella*. Various hedbergellids and *Globigerinelloides ultramicra* were recorded from sediments of Albian to Hauterivian age.

Luterbacher (1972) appeared to favor comparison of the Upper Jurassic faunal assemblage of the northwestern Atlantic with the "shelf assemblages" from the western interior of North America and those from Europe (eastern Swiss Jura Mountains and the Polish lowlands) (*cf.* Gordon, 1970) which were probably deposited in middle to outer neritic environments. Assemblages dominated by epistominids are comparable to similar faunas from relatively near-shore sediments of western Europe (*e.g.,* Aalénian of the Swiss Jura Mountains and the Dogger alpha of southwestern Germany). The agglutinated faunas might be comparable with those from the Lower Malm of the Aargauer Jura in Switzerland, or the type Kimmeridgian of southern England. Luterbacher (1972) discussed evidence of foraminiferal faunal associations of Late Jurassic age from the central Apennines which suggests that Upper Jurassic-Lower Cretaceous assemblages of the northwestern Atlantic were deposited at bathyal depths on the upper continental rise and slope.

The Upper Jurassic foraminiferal assemblages are comparable with correlative faunas from North America and with bathyal deposits of the Alpine-Mediterranean area. Lutherbacher (1972) concluded that the increase in foraminiferal number, variation, and taxonomic diversity, and the presence of outer neritic to bathyal ostracod faunas in the Upper Jurassic at Sites 100 and 105 suggest a gradual deepening of the sea above the basement in this part of the northwestern Atlantic, but that this region of the Atlantic was already at bathyal depths in Late Jurassic time.

The stratigraphic utility of the planktonic foraminifers begins with the Aptian-Albian (Bolli, 1957a, b, c; 1959). Numerous studies on Cretaceous planktonic foraminiferal biostratigraphy have been made in Europe and North America which have aid in an understanding of the biogeography of the late Mesozoic of the North Atlantic, including: 1) Europe-Brotzen (1936, Lower Senonian (Emscherian = Late Coniacian-Early Santonian) of Eriksdal, Skåne (Scania) Sweden); Barr (1962, Senonian of Isle of Wight, England); Berggren (1962, Maestrichtian of Denmark and southern Sweden); Hofker (1966, type Maestrichtian of Holland (Hofker has also described planktonic foraminiferal faunas from various areas of northern Europe in numerous publications—the interested reader is referred to the bibliography in Hofker, 1966); Douglas and Rankin (1969, Senomanian-Lower Senonian of Bornholm); and 2) North America-Bolli (1957a, 1959, Lower and Upper Cretaceous of Trinidad); Olsson (1960, 1964, Campanian-Maestrichtian of Atlantic Coastal Plain); Pessagno (1967, Upper Cretaceous of southwestern Gulf Coastal Plain).

A synthesis of the results of these and other studies leads to the following conclusions:

1. The Upper Cretaceous planktonic foraminiferal faunas described from northern Europe and North America are similar.

2. In general, compared to coeval Tethyan faunas, those of northern latitudes are less diverse (Berggren, 1962; Olsson, 1964). For the Santonian Douglas and Rankin (1969, p. 214) observed that northern planktonic foraminiferal faunas are about 2/3 as diverse as comparable Tethyan assemblages.

3. Senonian (pre-Maestrichtian) boreal faunas were dominated by globigerinid-like forms (hedbergellids and archeoglobigerinids) which occurred in approximately equal numbers with keeled species (Douglas and Rankin, 1969).

4. Late Cretaceous planktonic foraminifers do not exhibit mondial latitudinal and longitudinal distribution patterns.

5. Numerous Late Cretaceous species were cosmopolitan in distribution but apparently were unable to extend their range (except rarely) into high latitudes.

6. During Campanian-Early Maestrichtian time there were many cosmopolitan species, whereas during the Late Maestrichtian stratigraphically important planktonic foraminifers became increasingly restricted to the Tethyan region, suggesting a contraction of the tropical belt.

A comprehensive study of the paleobiogeography of Maestrichtian planktonic foraminifers was made by Davids (1966). He was able to delineate the northern limit of the Tethyan faunal province by changes in the frequency distribution patterns (northward diminution) of *Globotruncana, Praeglobotruncana, Schackoina* and *Trinitella* (see figs. 1 and 2) and estimate the geographic limits of the Maestrichtian paleoclimatic zones (fig. 3). However, as will be seen from the discussion below, his three-fold paleobiogeographic subdivision (and its boundaries) is an oversimplification, and to a certain extent misleading. A high concentration of warm-water forms extended from Alabama to New Jersey suggesting a northward flowing warm ocean current during Maestrichtian time. Recent results from the Deep Sea Drilling Project (Leg 12) indicate the existence of tropical planktonic foraminiferal faunas as far north as 54°N lat. (Orphan Knoll, Labrador Sea) during the Cenomanian.

Davids (1966) concluded that latitudinal control of Maestrichtian planktonic foraminiferal faunas suggests ocean water mass distribution not greatly unlike that existing today and that stratigraphic correlation along parallels of latitude is easier than along meridians of longitude.

A number of important observations on diversity and distribution of Maestrichtian planktonic foraminiferal faunas were made by Davids (1966). The genera *Globigerinelloides, Praeglobotruncana (vel Globotruncanella), Hedbergella* and, to a lesser extent, *Rugoglobigerina,* appear to have been rather tolerant of environmental changes.

A poleward reduction in the number of genera of planktonic foraminifers during the Maestrichtian was observed; similar observations

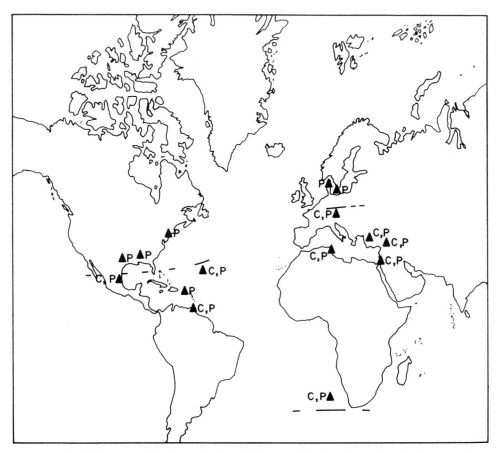

Fig. 1.—Paleobiogeographic determination of the north Tethys boundary based on species of *Praeglobotruncana* (after Davids, 1966, map 7).

were made on Cenomanian-early Senonian faunas by Douglas and Rankin (1969) supporting the suggestion that the genera *Praeglobotruncana (vel Globotruncanella), Globigerinelloides, Hedbergella* and *Heterohelix* are the only forms found in any high percentage in northern latitudes. The latter is generally the dominant form, followed by *Globigerinelloides*. Davids (1966, p. 60) observed that "the genera *Heterohelix, Globigerinelloides* and *Hedbergella* all show increases in number (northwards) suggesting tolerance of apparently radical ecologic change." We would suggest, however, that these ecologic changes were probably not "radical" in the Maestrichtian sea, but may be related to simple diversity gradients which are a reflection of an equatorial-polar temperature gradient which, though far less pronounced than during the Cenozoic, nevertheless affected the latitudinal distribution of the planktonic foraminifers of that time. Significant observations on Maestrichtian planktonic foraminiferal fauna diversity are outlined below:

1. In the Gulf Coast-Caribbean region *Heterohelix* is the dominant form; *Guembelitria* replaces it in some places; either of the two average over 75% of the fauna. *Globigerinelloides, Rugoglobigerina, Globotruncana, Hedbergella, Praeglobotruncana (vel Globotruncanella), Trinitella, Schackoina,* and *Abathomphalus* follow in abundance in that order. A reduction in *Trinitella* and *Schackoina* is observed north of the Gulf Coast-Caribbean region.

2. The alternation of assemblage composition at the northern edge of the Tethys in the North American region is far less marked than in Europe. *Praeglobotruncana (vel Globotruncanella), Trinitella,* and *Globotruncana* exhibit a decreasing relative abundance northwards which parallels European trends. *Globigerinelloides, Hedbergella* and *Rugoglobigerina* remain relatively stable northwards. *Heterohelix* (and the Heterohelicidae) increases northwards.

Environmental conditions in the northern part of this region (Atlantic Coastal Plain) were very different from those in southern Scandinavia. This is suggested by the larger number of genera that persisted in North America under similar depositional conditions indicated by similar percentages of genera of Globigerinaceae and Heterohelicidae in the two regions. Davids (1966, p. 63) concluded that "it appears that the environmental conditions existing in the low-latitude Tethys region extended to higher latitudes in North America than Europe." This suggests that the Gulf Stream was operative along the eastern margin of North America in the late Cretaceous.

3. In the Mediterranean-European region, the Northern Tethyan assemblages are characterized by *Globotruncana arca* and *G. tricarinata;* southern assemblages by *G. gagnebini, G. subcircumnodifer* and *G. gansseri.*

4. The northern Tethys assemblage is present in the Gulf Coast-Caribbean region. The north-ern area is dominated by *G. arca, G. tricarinata* and *G. mariei;* the southern area by *G. gagnebini, G. rosetta* and *G. stuartiformis.* The appearance of certain globotruncanid species (*calciformis, conica* and *falsostuarti*) in Mexico and localities to the south indicates the northern limit of the Tethyan influence. *Praeglobotruncana citae (vel Globotruncanella havanensis)* and *P. petaloidea* also serve to delimit the northern limits of Tethyan influence.

5. *Guembelitria* was not observed in deep sea cores of the North and South Atlantic but has been found in relatively shallow water deposits of New Jersey, the Gulf Coast, Scandinavia and Turkey. Davids (1966) suggested that the genus may be a) a benthonic or b) a planktonic form adapted to near shore and perhaps lower salinity waters.

6. The delineation of tropical, temperate and boreal temperature zones has been demonstrated to be possible for the Late Cretaceous (Maestrichtian).

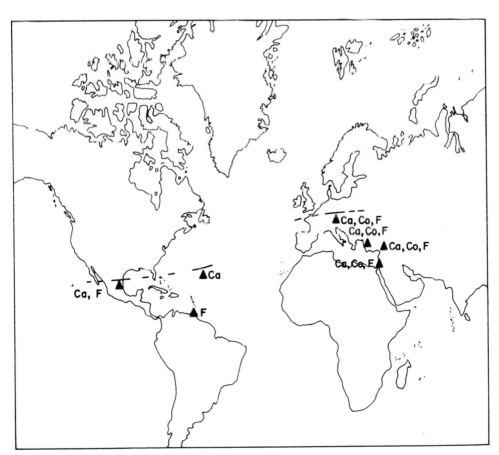

Fig. 2.—Paleobiogeographic determination of the north Tethys boundary based on species of *Globotruncana* (after Davids, 1966, map 4)

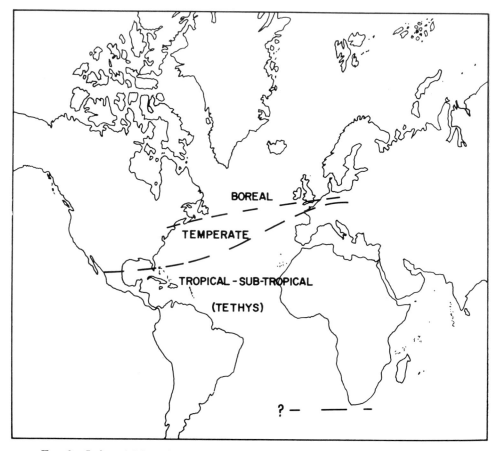

Fig. 3.—Inferred Maestrichtian paleoclimatic zones (after Davids, 1966, map 14).

7. Two basic eco-assemblages were observed: shallow water and deep water. The former (exemplified by assemblages found in North America) have the following characteristics:

a) persistently low planktonic/benthonic ratio and highest number of Heterohelicidae relative to other planktonic forms.

b) higher numbers of *Guembelitria*.

c) *Globigerinelloides* and *Rugoglobigerina* appear in relatively large numbers giving a pronounced inequality to faunal assemblage pattern.

d) *Globotruncana* fluctuates in abundance.

e) *Praeglobotruncana (vel Globotruncanella)* and *Trinitella* significantly reduced in abundance.

f) *Hedbergella* present in numbers similar to other regions.

g) *Schackoina* appeared only once in North America and everywhere in the Mediterranean and Mexico.

The deep-water eco-assemblage is exemplified

by associations found in the Tethys region. The assemblages, in general, exhibit a faunal balance and aspect of relative generic abundance which suggest open ocean conditions, namely:

a) planktonic/benthonic ratios are consistently high.

b) *Guembelitria* is rare or absent.

c) *Globigerinelloides, Rugoglobigerina* and *Globotruncana* common.

d) *Praeglobotruncana (vel Globotruncanella), Trinitella* and *Hedbergella* present in relatively large numbers.

e) *Schackoina,* though not common, occurs persistently.

f) *Abathomphalus* occurs in varying numbers.

Cretaceous benthonic foraminifers exhibit wide geographic distribution patterns. Major studies by Hofker (1966, and references to his earlier studies therein) and Cushman (1946, and references to his earlier studies therein) on the Cretaceous benthonic foraminifera of western Europe and North America, respectively, have shown that numerous species occur in common on both sides of the Atlantic. That certain benthonic foraminiferal species of the genus *Bolivinoides* were widely distributed (probably by surface currents) in the Cretaceous has been documented by Barr (1966, 1970) and Hiltermann (1963), among others. This genus, which began in the early-mid Santonian with the species *strigillata*, rapidly diversified into at least 3 lineages (Barr, 1970). The widespread occurrence of *B. strigillata* in NW Australia (Edgell, 1954), the SW Soviet Union (Vassilenko, 1961), NW Europe (Hiltermann, 1963; Hiltermann and Koch, 1950), England (Barr, 1966; Chapman, 1892) and Libya (Barr, 1970) as well as in the basal Taylor marl and part of the Austin chalk of Texas (where it had been recorded as *B. austiniana* Cushman) renders an interpretation of the area of origin of the genus indefinite. The fact that it is more common in the Tethyan and European regions suggests that it had its origin there and was subsequently transported to North America by means of a westward flowing equatorial current system. Indeed, several species have well-documented occurrences in the Tethys, western Europe, North America and Australia, which suggest transportation and dispersal along the Tethyan seaway and dispersal both eastwards (to Australia) and westwards, across the Atlantic. On the other hand, Hiltermann (1964) suggested that several evolutionary "pulses" must have originated in the American habitat with subsequent transportation and evolutionary radiation in Europe and the Tethys region.

The stratigraphic and geographic distribution of several species of *Bolivinoides* are shown in Figs. 4 and 5–8 respectively, as an indication of the widespread development of a stratigraphically significant late Cretaceous benthonic form.

The most recent and thorough survey of the geographic distribution of Cretaceous foraminifera is that by Dilley (1971). In his discussion he has considered the "larger" and "smaller" foraminifers separately and, in the latter category, he treats the benthonic and planktonic forms separately. We can summarize his main observations as follows:

1. A distinct "larger foraminiferal realm" is discernible throughout the Cretaceous as an extensive sinuous linear belt which essentially parallels the present day low to mid latitudinal belts in the Northern Hemisphere. It extends from approximately 30°–45°N in the Middle East, Africa and southern Europe—in the Tethys Sea; *Orbitolina* and *Trocholina* in the

Aptian of southern England (52°N) and *Orbitolina* alone in probable early Cenomanian of Ulster (54°N) represent the maximum poleward limit of this belt in time and space. In the New World this belt extends approximately from 8°–32°N and occupies the general area of the Caribbean-Antilles-Gulf of Mexico with rare occurrences of some genera at higher latitudes along the Atlantic Coastal Plain. *Orbitolina* has recently been found at Flemish Cap (46°30′N lat.) on the easternmost part of the western North Atlantic continental shelf (Sen Gupta and Grant, 1972) in sediments probably of late Aptian to early Albian age. Previously the genus had not been recorded north of Texas in North America. Additional occurrences of the genus can be expected along the Atlantic Coastal Plain where suitable facies are present.

2. During the Early Cretaceous this realm achieved maximum homogeneity, *i.e.* most of the genera achieving geographic distribution throughout its extent.

3. During Late Cretaceous the Americas are clearly distinguished from the Old World by the absence of the Alveolinidae and a majority of the complex Lituolidae (*e.g.*, Miliolidae: *Lacazina, Lacazopsis, Periloculina;* Soritidae: *Vandenbroeckia, Meandropsina, Broeckina, Edomia, Nummulofallotia;* Barkerinidae: *Nezzazata, Coxites* and *Rabanitina*, among others). These forms are restricted to the Mediterranean Tethys including the Middle East.

4. Orbitoidal foraminifers (such as *Omphalocyclus* and *Orbitoides*) appeared in the late Senonian; these two occur in both the Old and New Worlds. The Pseudorbitoididae are restricted to Central American forms. *Siderolites* was restricted to Europe and the Middle East in much the manner of the majority of orbitoidal foraminifers, whereas *Loftusia* exhibited the extreme of provinciality, being restricted to Asia Minor and southwest Asia—essentially the Middle East. Dilley (1971) suggested that the wider distribution of the "trans-Atlantic" orbitoidal genera might be related to their supposed heterohelicid nepiont (*i.e.*, planktonic early ontogeny).

5. Cretaceous planktonic foraminifers show indications from their initial radiation of latitudinal geographic distribution although the strong influence of other factors is indicated by distributional features in North America.

6. Smaller calcareous benthonic foraminiferal genera exhibit an insignificant tendency to provincialism during the Cretaceous. Discontinuities in the distributon of several calcareous and agglutinated forms suggest possible areas of origin and subsequent migration.

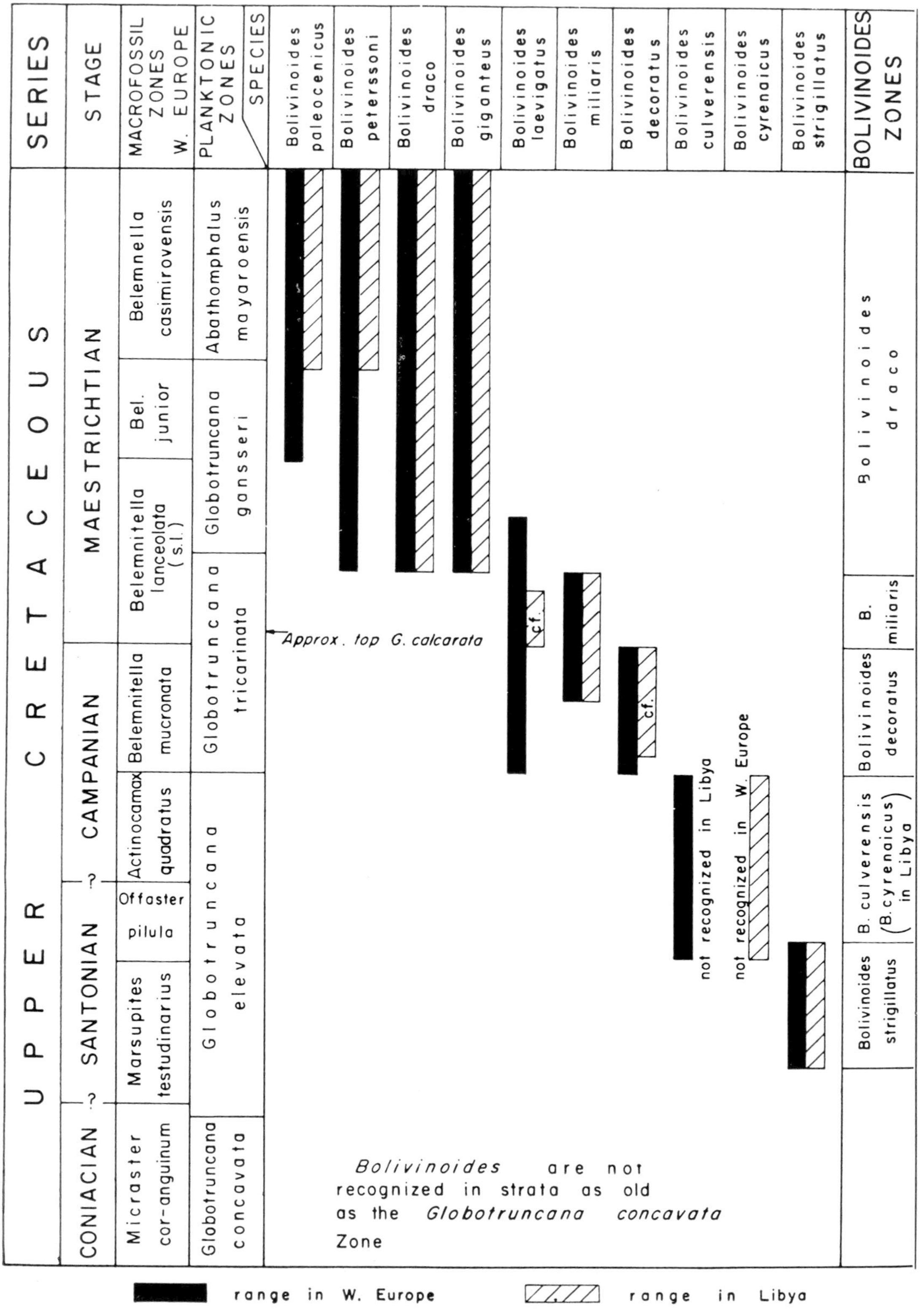

Fig. 4.—Stratigraphic range and geographic distribution of the benthonic foraminiferal genus *Bolivinoides* in western Europe and Libya (from Barr, 1970, fig. 2).

7. Two significant global patterns in foraminiferal distribution involve the "larger" foraminifers: restriction to a narrow, linear zone essentially parallel to present day latitudes and the change from a continuous, worldwide early Cretaceous distribution to a discontinuous distribution in late Cretaceous time separable into Old and New World "provinces." Dilley (1971) concluded that the first of these suggests: a) that the distribution was climatically controlled, and b) that Cretaceous latitudes were approximately oriented as they are today.

8. Cretaceous evidence suggests that East-West migrations across the Atlantic were probably easier than the opposite direction (cf. Adams, 1967, who suggested that West-East migration might have been easier during the Tertiary).

An example of provincialism among late Maestrichtian calcareous nannoplankton was presented by Worsley and Martini (1970). *Tetralithus murus* is restricted to tropical regions: *Nephrolithus frequens* occurs at high latitudes. They have been found together only in southwest France.

Funnell (1964) has presented a summary of the occurrence and distribution of Upper Cretaceous sediments and fossils in the North Atlantic. Most of the locations, as expected, occur in the eastern and western North Atlantic along the continental margin (shelf and slope) of North America and Europe, on seamounts and islands off Europe and Africa. Since then numerous data have accumulated revealing the presence of Upper Cretaceous sediments beneath the deep-sea floor (in particular in the Initial Reports of the Deep Sea Drilling Project). Funnell and Smith (1968) prepared a map showing the sequential opening of the Atlantic Ocean by sea-floor spreading which allowed an estimate of the region in which sediments of a particular age were likely to be encountered above basement, considering the age of the sediment immediately overlying the basement to be a function of distance from the centrally located Mid-Atlantic Ridge.

An analysis of the faunal evidence from different areas led Funnell (1964) to the following conclusions:

1. Upper Cretaceous sediments which occur on the continental margin of North America at depths greater than 200 meters, indicate accumulation in water less than 200 meters deep. This suggests post-Cretaceous subsidence and there is apparently a systematic increase in subsidence from north to south.

2. The existence of oceanic depths of water in the North Atlantic Basin during the late Cre-

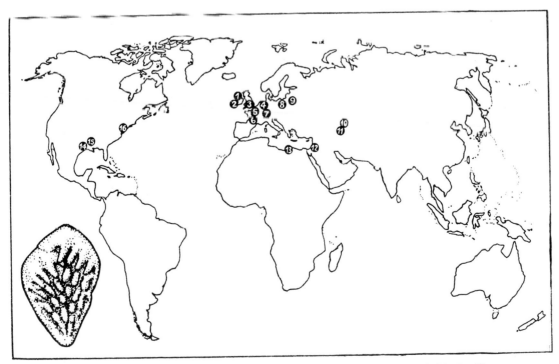

Fig. 5.—Distribution of *Bolivinoides decoratus* (Jones) (after Barr, 1970, fig. 5).

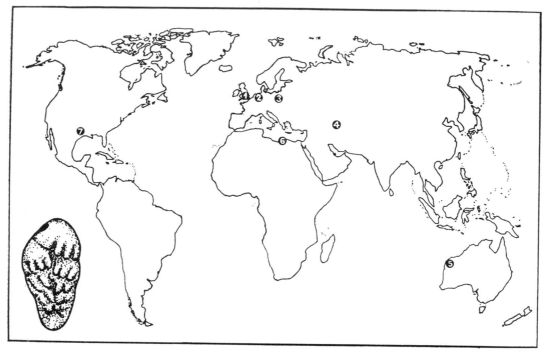

FIG. 6.—Distribution of *Bolivinoides strigillatus* (Chapman) (after Barr, 1970, fig. 7).

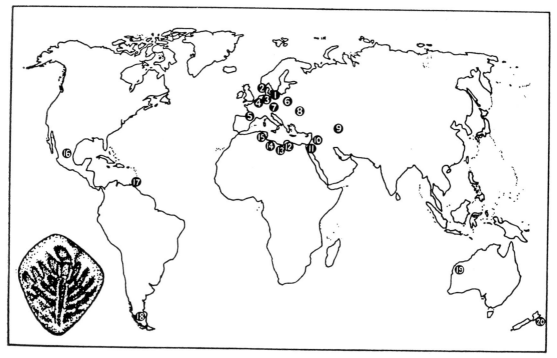

FIG. 7.—Distribution of *Bolivinoides draco* (Marsson) (after Barr, 1970, fig. 3).

taceous "cannot be regarded as established, although on general grounds it is not improbable." Leg 11 data of the Deep Sea Drilling Project suggest that bathyal depths existed in certain areas at least as early as the Late Jurassic to Early Cretaceous.

3. Neither continental slope occurrences off continental Europe and Africa, nor the presence of an Upper Maestrichtian planktonic foraminiferal fauna from Galicia Bank, provide substantial information regarding paleogeographical conditions along the eastern margin of the Atlantic during the Late Cretaceous. However, recent findings by the DSDP (Leg 12) indicate that the floor of the Bay of Biscay was at or near its present depth by the early Cenozoic (Paleocene-Eocene).

Tethyan warm water lithistid *Demospongia* and dictyonine Hexactinellida (siliceous sponges) appear in the Cretaceous of northern Europe (Reid, 1967). The influence of the Tethys is suggested by three factors:

1. Recognized derivatives of late Cretaceous and early Cenozoic Tethyan dictyonine Hexactinellida are most numerous in the Indo-West Pacific region and most abundant in the Indo-Malayan region.

2. Eight genera and six species appear to be distributed discontinuously between the Indo-West Pacific and the warm Atlantic.

3. Several genera (*Periphagella, Pleurochorium* and *Stereochlamis*) had Cretaceous species in Europe, but are now known only in the Indo-West Pacific and primarily from the Indo-Malayan region. The distribution of these and several other genera corresponds with that of many descendants of the former Tethyan fauna, now essentially restricted to the Indo-West Pacific but formerly present in Europe.

The relevant fossil record of these sponges occurs in the Jurassic and all evidence points to their distribution within warm-water reefal areas, generally in the Tethys region. The Aptian and Santonian faunas of the Tethyan region together contains 36 genera and 37 species which occur in the *Belemnitella quadrata* Zone of Germany, *i.e.*, one half of the genera and nearly half of the species. This is far too high a proportion of identity for these forms to have been cold-water elements (Reid, 1967). Furthermore, the Santonian was a time of the second Cretaceous climatic optimum (Bowen, 1961a, Fig. 2). The *quadrata* fauna of North Germany included species of the few genera common to the Cretaceous and the present day, including those restricted to warm water regions and the Indo-West Pacific region. Reid (1967, p. 177) suggested that the reason so many forms of inferred warm-water origin could occur in an area commonly called "boreal," and whose char-

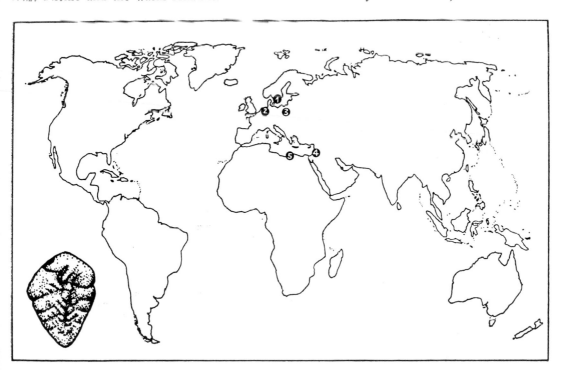

Fig. 8.—Distribution of *Bolivinoides paleocenicus* (Brotzen) (after Barr, 1970, fig. 6).

acteristic fossils of other groups (*e.g., Gonio-teuthis, Belemnitella, Ancellina*) have been considered cold-water animals, was that "boreal" Europe was only boreal geographically, not climatically (Reid, 1967, p. 178). He observed further that the Late Cretaceous climate of northwestern and central Europe never fell within the present range of the mean yearly temperatures in the North Atlantic (2–3°C north of Norway to 12–13° at the western end of the English Channel). The Cretaceous "boreal" province was properly a subtropical/warm temperate region—basically an area of overlap between tropical/subtropical (Tethyan) and warm-temperate/subtropical faunas. The latter has been denoted "boreal" but is not comparable zoogeographically with the modern boreal fauna. Reid (1967) concluded by comparing the north European Late Cretaceous to the present day Mauretanian/Luisian region (the boundary between these two provinces is at about 40°N along the western coast of Europe) or the area from the Philippines to southern Japan.

During the Late Cretaceous the strongest affinities of the South American vertebrate fauna were with North America and Europe. The close relationship which had existed with Africa was lost suggesting that the separation of South America and Africa had occurred by this time. This is in accord with evidence obtained from Leg 3 of the Deep Sea Drilling Project (Maxwell and others, 1970), which suggests an age of separation of about 130 million years ago (*i.e.*, Early Cretaceous). The rich Late Cretaceous vertebrate faunas of Asia and North America are considered to be more closely related to each other than to those of Europe, Africa and South America suggesting that migration between Eurasia and North America occurred by way of the Bering Straits Land Bridge during the Late Cretaceous (although Pitman and Talwani, 1972, indicated that the existence of the Bering Land Bridge at this time is problematic), while at the same time migration between North America and Europe occurred via Spitsbergen (Pitman and Talwani, 1972).

Hallam (1967) summarized Cretaceous paleozoogeographic data on the molluscs (pelecypods, gastropods, belemnites and ammonites). His data indicate a closer relationship between areas now separated by extensive oceanic distances and latitudinally distinguishable zoogeographic provinces.

A sedimentary sequence over 2 km thick in West Greenland (69°–72°N) (Rosenkrantz, 1970) contains rich marine faunas (ammonites, baculitids, inoceramids) of Cenomanian to Maestrichtian age. Scaphitid and sphenoceramid faunas were recorded as the dominant forms. *Pteria (Oxytoma) tenuicostata*—which occurs in the Lower Campanian of Germany, England, Belgium, Russia and central Europe and is considered to be a boreal element—is found in the Santonian on both the east and west coasts of Greenland.

Ravn (1918) observed that a number of the Greenland species also occurred in Upper Cretaceous deposits of the western interior of North America, but no affinity was observed with the American Coastal Plain faunas. Teichert (1939, p. 155), in agreeing with Ravn's (1918) results, indicated that an Upper Cretaceous transgression could not have occurred from the south, via the Davis Strait, but must have come around the northern margin of the Canadian Shield through the Sverdrup Basin (*i.e.*, from the northwest).

In view of the fact that the Labrador Sea was being formed by sea-floor spreading during the Late Cretaceous, it would seem equally likely that the marine sediments of West Greenland were deposited in the northward expansion of the North Atlantic Ocean during this time. This is consistent with the history of the opening of the Labrador Sea and North Atlantic by sea-floor spreading during Late Cretaceous time (Le Pichon and others, 1971; Pitman and Talwani, 1972). Alternatively, it is possible that the Sverdrup Basin and Labrador Sea were connected during the Cretaceous and that faunal exchange between central North America and the North Atlantic via this connection occurred. It is significant that the ammonite-belemnite-inoceramid fauna of the Sverdrup Basin and West Greenland indicate the presence of relatively warm seas and climates in the Arctic-Subarctic region during the Cretaceous.

It is unlikely that any single factor will, alone or in combination with a few secondary factors, suffice to explain the complex problems of the taxonomic diversification and geographic provincialization of marine invertebrate faunas during Mesozoic time. Rather it is more plausible to seek a general explanation for these facts in rising latitudinal temperature gradients on the shelves and to the fragmentation and isolation of shelf environments and the formation of deep ocean basins by continental drift as suggested by Valentine (1969) and Valentine and Moores (1970).

CENOZOIC BIOGEOGRAPHY

Introduction

Cenozoic biogeography of the North Atlantic

and marginal (*i.e.*, adjacent) land areas is intimately related to the continuing process of fragmentation of Laurasia. During the early part of the Cenozoic the active phase of sea-floor spreading in the North Atlantic shifted from the Labrador Sea Ridge to the Reykjanes Ridge. This had the effect of separating northern Europe (Scandinavia) from Greenland and, with the final separation of Spitsbergen in early-middle Eocene time, of establishing an Arctic province with direct deep-water connection to the North Atlantic. Distinct faunal changes occurred as a result of these modifications to land and sea configurations. Superimposed upon these changes are those caused by a gradual lowering of temperature during the Cenozoic and the gradual southward displacement of paleolatitudes as the crust moved northwards over the mantle (Berggren and Phillips, 1971).

Cenozoic geologic history of the marginal areas of Europe and North America is, generally speaking, an alternation of marine transgression and regression on slowly subsiding shelves or basins.

Faunal exchange continued between the Tethys and western Atlantic (Caribbean-Gulf Coast) regions into the middle Tertiary. The junction of Asia and Africa in the Early Miocene separated the Tethys into two distinct regions. The junction of Europe and Africa in the Middle Miocene restricted circulation within the western Tethys and effectively prohibited benthonic faunal interchange during late Middle and Late Miocene time. The modern Mediterranean has developed since the early Pliocene transgression of the Atlantic.

During the Cenozoic, mammalian migrations between Eurasia and North America and North Africa and Europe provide valuable data which place constraints on reconstructions of land-sea relationships during this time. Simpson (1947a, b) has indicated that major faunal interchange took place between Eurasia and North America during the Early Eocene, Late Eocene, Early Oligocene, Late Miocene, Middle-Late Pliocene, and Pleistocene. Little or no faunal interchange occurred during the Middle Eocene and during Middle and Late Oligocene times, although some vertebrate investigators believe that early Cenozoic migration took place via the Bering Land Bridge. Kurtén (1966, 1967) has indicated that this is unlikely and that migration more likely took place via a land bridge across the North Atlantic. The recent study by Pitman and Talwani (1972) provides the necessary northern migration route via Spitsbergen. They show that the final severance between North America and Eurasia occurred with the separation of Spitsbergen from Scandinavia during the early Eocene about 50 million years ago (see also McKenna, 1971, 1972). From that time on migration between Eurasia and North America occurred via the Bering Land Bridge, as is indicated by the fact that Asian and North American faunas resemble each other more closely than the European (Szalay and McKenna, 1971).

Regional Distribution Studies

The most comprehensive summary of Tertiary faunal biogeography remains that of Davies (1934–1935). He traced the sequential development of marine and terrestrial faunas on both sides of the Atlantic and the Tethys region in painstaking detail. The gradual constriction of the tropical regions and attendant modifications to circulation patterns during the Paleogene is reflected in the fact that by the end of the middle Eocene (Lutetian) the influx of Tethyan forms had almost ceased in the Paris Basin. Nevertheless, various Tethyan elements persisted in northern Europe (nummulites in North Germany) into the early Oligocene attesting to the relatively warm surface waters along the coasts of western Europe during the mid-Cenozoic. The gradual provincialization of marine invertebrate faunas in the Atlantic is carefully traced and this book is recommended as stimulating reading to the reader interested in forming a more comprehensive acquaintance with the biogeography of Tertiary faunas.

Hazel (1970) has provided additional valuable information on ostracod zoogeography along the continental margin of North America. Significant for our discussion here are the following points:

1. Many sublittoral cryophyllic species are not present south of Cape Cod or the Northeast Channel and several thermophilic species are not found north of Cape Cod or Georges Bank.

2. Ostracod assemblages in the southern part of the cold-temperate Nova Scotian province are a mixture of amphi-Atlantic cryophyllic species and endemic, mostly thermophilic, species.

3. European forms make up about 50% of the species. Less than 25% of the species known from the mid-temperate Virginian province have been reported from European waters. More endemic species pass Cape Cod from the south than amphi-Atlantic cryophyllic species do from the north.

Information on the distribution of fossiliferous sediments along the east coast of the United

States has been provided by Gibson, Hazel and Mello (1968). They recorded fossiliferous sediments from submarine canyons off the NE United States (37°–42°N lat.) ranging in age from Late Cretaceous (Campanian-Maestrichtian) to Late Cenozoic. The following observations are relevant to the present discussion:

1. Upper Cretaceous subtropical-tropical planktonic faunas were recorded from Hudson, "70–30," Oceanographer and Lydonia canyons.

2. Paleocene and/or Eocene keeled globorotaliids (morozovellids) and acarininids (listed as globorotaliids) were recorded from Hudson, Oceanographer and "70–30" canyons.

3. Oligocene assemblages were reported from Oceanographer Canyon although Oligocene is not known to outcrop on the Atlantic Coastal Plain north of North Carolina.

4. Samples dated unequivocally as Pleistocene contain ostracod species whose modern southern limits are north of the northernmost canyon, indicating southward displacement during glacial intervals.

Adams (1967, 1970) has discussed the geographic and stratigraphic distribution of Tertiary larger foraminifers in the Tethyan, American and Indo-Pacific provinces. He suggested that present day circulation patterns in the North Atlantic can be used to account for the transportation of certain genera between the Tethys (ancient Mediterranean) and American provinces.

The following is a summary of some of the interesting conclusions reached by Adams (1967, 1970):

1. The American province was fairly well isolated from the Tethyan and Indo-Pacific provinces throughout the Tertiary. Species of *Lepidocyclina* reached the Tethyan region from America at least twice, during the Late Eocene and again during the Oligocene. Some miogypsinid species may have migrated in the same manner.

Several important Tethyan genera did not reach the Americas (*Assilina, Miscellanea, Fasciolites, Orbitolites, Opertorbitolites, Somalina, Cycloclypeus*) nor did any of the known European species of *Nummulites*.

2. The western Tethys, or Mediterranean area, was the center of dispersal of several important genera: *Nummulites, Fasciolites, Orbitolites*, during the Paleogene.

3. Successful east-west crossing of the Atlantic is indicated by the occurrence of two species of *Nummulites* and one of *Spiroclypeus* in the Americas, although Adams (1967, p. 210) qualified this with the reservation that *Spiroclypeus* may have had a polyphyletic origin.

4. Paleogene faunas in the Indo-Pacific were broadly similar to those in the Tethyan region. Few of the true Miocene Indo-Pacific spiroclypeids and cycloclypeids are known from the Tethys: *Flosculinella* did not reach the Tethys, which may indicate that "east-west migration was rather more difficult than from west to east" (Adams, 1967, p. 210, 211).

5. The Oligocene reticulate *Nummulites* migrated eastward and were abundant from Spain to the central Pacific. *Eulepidina*, after crossing the Atlantic Ocean from America, spread eastwards and achieved a geographic distribution similar to that of the reticulate *Nummulites*.

6. Certain genera (*Discocyclina, Operculina, Miogypsina*) are common to all these provinces. Adams (1967) was not able to state with certainty whether they appeared earlier in one province or another. It is possible, he suggests, that all evolved in the Americas and spread eastwards to the Tethys, and hence to the Indo-Pacific province.

7. Some genera are restricted to the Americas (*Pseudophragmina, Helicostegina, Helicolepidina*), indicating that migration did not always occur despite its possibility.

During the Paleogene the faunas of the Mediterranean and the Indo-Pacific exhibit pronounced similarities which indicates that the connection between the two areas was maintained by a marine seaway. By mid-Miocene time the marine seaway connection between the two areas has been lost and thereafter foraminiferal faunas in the two areas became sharply differentiated. Such typical Mediterranean forms as *Borelis melo curdica* and *Discospirina* were unable to reach the Indian Ocean, whereas such Indo-Pacific forms as *Alveolinella quoyi, Katacycloclypeus annulatus, Flosculinella bantangensis, i. al.*, were unable to reach the Mediterranean area. *Borelis melo* appeared in the Mediterranean region at about the same time as the planktonic foraminiferal genus *Orbulina*. The *Orbulina* Datum has been dated at about 15 my B.P. by Ikebe and others (1971). The migration of proboscideans and other mammalian groups from Africa into Eurasia during the early or middle "Burdigalian" land mammal age (about 18 my ago) (Van Couvering, 1972) provides a date for the closing of the connection between the Tethyan/Mediterranean and Indo-Pacific faunal provinces during the early Miocene (Berggren, 1972).

Adams (1967, p. 211, 212) concluded that the Atlantic constituted a major barrier to migration throughout the whole of the Tertiary. He suggested that exceptional crossings did occur at times of tropical storms when masses of seaweed might have become detached from the sea floor and set adrift. Drifting material could cross the Atlantic on the Gulf Stream or, less probably, by means of the Equatorial Counter Current and reach the Tethyan region by way of the Azores or West Africa. This interpretation is supported by recent evidence that the Gulf Stream has been operative since at least the Cretaceous (Laughton and others, 1972).

Adams (1967) also concluded that the continents of Europe, America, and Africa and Asia have occupied much the same positions during the Tertiary as they do today. If this were not so, he suggested, greater faunal similarity in American and Mediterranean/Tethyan faunas would be expected and the Atlantic would not have been such an effective barrier to migration. However, recent advances in geological-geophysical studies of the Atlantic Ocean would seem to provide ample documentation of the gradual break up and lateral movement of a large continental mass in the mid-Mesozoic (some 150–200 my ago). The locus of this rifting is the Mid-Atlantic Ridge, a prominent topographic feature which extends throughout the Atlantic Ocean in a N-S direction (with prominent offset in the equatorial region) and which connects with other prominent ridges in a world-encircling rift system. Lateral movement of the sea floor appears to be equally well documented now and a model has been recently constructed by Funnell and Smith (1968, Fig. 4) to illustrate stages in this phenomenon.

An important idea which Adams (1967, p. 214) discussed is that the eventual distribution of warm-water larger foraminifers during the Tertiary depended largely on the area in which they originated. For example, a species evolving in the western Tethys could reach the Indo-Pacific but not, as a rule, the Americas. A species originating in the Indo-Pacific was more likely to remain in that province, although it could penetrate into the Mediterranean region in some instances. A species originating in the Americas, on the other hand, could achieve worldwide distribution by migrating in a westerly direction, although it could also remain restricted to that province. The first step was the hardest: the passage of the Atlantic was in Adams' words, "fortuitous."

Data on Caribbean echinoid faunas have been summarized by Fell (1967). He makes the following observations based upon a review of the generic content of 30 families of shelf echinoids with representatives in both the Caribbean and Atlantic coasts of the Old World:

1. Of 28 families with representative genera in both American and Tethyan faunas, the Tethyan representatives appear earlier in the geologic record than the American occurrences.

2. The Caribbean-western Atlantic fauna has always had its strongest affinities with the West Tethyan fauna (that part of the Tethys which developed into Mediterranean Sea during the Pliocene).

3. Caribbean-western Atlantic faunas have always been relatively poorer in comparison with West Tethyan faunas. 314 genera have been recorded from the West Tethys compared to only 137 genera from the Caribbean-western Atlantic region.

4. The West Tethys contributed numerous genera to the Americas. In contrast, those families which originated in the Old World have not contributed a single genus to European, Mediterranean or West African seas, nor have they any representative in any West Tethyan Tertiary fauna.

5. Several losses of genera have occurred in the Caribbean at various intervals during the Tertiary. In this way genera which continued to flourish in the Indo-West Pacific area were excluded from the Caribbean-western Atlantic area. This substantiates observations made on other groups, such as foraminifers, ostracods, corals, and molluscs, generally attributed to the break up and isolation of the Tethyan seaway during the mid-late Cenozoic, approximately 15 my ago.

McKenzie (1967) has provided evidence of widespread distribution of marine ostracods in the Cenozoic. Among the main conclusions of his study are the following:

1. The Tethys played a significant role in the distribution of many ostracod faunules in the Caribbean, Mediterranean, Indo-Pacific and Australian provinces by allowing relatively rapid dispersal of genera, especially during the Paleogene.

2. This corridor was gradually disrupted during the Neogene and from the Neogene to the present provincial faunules have developed more or less independently.

3. The Mediterranean faunule, impoverished during the close of the Miocene, was replenished via the Gibraltar filter because communication with the Indo-Pacific was impossible since Vindobonian time (should be Burdigalian, see Berggren, 1969b, 1972; Berggren and Phillips, 1971). This accounts for the Atlantic (non-Tethyan) aspect of many living Mediterranean species.

4. Panamanian Straits provided access to the Pacific Coast of the Americas for many Caribbean forms.

The discovery of a cosmopolitan fauna of

ostracods in the Paleogene and Neogene of the Mediterranean and northern Italy indicate that the Tethys was indeed a deep-sea oceanic region during the Cenozoic (Benson and Sylvester-Bradley, 1971). The absence of most of the elements of this fauna in the present Mediterranean is ascribed to the hydrologic barrier which developed along with Pleistocene climatic deterioration. These faunal elements were derived from populations inhabiting the oceanic environments of the Mesozoic Tethys. Oceanic connection was maintained through the Middle Miocene with the Atlantic Ocean; this cosmopolitan fauna was reported as far east as Crete in the Miocene. At this time the east-west communication of Tethys was sealed off and the Paratethys Sea—an extensive epicontinental sea developed over southeastern and central Europe (Balkan countries, Rumania, Hungarian-Vienna Basins).

The fact that this cosmopolitan fauna survived the severe Late Miocene change in hydrologic and climatic conditions (evaporation and desiccation) in the western Tethys Sea suggests two possibilities:

1. Cosmopolitan conditions were reestablished with the Pliocene transgression of the Atlantic Ocean from the west.

2. Some areas of the Mediterranean never suffered the evaporitic conditions of the *gessosa solfifera* (evaporite deposits developed extensively in the Mediterranean during Messinian time). In these areas the cosmopolitan fauna not only survived, but maintained a link with the outer oceans.

Today the sill of the Straits of Gibraltar stands as an effective barrier to the entry of the cosmopolitan ostracod fauna. The differentiation of the cosmopolitan Neogene benthonic foraminiferal fauna of the Tethys occurred in Middle Miocene time (*ca.* 12–14 my ago) as a result of the junction of Europe and Africa and the probable formation at that time of the Gibraltar Sill. Following the Pliocene transgression Atlantic benthonic foraminifers could again enter the newly formed Mediterranean Sea but in a manner substantially restricted in comparison to conditions which existed during pre-Middle Miocene (Berggren, 1969b, 1972; Berggren and Phillips, 1971). This suggests that the Pliocene development of the cosmopolitan ostracod fauna in the Mediterranean was due to reinvasion of these faunas from the Atlantic, but it is unlikely that a "relatively wide and deep gateway lay between Spain and Morocco" during the Pliocene as Benson and Sylvester-Bradley (1971) suggested. The Gibraltar Sill has probably existed in its present

form since the Middle-Late Miocene and formed an effective barrier to the Atlantic as sea-level fell during the Late Miocene initiating a period of excessive evaporation in the extensive western Tethys Sea (Ryan and others, 1970).

Paleogene

Rich molluscan faunas (pelecypod, gastropod, scaphopod and some hercoglossids) of Danian age occur in West Greenland. Echinoid, serpulid, coral (scleractinians, octocoraliids), arthropod (crustaceans: balanomorph cirripeds and caliannassids), fish (elasmobranchs, batoids, actinopterygiids), bryozoan and brachiopod faunas have also been reported as well as foraminifers and ostracods. Although taxonomic work is still in progress on these faunas, Rosenkrantz (1970) indicated that Early Danian fish faunas show great affinities to the Early-Middle Danian fauna of Dano-Scania, whereas the Late Danian fish fauna exhibits some affinities with younger Paleocene deposits of Europe and the Early Selandian fauna of Denmark. The Danian molluscan, benthonic foraminiferal and coral faunas of West Greenland exhibit marked affinities with contemporaneous faunas in the type area of the Danian of Denmark and southern Sweden. At the Mesozoic-Cenozoic transition, Greenland and Europe were essentially contiguous and transport along the broad shelves of the northern perimeter of the North Atlantic would have been relatively easy. Faunal elements of this time are found throughout northwestern Europe and as far south as the Crimean peninsula and even further eastwards within the Tethys province proper.

Hansen (1970) has recently made a significant contribution to early Cenozoic biogeography of the North Atlantic in describing Danian foraminifers from Nûgssuaq, West Greenland (lat. 70°N). The association of *"Globigerina" compressa* with *Subbotina pseudobulloides, S. triloculinoides* and *Globoconusa daubjergensis* suggests a Late Danian age for these sediments (Sonja Member of the Agatdal Formation). Fifty-seven benthonic foraminiferal species were recorded, 11 of which were described as new and 11 were not specifically determined. Of the remaining 38 forms, 18 occur in both Europe and North America, 13 only in Europe and 7 only in North America. Amphi-Atlantic benthonic foraminiferal distribution was common in the early Cenozoic and the occurrence of these Danian forms in West Greenland is the northernmost known to this writer in the North Atlantic.

The Upper Danian flora (which includes the deciduous conifer *Metasequoia occidentalis,* whose only known living representative is presently living in central China) and marine invertebrate fauna present a complementary climatic picture. The flora indicates a temperate, and the marine fauna a warm temperate, climate. The presence of large cucullaeids, comparable to species in the Aquia Formation of Maryland and a species in the Thanetian of the Paris Basin, would seem to point to warm conditions, because the living descendants of these forms currently live in the Indo-Pacific area. The nautiloids, cypraeids, and *Isognomon* point in the same direction, whereas the Astartidae, Cyprinidae and Aporrhaidae are currently restricted to colder areas.

The faunal and floral characteristics mentioned above would appear to reflect the marginal situation of West Greenland in the North Atlantic in the early Cenozoic. It can be expected that the northward expansion of the North Atlantic during the late Mesozoic-early Cenozoic would place this area in an intermediate position, in which faunal mixing (temperate and tropical forms) would be common.

A late Paleocene foraminiferal fauna was described from the Norwegian Basin (lat. 66°N) by Saito and others (1967). The benthonic faunal affinities are with the circum-Atlantic and Tethyan region (Caribbean region, Gulf and Atlantic Coastal Plains of North America, North Africa, western Europe– in particular with the Swedish-Danish Paleocene). Differences in faunal composition between the Norwegian Basin and Scandinavia were ascribed to different water depths: shelf depths in Scandinavia and an upper bathyal depth in the Norwegian Basin. Planktonic foraminifers (*Globigerina triloculinoides, G. triangularis, Globorotalia imitata, G. varianta*) were also recorded; they represent the northernmost known occurrence of Paleocene planktonic forms in the northeastern Atlantic and indicate the presence of a relatively deep marine seaway between Greenland and Norway in the Paleocene.

The evidence that a distinct boreal zoogeographic province evolved in the North Atlantic during the Paleogene comes from several groups. Although the Late Paleocene (post-Danian) faunas of western Europe contain various Tethyan elements, the appearance of several boreal molluscan genera indicates that a process of bioprovincialization was underway. Lower or Middle Eocene molluscan faunas of East Greenland (Ravn, 1904) contain *i. al., Cyprina, Astarte, Thyasina* and *Aporrhais*— typical boreal forms—and are characterized by an absence of characteristic warm-water forms. The appearance of cold-water fishes in the Lower Eocene of England (White, 1931), contemporaneously with warmer water molluscs, would appear to indicate the development of significant temperature stratification of the sea.

Mediterranean and Caribbean-Gulf Coast Paleocene benthonic foraminiferal faunas exhibit a marked similarity (Berggren, 1969; Berggren and Phillips, 1971). Brotzen (1948) was the first to point out the strong faunal affinities between the Paleocene of Denmark and southern Sweden and the Midway of the Gulf Coast (Plummer, 1926; Cushman, 1951). Haynes (1955, 1956, 1958) made a detailed study of the foraminifera of the Thanet sands of England and drew attention to similarities with the Danish-Swedish Paleocene. Pozaryska (1965) and Pozaryska and Szczechura (1968) have made comprehensive studies on the foraminifers of the Paleocene of Poland and Hofker (1966) has presented a synthesis of his many years of study on the Paleocene of Holland-Belgium and Denmark. Other basic studies dealing with the Paleocene-Lower Eocene stratigraphy of northwestern Europe include: Staesche and Hiltermann (1944), Holland; and Kaaschieter (1961), Belgium. A general synthesis of these various works yields the following points:

1. A strong similarity exists between Caribbean-Gulf and Atlantic Coastal Plain Midway faunas and southern Scandinavia and Polish Paleocene faunas.

2. A striking similarity is seen between Danian and lower Paleocene benthonic foraminiferal assemblages of Poland and Sweden (about 80% of the species occur in common according to Pozaryska, 1965, p. 44).

3. Boreal and meridional environments merge in Poland. The boreal influence is somewhat stronger at the base of the Paleocene; the meridional (non-Mediterranean) influence increases in the upper part of the sequence (fig. 9). In general, the boreal influence is the stronger of the two. About 15% of the species are subtropical.

4. Dominant forms in the Polish Paleocene are the Cibicididae, Nonionidae, Polymorphinidae, Discorbidae, and Anomalinidae, which suggests that the water depth was "not considerable" (Pozaryska and Szczechura, 1968, p. 14); a direct connection with the sea to the northwest existed at the time as indicated by the presence of planktonic foraminifers. The absence of *Palmula, Planularia,* and the scarcity of *Robulus* (*vel Lenticulina*), *Lamarckina rugulosa* and *Ceratobulimina tuberculata* in the

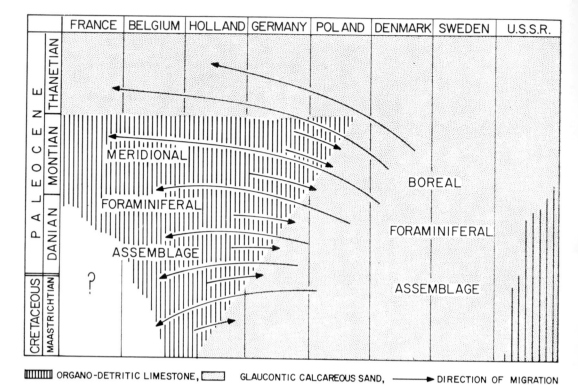

ORGANO-DETRITIC LIMESTONE, [   ] GLAUCONTIC CALCAREOUS SAND, ———▶ DIRECTION OF MIGRATION

FIG. 9.—Paleocene foraminiferal biogeography of Europe (after Pozaryska and Szczechura, 1968, fig. 4).

Pamiętowo boring, differentiates the fauna from central Poland and Scandinavian Paleocene foraminiferal faunas. The authors observed that "the majority of species present in the Pamiętowo boring, as well as in Central Poland, also occur not only in the Paleocene of Denmark and Sweden but in the Paleocene in Austria, England, European and Asiatic U.S.S.R., North and Central America (U.S.A.) and Australia (Pozaryska and Szczechura, 1968, p. 14).

5. These representative foraminiferal faunal elements, listed above as common to several areas, are less abundant in the Paleocene of Germany, southern Holland, and northeastern Belgium (Limburg Province), and are still less numerous in southwestern Belgium (Mons Basin) and France (Paris Basin). These latter areas, according to Pozaryska and Szczechura (1968, p. 14, 15) should be considered as a different province—a tropical or subtropical one, i.e., meridional (non-Mediterranean).

6. Some Paleocene boreal benthonic foraminifers occur in the Paleocene of the meridional (non-Mediterranean) province in western Europe (Limburg Province, Mons and Paris Basins). The number of boreal species decreases westward, indicating the possible presence of northward flowing currents from the Tethys

Sea bringing in warm water forms. In the meridional province the tests of benthonic foraminifers are smaller and less numerous than in the boreal region. In the Thanet beds of England the boreal fauna appears as an almost exclusive assemblage.

7. In the Early Paleocene of western Europe (southern Scandinavia, Poland and the European part of the Soviet Union) an extensive boreal basin developed which was strongly under the influence of the North Atlantic circulation (figs. 10, 11). The boreal basin was not an extensive sea but rather it was composed of several, elongated, narrow, intercontinental basins having the character of narrow straits between surrounding continents which supplied the sea with considerable amounts of terrigenous material. During the Late Danian (as used here) the climate was favorable in western Europe for meridional faunas—the result of warming of the climate around the western periphery of the boreal basin. As a result there was a two-directional faunal interchange from E→W and W→E. Pozaryski and Pozaryska (1960) had indicated that various warm water Cenozoic foraminiferal elements appeared slightly earlier in western Europe (in the Upper Maestrichtian of the Belgian-Dutch Limburg

area) than in eastern Europe due to more favorable ecologic conditions.

DSDP Leg 12 in the North Atlantic (Laughton and others, 1972) has yielded Paleocene foraminiferal faunas on Hatton-Rockall Bank and Lower Eocene faunas in the Labrador Sea (Orphan Knoll, 54°N Lat.) which have affinities with correlative North American and European faunas. A primitive operculinid was recorded from the Paleocene at the Rockall site—the most northerly location recorded to date for this genus.

Preliminary investigations on late Paleocene and Oligocene bryozoan (Cheetham and Håkonsson, 1972) and ostracod (Benson, 1972) assemblages from Rockall Bank have yielded valuable data on the Paleocene biogeography of the North Atlantic. Although the data of both groups suggests submergence of Rockall Bank during the Paleogene, the authors differ to some extent in their quantitative estimate of this submergence. The bryozoans suggest depths ranging from slightly less than 60 m during the Late Paleocene to slightly more than 200 m during the Oligocene, whereas the ostracod as-

semblages indicate depths of water ranging from 100–600 m (Late Paleocene) to depths in excess of 1000 m (Oligocene).

Of particular interest are the data which these two groups have yielded with regard to the progressive separation of Europe and North America and the development of a boreal faunal province. Close biogeographic connections with both Europe and North America are indicated by the Paleocene bryozoan fauna; the Oligocene faunas indicate stronger relationships with Europe than North America. Cheetham and Håkonsson (1972) suggest that the marked reduction of amphi-Atlantic species alone—from 31 percent in the Late Paleocene assemblages to 7 percent in the Oligocene ones—indicates that progressive isolation of the Rockall area may have had a bearing upon this reduction in trans-Atlantic faunal interchange. The Late Paleocene bryozoan assemblages indicate relatively warm-water conditions; the presence of *Porcillaria* is cited by Cheetham and Håkonsson (1972) as significant because modern representatives of this genus are tropical reef-associated forms not found at depths greater than about

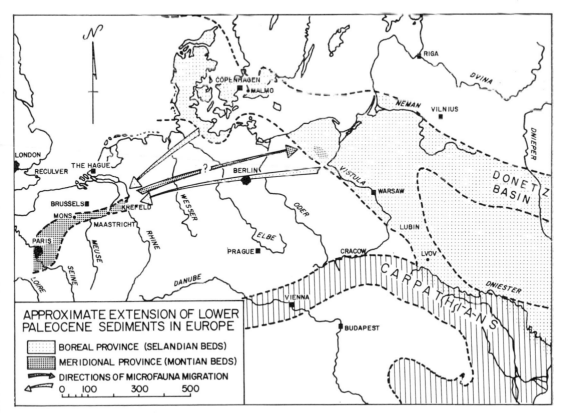

Fig. 10.—Approximate extension of lower Paleocene sediments in Europe
(after Pozaryska and Szczechura, 1968, fig. 3)

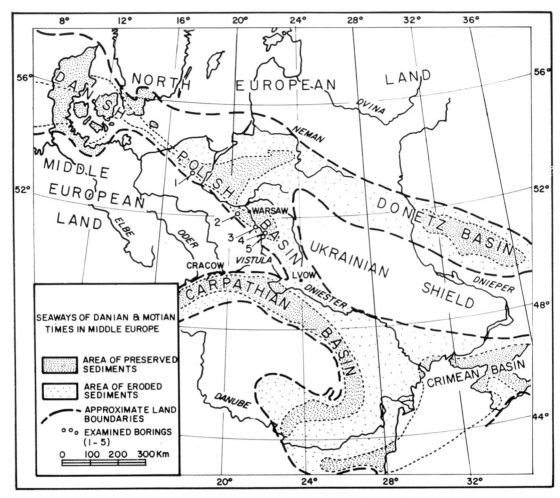

Fig. 11.—Seaways in Danian-Montian time in Central Europe
(after Pozaryska, 1965, text-plate 1).

60 m. The Oligocene bryozoan assemblages "conspicuously lack genera having modern representatives restricted to tropical and subtropical zones," although the authors point out that some of the species having numerical dominance, such as *Adeonellopsis* and *Floridina,* are at present most common in tropical to warm temperate regions. This would tend to suggest that the eastward trans-Atlantic flow of the Gulf Stream continued in the vicinity of the Rockall region throughout most of the Paleogene. Indeed, available evidence indicates that it has flowed across this region at least into the late Neogene (Pliocene). The presence of a typical deep-water (psychrospheric) ostracod assemblage in the late Eocene sediments of Rockall Bank is interesting in that it suggests that this area may have sunk to its present depth (a little over 1000 m) between Late Pa-

leocene and Oligocene time. The genera in the Oligocene are all blind, a condition which Benson (1972) indicates occurs below about 800 m.

In brief then, peri-Atlantic and Tethyan benthonic foraminiferal and invertebrate faunas exhibit a marked degree of similarity and indicate widespread dispersal during the early Paleogene, a pattern which continued into the middle part of the Neogene.

That significant changes occurred in the North Atlantic during the early Cenozoic (Paleocene-Eocene) can also be seen by distribution patterns in the planktonic foraminifers. During Late Cretaceous (Maestrichtian) time tropical-subtropical water forms occurred in New Jersey (Olsson, 1960, 1964; Davids, 1966) and even as far north as the Labrador Sea (Orphan Knoll, 56°N Lat.) where *Globotruncanella mayaroensis, G. havanensis, Globotruncana contusa, G.*

stuarti, G. gansseri, i. al., were found by Leg 12 of the DSDP. Bartlett and Smith (1971) report similar faunal associations from the Grand Banks of Newfoundland. Similar faunas occur in northwestern Europe; in Holland (Hofker, 1966) and as far north as southern Scandinavia (Troelsen, 1955; Berggren, 1962).

In the Paleocene there is a marked change in the planktonic foraminiferal fauna following the extinction of the Cretaceous forms. In the Danian planktonic foraminiferal diversity is low (3–4 species in Lower Danian strata) but these faunas are essentially cosmopolitan. By Late Danian time some differentiation of faunas can be seen with such forms as *Morozovella uncinata, Subbotina praecursoria* (=*trinidadensis*) being essentially restricted to low latitudes and *Planorotalites compressa* extending to high latitudes (Berggren, 1971). Further diversification of faunas is seen in post-Danian Paleocene faunas; keeled morozovellids in the Atlantic Coastal Plain of New Jersey are similar to those from the Gulf Coastal region (Olsson, 1960, 1970a,b). By Early Eocene time a marked differentiation had occurred within planktonic foraminiferal faunas whereby keeled morozovellids and acarininids had established themselves as the dominant elements in low latitudes and high latitudes, respectively.

In an interesting study of Paleocene planktonic foraminiferal diversity patterns Olsson (1970a) has made the following observations:

1. The low diversity in the Paleocene which stands in marked contrast to the large and varied fauna at the top of the Cretaceous (Maestrichtian) has been observed throughout the Atlantic Province and indicates a low biomass in the Danian (see also Berggren, 1971).

2. Jaccard matching coefficients (Olsson, 1970a, Fig. 4, p. 594) show a remarkable faunal similarity over 30° latitudinal span (New Jersey to Trinidad) in the lower 3 zones of the Paleocene (*i.e.,* Danian time).

3. In Zone 4 (*angulata* Zone) and Zone 5 (*pusilla* Zone) the matching coefficient curve approaches 50%, which suggests that substantial faunal differentiation had occurred along latitudinal lines so that water masses were more clearly defined biologically. In terms of Berggren's Cenozoic time-scale (1972) this would be about 60 million years ago, or about the time of initial rifting along the Reykjanes Ridge and deepening and extension of the eastern North Atlantic basin into the Arctic region; see further discussion below.

4. There is a reduction in keeled morozovellids and an increase in acarininids at this time. The uniformity of early Paleocene faunas changed by replacement and speciation to more provincial faunas reflecting temperature (or climatic) belts.

5. Preferential coiling modes in *Morozovella acuta* were observed, indicating that a sudden southward shift of sinistral populations into low latitudes must have occurred. A similar shift at the base of the *Planorotalites pseudomenardii* Zone is also seen in the *Morozovella angulata-aequa* lineage; in the latter case dextrally coiled populations shifted into lower latitudes.

6. Middle-Late Paleocene changes in coiling patterns appear to have occurred earlier in high latitudes, later in low latitudes and may be a reflection of lowered temperatures (warmer→ cooler climate). This is in accord with evidence of a Paleocene-Eocene fauna in Spitsbergen indicating a winter surface temperature of 5°–8°C (Durham, 1952); and Chaney (1940, 1964) and Dorf (1955, 1964) have described terrestrial cold temperate Eocene floras from areas on the periphery of the Arctic Ocean.

In general, a broad patern of distribution in the North Atlantic can be seen: in the Cretaceous globotruncanids occur on both sides of the Atlantic to about 55°N; in the Early Cenozoic keeled morozovellids occur on the western side of the Atlantic to at least 54°N (Labrador Sea), whereas in Europe they occur to about 45°N, and only rarely north of that.

Kurtén (1967, p. 4) has observed that mammalian geography indicates that a Europe-North America land bridge "was in function up to and including the Early Eocene, then foundered." The remaining part of Laurasia-Eurasia remained a single continental block but was longitudinally divided into a European and an Asiatic part by an internal seaway—the Turgai Straits—which extended from the Arctic to the Tethys, east of the Urals. This marine seaway formed an effective barrier between land faunas of Europe and Asia up to the Middle Eocene when the sea retreated from this region.

During the Early Eocene the similarity between European and North American mammalian faunas is so great that Simpson (1947) referred to the two continents as "zoogeographically essentially a single region." Kurtén (1967) noted that numerous genera are identical: *Phenacodus, Coryphodon, Hyracotherium, Esthoryx, Ectogonus, Paramys, Dissacus, Pachyaena, Palaeonictis,* and that some species are probably identical. He further observed that all forms known to be common to Europe and North America are absent in the Gashato assemblage, near the Bering Land Bridge in eastern Asia, so that migration across the latter is ruled out. The evidence points to a North

Atlantic route, although recent geophysical studies (Pitman and Talwani, 1972) suggest that it may have been via Spitsbergen and the Arctic region and not via a trans-Atlantic "Thulean" land bridge extending northwestwards from present day England to Greenland and thence to North America as thought by Kurtén (1967, Fig. 1: an Eocene paleogeographic reconstruction after Schaffer). McKenna (1971, 1972) has referred to this trans-Atlantic migration route as the "De Geer route" after the De Geer line (=Spitsbergen Fracture Zone, a right-lateral ridge-ridge transform fault) where the northern Greenland Sea terminated against the transform fault zone and the exposed Barents Shelf.

Subsequent migration between North America and Eurasia occurred via the Bering Land Bridge (Middle-Late Eocene). By this time Greenland and Scandinavia were separated by oceanic depths and Spitsbergen had separated and rotated from its connection with Eurasia. In terms of mammalian biogeography there was no unified Paleoarctic zoogeographic region in the Paleocene and Early Eocene. The Holarctic region of the present day was divided into three separate regions: European, Asiatic and Nearctic.

The paleogeography of the London Clay Sea (early Eocene time) has ben discussed in detail by Davis and Elliott (1957). The London Clay is a lithologic unit of widespread distribution in northwestern Europe (London-Hampshire Basins of southeastern England, Denmark, NW Germany, Holland and Belgium). It transgressed from an area of continuous sedimentation in the Danish-NW German region southwards over the Hampshire Basin to a Tethyan connection over the English Channel and then retreated over SE England. Tropical floras, whose modern analogs are to be found in the Malayan peninsula, are considered to have grown on the SW coasts of England during the Early Eocene.

The molluscan fauna is the most common invertebrate group represented in the sediments of the London Clay. Over 150 genera have been recorded in the British London Clay alone. Eighty of them are known in the Paleocene of Denmark, Belgium, France (the so-called northern forms of Davies, 1934–1935). Twenty-six genera occur in both Tethyan and northern regions. About 20 or more exclusively Tethyan genera are present, but northern forms outnumber strictly Tethyan forms. Among them are such cool water forms as *Cyprina, Astarte, Pholadomya, Thyasira* (*Axinus*), and *Aporrhais*.

Aside from diatoms, the fossil flora is represented mostly by dicotyledons, with a few palms and conifers. Reid and Chandler (1933), Chandler (1954) and Edwards (1936, 1955) studied the London Clay flora and essentially agreed that the affinities of the flora are overwhelmingly with modern tropical floras of the Indo-Malayan area. Seventy-three percent of living genera to which London Clay genera were ascribed occur in that region. They concluded that the London Clay flora was living at its northernmost limits, and cited evidence of stunting.

Conclusions about the climate of the time may be summarized as follows:

1. Uniform climate.

2. Suitable balance between precipitation and evaporation.

3. Suitable seasonable distribution of rainfall; frostless winters.

4. Mean annual temperature of 70° (~21°C).

This climate may well have been the result of the ameliorating effect of warm currents coming from the Tethys Sea, along whose shores the flora migrated. These climatic conditions should be viewed in the light of evidence of winter surface temperatures of 5°–8°C near Spitsbergen (Durham, 1952). The Early Eocene was a time when the Arctic province was being established by the opening of the North Atlantic between Greenland and Scandinavia.

The distribution of a Tethyan molluscan fauna (*Velates perversus* group) in the Gulf Coast-Caribbean region and California has been summarized by Palmer (1967). Various molluscan genera with widespread occurrence in the Tethys and Western Hemisphere (Gulf Coast, West Indies, Caribbean region) include, *i. al., Velates, Gisortia, Terebellum, Bellatara, Eovasum, Vusella* and *Carolia*.

Eocene, Oligocene and Lower Miocene benthonic faunas continue to exhibit a marked degree of similarity between the Mediterranean and Caribbean-Gulf Coast regions (Berggren, 1969a; Berggren and Phillips, 1971). Strong similarities between the Eocene benthonic foraminiferal faunas of coastal Ecuador and the Gulf Coast-Caribbean region were demonstrated by Hofker (1956). Numerous species were said to be identical or closely related in the following groups: bolivinids, buliminids, uvigerinids, lagenids (including stilostomellids, plectofrondiculariids, lenticulinids), pleurostomellids, parrellids (including osangularids and planulinids), anomalinids, valvulinerids, alabaminids (gyroidinids), gavelinellids (Hofker, 1956, p. 948, included "*Cibicides perlucidus*" in *Gavelinopsis*) and eponidids. Similarly, marked faunal affinities were shown to have existed between

Oligocene faunas of Ecuador and the Gulf Coast-Caribbean region (Hofker, 1968). Most of the forms (or closely related ones) occur in the European-Tethyan Oligocene as well. Caribbean Oligocene foraminiferal faunas exhibit certain affinities with those described by Batjes (1958) from Belgium and northern Germany. Faunal interchange between the Atlantic and Pacific took place through the Balboa Straits (Isthmus of Panama) which remained open until Early Pliocene.

Bartlett (1968) has discussed the affinities between mid-Tertiary planktonic and benthonic foraminiferal faunas of the continental slope of Nova Scotia and the Caribbean region. Leg 12 of the DSDP recovered numerous mid-Tertiary benthonic foraminifers from the Rockall Bank region and Bay of Biscay, which were originally described from the Caribbean region.

The planktonic foraminifers underwent relatively rapid evolution and diversification during the Late Paleocene and Early Eocene, but experienced a gradual but significant decline during Middle-Late Eocene (Berggren, 1969c). Distinct latitudinal zonation of planktonic foraminifers is seen in the Eocene, keeled morozovellids, *Hantkenina* and *Globigerapsis* characterizing the low latitude tropical regions and the group of *Acarinina-Truncorotaloides* and *Pseudohastigerina*, though present in low latitudes, extending to about 55°N. The continued presence of a northward flowing warm current —"the Gulf Stream"—is seen by the presence of keeled morozovellids of Early Eocene age (*ca.* 53 my ago) in a grab sample from 1675 m at a point south of Cape Cod (Gibson, 1965) and in the Labrador Sea (Orphan Knoll) at about lat. 54°N (Laughton and others, 1972). Oligocene planktonic foraminiferal faunas consist primarily of morphologically conservative groups (globigerinids, globigerinitids). The decrease in diversity in the planktonic foraminiferal fauna during the Late Eocene-Oligocene exhibits a strong parallelism with the decrease in temperature shown by Devereux (1967) during that time and this writer has suggested (Berggren, 1969c) that temperature was probably one of the main factors controlling the rates of evolution of Cenozoic planktonic foraminifers.

Oligocene planktonic foraminiferal faunas of northwestern Europe exhibit distinctly boreal characteristics (Hofker, 1966; Berggren, 1969b). In the North Atlantic between 50° and 60°N lat. planktonic faunas exhibit extremely low diversity, and, in some instances, consist essentially of only one or two species, *Globigerinita dissimilis* and *G. unicava* (Laughton

and others, 1972). Tropical Oligocene assemblages have been described from East Africa (Tanzania) by Blow and Banner (in Eames and others, 1962; Blow, 1969). Faunas exhibiting intermediate characteristics between tropical and boreal regions occur in the Blake Plateau core holes drilled during the first part of the JOIDES program (Bunce and others, 1966).

Neogene

The Neogene is characterized by a gradual decrease in temperature, particularly since the Middle Miocene (Devereaux, 1967). Foraminiferal biogeography in the North Atlantic was affected by this and other factors. Among the main events which occurred are the following:

1. The junction of Eurasia and Africa-Arabia closed off the eastern and western Tethys and isolated Indo-Pacific and Atlantic faunas. This occurred during Burdigalian time, about 18 million years ago (van Couvering, 1972; Berggren, 1972).

2. The junction of Europe (Spain) and Africa (Morocco) probably occurred about 14–15 million years ago. Circulation between the Atlantic and western Tethys Sea was gradually inhibited and during the Late Miocene (approximately 5–7 my ago) there is evidence of evaporation of the western Tethys concomitant with a drop of sea-level of several thousand feet (Ryan and others, 1970). During the Middle and Late Miocene faunal interchange between the western Tethys and Atlantic Ocean was severely inhibited and few benthonic forms are found in common between the western Tethys and the Caribbean-Gulf Coast region (Berggren, 1969b; Berggren and Phillips, 1971). Faunal interchange was once again established following the basal Pliocene transgression about 5–6 my ago (Ryan and others, 1973).

3. The uplift of the Isthmus of Panama cut off the marine connection between the Atlantic and Pacific Ocean, isolated the Pacific and West Indian faunas and allowed a two-way migration of terrestrial mammals between North and South America. This event has been generally ascribed to the Late Miocene (based upon inaccurate correlation by vertebrate paleontologists with European stages). It can now be dated relatively precisely as Early Pliocene, between 3.5–4 million years ago (Kaneps, 1970).

4. The initiation of glaciation in the North Atlantic occurred about 3 million years ago (Laughton and others, 1972; Berggren, 1972). Warm currents which had been flowing into the Labrador Sea since the Early Cretaceous,

were abruptly displaced southwards by the cold Labrador Current. Since the mid-Pliocene the history of circulation in the North Atlantic has been one of latitudinal migration of the polar front in a response to glacial/interglacial fluctuations (Ruddiman, 1969; McIntyre, Ruddiman and Jantzen, 1971). Planktonic foraminiferal diversity in the North Atlantic has decreased during the Neogene. Faunal similarities are seen with New Zealand, particularly in the ability to use the *Globorotalia miozea-conoidea-sphericomiozea-puncticulata* group to zone the Middle Miocene-Lower Pliocene interval of the North Atlantic. During the Pliocene, diversity was further reduced and in the Late Pliocene; *Globigerina pachyderma* established itself as the dominant, and, at times, exclusive element in North Atlantic planktonic foraminiferal faunas. *Globigerina bulloides* and *Globorotalia inflata* are commonly associated with *G. pachyderma* during relatively milder intervals (interglacials) at about 60°N lat.

That biogeographic relationships during the Miocene along the east coast of North America may have varied somewhat from present day conditions has been illustrated by Gibson (1967) who made a study of the phosphatic Pungo River Formation and the overlying Yorktown Formation in eastern North Carolina. The Pungo River Formation was correlated with the *Globigerinatella insueta* Zone of Burdigalian age, late Early Miocene. The Yorktown Formation is of early Late Miocene age. Gibson reached the following conclusions:

1. Cool-temperate water conditions existed in this area during the deposition of the Pungo River sediments, indicating that circulation patterns of oceanic currents and the resultant faunal provinces were not the same as at present and later in the Miocene.

2. Cool-temperate conditions during lower Yorktown deposition (early Late Miocene, Tortonian) changed to warm-temperate to subtropical in later Yorktown time. Circulation patterns reached their present state during later Yorktown deposition.

Gibson (1967) noted that the presence of the same species of benthonic foraminifers and molluscs in eastern North Carolina, Maryland and farther north in the Atlantic Coastal Plain indicates that marine faunal provinces did not have their present geographic boundaries in the Early Miocene. At present a marked marine faunal boundary occurs in the vicinity of Cape Hatteras in the central North Carolina coast. Cape Hatteras is the northern limit of numerous living invertebrate species having subtropical distribution and the southern limit of many cool-temperate species. The lack of a faunal gradient in North Carolina in the Early Miocene, together with cool water fauna, indicates that the southern boundary of the temperate province must have been further south than at present. This observation stands in marked contrast to the general situation of a gradual southward displacement and elimination of warm-water planktonic foraminiferal faunal elements in the North Atlantic observed by this writer.

Gibson (1967) also observed that mixing of planktonic faunas (5–10% = subtropical forms) suggests that despite cool-temperate bottom and inshore currents, a warm current, "possibly the Gulf Stream," must have been located somewhere off the North Carolina coast during the time of deposition of the Pungo River sediments (late Early Miocene), but not as close to the coast as at present. The Calvert Formation (Maryland-Virginia) contains a lower percentage (1%) of warm-water species and suggests a gradient away from the warm current to the N-NW; reflecting the same pattern as found at present off the North Carolina coast northward to Maryland. Gibson (1967) suggested that southward flowing cool-temperate currents may have flowed further south inshore from the Gulf Stream during Early and Middle Miocene time than at present.

Savage (1967), van Couvering (1972) and van Couvering and Miller (1971) have discussed the migration of North African mammalian faunas into Europe during the Early Miocene (Burdigalian). This would be about 18 million years ago and provides an estimate of the time at which the junction of Eurasia and Africa separated the Tethys Sea into two distinct parts. From this time onwards the Indo-Pacific faunas were isolated from western Mediterranean and Atlantic faunas. Although there may have been migration between North and South America in the Early Cenozoic, the Atlantic and the Pacific were connected by marine straits which linked the marine faunas of the Caribbean (and indeed the Atlantic and Tethyan faunas in general) with those of the west coast of South America and to some extent with those of the west coast of North America. This link was severed by the emergence of Panama, which has been believed by most investigators to have occurred during late Miocene-Pliocene time (over 10 million years ago). This belief has been based on incorrect correlation between invertebrate faunas of Central America with those of the type sections of Europe as well as inaccurate correlations between vertebrate and invertebrate faunas in terms of the time-stratigraphic scale established in Western Europe. Planktonic foraminiferal evidence (the presence of *Globorotalia miocenica* in the Atlantic and its absence in the Pacific and the presence of *G. multicamerata* in both oceans and the interruption of the evolution of the genus *Pulleniatina* in the Atlantic Ocean) suggests that the uplift of Panama, which eliminated the marine connections between the Atlantic and the Pacific occurred as late as Early Pliocene, about 3.5–4 million years ago (Kaneps, 1970).

Continued cooling of the earth resulted in stronger latitudinal temperature gradients. This process was accelerated by the initiation of glaciation in the Northern Hemisphere about 3 million years ago. At that time the present polar biogeographic realm evolved and the present day latitudinally controlled faunal provincialization was established (Bé, 1959, 1960b).

The biogeographic history of the Atlantic Ocean during the past 3 million years has been essentially one of fluctuating faunal province boundaries in response to glacial/non-glacial conditions. This process was accelerated about a million years ago as a result of increased severity of climatic cooling. The Holocene is a typical interglacial interval; one of many which have punctuated the last million years. It represents an insignificant amount of time in comparison with the last 200 million years of earth history which we have considered above.

PALEOTEMPERATURES

A comprehensive discussion of paleoclimatology would involve consideration of such diverse topics as paleo-wind directions, paleosoils, distribution of evaporites, corals, coals, glaciated bed rock, and so forth. We present here a brief discussion of one aspect of paleoclimatology, namely, paleotemperature as it is reflected in the distribution of Mesozoic and Cenozoic floras and faunas in the Atlantic region.

During the Mesozoic large areas of the world which are today above sea-level were submerged beneath relatively shallow seas. With the low-relief continental masses closer together and essentially distributed along meridional lines, only weak north-south thermal gradients were developed. As a result climate was rather uniform over a wide latitudinal range and the tropical region extended much further north and south of the paleoequator than it does today (see figs. 12–20). Polar waters were, concomitantly, warmer; Emiliani (1961b) estimated Arctic mean temperatures of 14°C during the Cretaceous whereas the present ice-covered Arctic mean is − 1.5 to − 1.8°C.

Paleotemperature studies on the Upper Cretaceous of western Europe (Lowenstam and Epstein, 1954; Bowen, 1961b) indicate a high in late Albian (24°C), a low (16°C) in the Cenomanian followed by a gradual increase until the Conician-Santonian (about 20°C), followed by a decline to about 16° in the early Maestrichtian. These values indicate tropical-subtropical surface marine temperatures for western Europe during late Cretaceous time. Thermal gradients less than half of the present values in the late Cretaceous (Douglas and Sliter, 1966) would suggest broadly distributed faunal patterns in the late Mesozoic. This is supported by a broad spectrum of data from various fossil groups: the essentially identical geographic distribution of Cretaceous rudistids in Europe between lat. 30° and 50°N and in the Caribbean between lat. 5° and 30°N (Dacque, 1915, and the "larger" foraminifers (Maync, 1961; Dilley, 1971); the development of Tethyan dictyonine Hexactinellida (siliceous sponges) in the late Cretaceous of northern Europe (Reid, 1967); and the relatively homogenous latitudinal distribution of late Cretaceous planktonic foraminifers (Davids, 1966; Douglas and Sliter, 1966). Douglas and Sliter (1966) have pointed out that at present no exclusively "Boreal" planktonic foraminiferal genera have been recognized and only a few species are restricted to that area and that this lack of restriction is unlike that seen in the ammonites and baculitids. They suggest that planktonic foraminifers were largely restricted to tropical waters of the Tethys during the late Mesozoic and that the few inhabitants of higher latitudes in Late Cretaceous time were eurythermal cosmopolitans (the characteristic difference between the Tethyan and "boreal" regions was at the specific level rather than generic and involved relative abundances). The northern regions are characterized by the absence of warm water faunas rather than by endemic temperate elements. The gradual replacement northwards of *Rotalipora* by *Hedbergella* in shallower waters in early Late Cretaceous and of *Globotruncana* by *Hedbergella* in the Senonian is broadly analogous to the present day relationship between *Globorotalia* and *Globigerina*.

The available evidence indicates that the Mesozoic was a time of relatively uniform warm climates with only moderate latitudinal variation. There is no definite evidence of glaciation during the Mesozoic and this, in addition to various other lines of evidence discussed elsewhere in this paper, suggest that it is unlikely that a Boreal Faunal Province (as the term is applied in modern biogeography) developed in the Atlantic and/or adjacent areas (cf. Schwarzbach, 1963; Hallam, 1967).

The history of the Cenozoic has been one of continental uplift (mountain building which produced the Rockies, Andes, Alps, and Himalayas). The increased amount of surface relief led to a gradual climatic cooling due to the lessened amount of absorbed radiation by dry land (albedo effect). Concomitant with this was the effect of the Arctic-Atlantic connection in the early Cenozoic and the establishment of a stronger equatorial-polar thermal gradient. This thermal gradient developed as the continents moved northwards (and the paleolatitudes were displaced southwards) with the result that distinct latitudinal climatic belts were established.

Emiliani (1956) has shown that a gradual decline in surface water temperature occurred in the Atlantic Ocean during the Cenozoic. During the early Cenozoic tropical conditions existed as far north as southern England during the Early Eocene (Davis and Elliott, 1957), with mean annual temperatures of about 21°C. The marine molluscan faunas of the Paris Basin indicate subtropical conditions in that area during the Middle Eocene. Barghoorn (1966) has shown that floral evidence indicates cooling in the Northern Hemisphere beginning in the Late Eocene and culminating in the Pleistocene.

Chaney (1940) discussed fossil floras of the Northern Hemisphere and concluded that the geographic position of the continents has remained constant throughout the Tertiary and that subtropical floras extended much further north during the early Tertiary than at present. He concluded that early Tertiary climatic zones were similar to those of today but that their boundaries were more poleward.

Durham (1950, 1952) has discussed the Tertiary marine paleoclimatic history of the Pacific coast of the United States and the Eocene marine climates of the world. His interpretations were made within a framework of static continental-oceanic relationships; correcting for continental drift, his data indicate that the Eocene marine tropical zone extended to about lat. 50°N on the Pacific Coast (Eocene paleolatitude of about lat. 45°N) and to about lat. 60°N on the west coast of Europe (Eocene paleolatitude of about lat. 50° N) (see fig. 16). Since that time the tropical zone has retreated southwards during the mid-late Cenozoic as equatorial-polar temperature gradients increased. Similar conclusions had been expressed by Chaney (1940) and Dorf (1955) based on Cenozoic flora and by Colbert (in Shapley and others, 1953) based on terrestrial vertebrates.

Paleotemperature investigations indicate that subtropical-tropical conditions existed on the northern shores of the Tethys (in south-central and southwestern Europe). Estimates of 22°–25°C were made for the Oligocene Liguro-Piemontais region (southwestern part of northern Italy) based upon paleobotanical studies which support comparison with the present day flora of Java and Sumatra (cited in Lorenz, 1969, p. 813). Marine microfaunas and macrofaunas of warm water affinities corresponding to those of present day tropical reef conditions in the Pacific (Schwarzbach, 1966, p. 168) indicate marine paleotemperatures of about 18°C for Oligocene sediments near Cologne which would be several degrees cooler than those of the Liguro-Piemontais region. Comparable values were obtained by Allegre, Boulanger and Javoy (1963) by paleotemperature measurements of about 23°C on *Nummulites intermedius* in the Stampian of the Aquitaine Basin. Tropical climatic conditions for the Stampian of Duance and the Aquitanian of Bresse were also deduced by Sittler and Millot (1965) based on paleobotanical studies (pollen).

Axelrod and Bailey (1969, p. 168) indicated that the peak of the Miocene warming trend in several areas (Devereux, 1967) coincided with the time of closing of the Tethys (ca. 16–18 my ago, Berggren, 1972) and that this may have brought a sufficient increase in warmth and equability to the western side of the oceans to significantly offset the near-shore climate temporarily. The cooler eastern sides of the oceanic basins would be less affected. However, closure of the Tethys seaway would have reinforced the Gulf Stream gyre and allowed it to develop as a self-contained system. A natural consequence of this may have been the development of the North Atlantic Current which traverses the North Atlantic diagonally and warms the west coast of Europe and Norway. Alternatively, warm currents issuing from the restricted Tethyan Sea may have flowed northwards along the coast of Europe. The development of either or both of these currents in the North Atlantic might be expected to have had an ameliorating effect on the climate of western Europe about 15–20 my ago. We know of no definitive evidence concerning this point, other than the general evidence of a continued, gradual cooling of marine, near-shore waters during the middle-late Cenozoic (Strauch, 1958).

Tertiary floras indicate that there has been a

general trend toward lowered annual temperatures and increasing ranges (and extremes) of temperature in the western United States and that changes were more pronounced in interior than in coastal regions (Axelrod and Bailey, 1969). Data are as yet inconclusive in regards to major worldwide fluctuations in temperature during the Tertiary.

Sorgenfrei (1958) studied molluscan faunas of southern Jutland and estimated that temperatures in the North Sea during the Miocene were some 5°C higher than today (winter ca. 6°C; summer ca. 16°C). He interpreted the range to have been similar to today. This invites comparison with present day circulation off Monaco and indicates a southward displacement of isotherms of about 20°C since the Miocene. Baden-Powell (1955) utilized molluscan faunas to interpret late Cenozoic climates. He suggested Early Pleistocene isotherms similar to those now found south of Newfoundland—and that the isotherms seem to have been closer together along the European coast than at present. During Early Pleistocene time he indicates that temperatures at the latitude of southern Iceland were equivalent to those of the present northern coast of Ireland and that conditions now found on the Senegalese coast occurred in the Biscay area.

Spaink (1958), from an analysis of Dutch Fen Sea Quaternary sediments, concluded that temperatures of the last Interglacial match those of the Bay of Biscay today. Strauch (1968, p. 215, 216) indicated that this mean value of 14°–15°C may be high and that a temperature 3°–4°C above that of the present, rather than his figure of 4°–5°C, is probably adequate in explaining the observed differences.

Strauch (1968) investigated the geographic and stratigraphic distribution of the mussel species *Hiatella arctica* (Linné) (syn. *Saxicava arctica*), a worldwide boreal-arctic, predominantly shallow-water form which lives to a depth of 2,000 m. Using the observation that shell size bears an inverse relationship to water temperature (*i.e.* larger forms occur in colder waters) he estimated paleotemperatures for the central Europe region during the Cenozoic (table 1).

Strauch (1968, p. 226) noted that the Oligocene values are somewhat high in comparison with data published on Oligocene sea-temperatures, but they are in agreement with continental climate estimates for the same time by Schwarzbach 1952, 1961). It should be recalled that during Late Eocene and Early Oligocene time warm currents from the Tethys region were still bringing *Nummulites* into the northern European Belgian, North German and Hampshire Basins.

TABLE 1.—CENOZOIC PALEOTEMPERATURES FOR CENTRAL EUROPE ESTIMATED BY STRAUCH (1968)

Geological time	Winter (°C)	Summer (°C)	Yearly average temperature (°C)
Middle Eocene	26.0	28.0	27.0
Late Oligocene	20.5	27.0	23.5
Miocene ca.	17.0	27.0	22.0
Pliocene	13.5	22.0	17.5
Waltonian	12.0	21.0	16.5
Newbournian	8.0	19.0	13.5
Butleyan	5.0	17.5	11.0
Eem-Interglacial ca.	10.0	20.0	15.0
Late Würm	−1.0	11.0	5.0
Recent (Dogger Bank)	6.0	16.0	11.0

The Cenozoic has been characterized by gradual cooling which probably began in the Late Eocene and Oligocene, accelerated in the Miocene and culminated in the Pliocene-Pleistocene. The relatively warm climate of Europe during the Paleogene was due to the continued, if somewhat reduced, presence of the extensive Tethys Sea which connected with the Pacific Ocean in the west. The gradual restriction of this seaway in the Miocene, concomitant with the rise of the Alpine mountain chain and the general cooling of the earth, resulted in a distinct climatic zonation in Europe as well as in the marine environment. In the Atlantic a marked temperature gradient from equator to pole has resulted in a significant latitudinal provincialization of faunas beginning in the early Cenozoic (Paleogene) and becoming well-established by mid-late Cenozoic (Neogene).

Comparison of Figures 12–20 show that the position of the pole (and, concomitantly, the disposition of the paleolatitudes) has changed over the past 200 million years. However, the data indicate that this relative movement has not been great. During the past 150 my the southern tip of Greenland appears to have moved about 15°, from about 45°N to its present position at about 60°N, but during the Mesozoic and early Cenozoic the fauna and flora of Greenland indicate subtropical conditions in the area. The same is true of the Labrador Sea and western Europe. It would appear that relative latitudinal position has played a subsidiary role in the paleoclimatic history of the Atlantic. It has been the relative relationship between land mass and ocean which has influenced the flow of surface and deep currents and has played the dominant role in the modification of climate through time.

CIRCULATION OF THE ATLANTIC OCEAN

Introduction

Just as the present circulation pattern of the surface and deep waters controls modern patterns of biogeography, patterns of paleo-circulation control patterns of paleobiogeography. In order to establish the bases for inferring patterns of paleocirculation it is useful to review the character of modern water masses and their current patterns and then to discuss the development of circulation for each of the time periods indicated on the maps of Figs. 12 through 20.

The driving power for circulation is drawn ultimately from the sun. The differential heating of air masses creates wind, driving the vigorous surface currents. Currents in the deep sea, on the other hand, are driven by the earth's gravitational pull on water masses of differing density. Water density increases by evaporation which cools the water and increases the concentration of salts. Cooling also results from the radiation loss of sensible heat to an overlying cold air mass. The cold deep and bottom waters of the ocean mainly originate in the polar regions where winter freezing leads to the formation of dense, cold waters which sink and move steadily, towards lower latitudes.

The deep waters formed in the south are denser than the northern waters; the southern waters flow as a wedge beneath the northern ones, reaching far into the Northern Hemisphere. These abyssal waters, which collectively constitute the "cold water sphere" ($< 4°C$), are capped by a thin protective blanket of the solar-heated "warm water sphere" which extends throughout temperate latitudes. However, within the limits of the polar front a warm surface layer is lacking and the cold water sphere outcrops at the surface.

The North Atlantic is unique in that it is the warmest and saltiest of the world's oceans and its deep waters, particularly along the continental margin, are competent to move fine grained sediment and often flow at comparatively high velocities (Heezen and others, 1966; Hollister and Heezen, 1972). In order to understand global patterns of upwelling and productivity and in order to predict the distribution of deep benthic communities and the migration of bathyal and abyssal organisms it is necessary to understand the circulation of the main water masses of the cold-water sphere in the Atlantic and the wind-driven circulation of the warm water sphere that governs the geographic patterns of organisms that live near the sea surface.

Antarctic Bottom Water

This distinctive water of the deep-sea floor apparently originates on the Antarctic continental shelf and slope (Brennecke, 1921; Mosby, 1934). The relatively heavy water, generated by the freezing of sea-ice, sinks by thermohaline convection to the floor of the Southern Ocean and from there it spreads along the bottom of the Atlantic, Indian, and Pacific Oceans, moving generally eastwards and northwards with highest velocities concentrated along the western sides of the basins. In the South Atlantic the Antarctic Bottom Current flows along the continental rise of Brazil and Argentina with near-bottom velocities of about 15 cm/sec (Wüst, 1955, 1957).

After crossing the equator (where the horizontal component of the Coriolis force is zero) Antarctic Bottom Water is deflected towards the right against the western flank of the Mid-Atlantic Ridge. The invasion of the cold Antarctic Bottom Water into the western basin of the North Atlantic takes place between the continental rise of Brazil and the Mid-Atlantic Ridge. The cold water then works its way along the western slope of the Mid-Atlantic Ridge becoming somewhat warmer as it goes, and eventually appears as a ring of cool (potential temp. less than $1.8°C$) water surrounding the Bermuda Rise (Wüst and Defant, 1936; Worthington and Wright, 1970).

As the last traces of the Antarctic Bottom water flow across the ocean basin floor on the western margin of the Bermuda Rise it apparently turns to the west (between 40 and 45°N) and then south along the continental margin of eastern North America where it mixes with the southwesterly-flowing North Atlantic Deep Water flowing as the Western Boundary Current. This water mass occupies the deepest portions of the basins, effects the distribution and physiography of the bottom sediment (Heezen and Hollister, 1964; Hollister and Heezen, 1972) and is the principal agent aerating the abyss; however, it does not directly effect patterns of biogeography except in the immediate circum-Antarctic region near its source, where its nutrient rich water is found at the surface.

Norwegian Sea Overflow Water

This cold North Atlantic water mass is a mixture of Iceland-Scotland Overflow Water and Denmark Strait Overflow Water. This Arctic Bottom Water with temperatures of less than $0°C$ flows from the Norwegian Sea through gaps in the submarine ridge linking

Greenland, Iceland and Scotland and leaks into the Atlantic. Approximately $2 \times 10^6 m^3/sec$ enters the Atlantic where it picks up another $3 \times 10^6 m^3/sec$ of North Atlantic Water to become a well-developed contour-following deep current south of Iceland (Worthington, 1971).

Direct current measurements (Steele and others, 1962) in this water, made along the continental slope south of Iceland, indicate near-bottom velocities as high as 23 cm/sec (at 1300 m). These currents which transport and deposit sediment along bathymetric contours along the flanks of Rockall Plateau and then along the eastern side of the Mid-Atlantic Ridge enters the western North Altantic at 53°N (Worthington and Volkmann, 1965).

This current is augmented by water which flows ($4 \times 16^6 m^3/sec$) through the Denmark Strait and cascades down into the Atlantic, picking up approximately $1 \times 10^0 m^3/sec$ of North Atlantic Water. This cold (0-2°C) bottom water flows at about $10 \times 10^6 m^3/sec$ along the continental slope and continental rise east of Greenland, north along the western margin of Greenland and then south along the continental rise of Labrador at velocities of about 10 cm/sec near the bottom (Swallow and Worthington, 1969). East of Newfoundland it is no longer distinguishable from North Atlantic Deep Water (Dietrich, 1956, 1957; Cooper, 1955; Worthington and Metcalf, 1961).

The southward migration of benthic faunal elements and the unconformities and accumulations of redistributed sediment (Hollister and others, 1972) may be related, at least in part, to the flow patterns of this cold, nutrient-rich water mass.

North Atlantic Deep Water

The North Atlantic Deep Water (between about 500 and 4500 meters) is the largest water mass in the entire Atlantic comprising about 98 million km³ or about 70% of the North Atlantic Water colder than 4°C (Wright and Worthington, 1970). North Atlantic Deep Water is characterized by comparatively high values of oxygen (5-7 ml/1). Temperatures range between 1.8° and 4.0°C and salinities range between 34.89 ‰ and 35.00 ‰. It lies beneath the warm water sphere and above the Antarctic Bottom Water.

The North Atlantic Deep Water is a mixture of water from the Norwegian, Mediterranean and Labrador Seas and it also includes varying amounts of Antarctic Bottom Water.

Current velocities measured in this water mass are among the highest values recorded in the deep sea. Swallow and Worthington (1961), working just seaward of the Gulf Stream axis off Cape Hatteras, measured southerly-flowing near-bottom currents (about 300 m off bottom) of 18 cm/sec using neutrally buoyant floats. A photographic current meter (less than 1 meter off the bottom) indicated a southerly-flowing current of 11 cm/sec. These and other deep current observations (Zimmerman and Hollister, 1970; Barrett, 1965) suggest that an intensified flow of the North Atlantic Deep Water moves along the bottom parallel to local contours as a Western Boundary Undercurrent (Heezen and others, 1966; Hollister and Heezen, 1972).

The North Atlantic Deep Water is thought to be partially responsible for certain benthic-biogeographic zones of the modern ocean (Rowe and Menzies, 1968) and no doubt many forms that live at intermediate depths owe their present (and past) patterns of distribution to the southward flow of North Atlantic Deep Water.

In this region the shallow as well as the deep ocean circulation is also strongly affected by the wind-driven Gulf Stream, a high velocity (up to 200 cm/sec), narrow (< 200 km), northeasterly flowing western boundary current that lies between the warmer Sargasso Sea and the colder Slope Water (Iselin, 1936; Stommel, 1960).

Temperature and salinity profiles suggest that the horizontal density gradient associated with the Gulf Stream may persist to the bottom in depths of over 4500 m along the continental rise off the northeastern United States, Nova Scotia, and the Grand Banks (Fuglister, 1960). In addition, direct measurements (Knauss, 1965; Zimmerman and Hollister, 1970) of northerly flowing bottom currents beneath the Gulf Stream on the continental rise north of Cape Hatteras show that currents associated with the Gulf Stream may at times reach the deep-sea floor.

The Gulf Stream was the principal agent transporting tropical organisms northward into the colder North Atlantic prior to the ice ages and has since that time been a key factor in the clockwise transatlantic transport of benthonic and planktonic forms.

Slope Water

Between the seaward limit of the relatively fresh coastal water that lies on the continental shelf and the Gulf Stream is the Slope Water (Iselin, 1936). This distinctive band of water ranges in width from about 50 miles off Chesapeake Bay to over 170 miles off Nova Scotia. The upper 200 meters is a mixing zone of coastal water and Gulf Stream Water and in this zone seasonal changes in temperature and salinity are large (12–26°C and 33.5 to 34.5 ‰). The deeper Slope Water from below about 2000 m with a potential temperature less than 2.4°–3°C is relatively oxygen-rich and may contain appreciable quantities of bottom water from the Labrador Basin which often contains as much as 7 ml/1 of dissolved oxygen (Wüst, 1936). Slope Water of 3°–3.8°C may consist of Norwegian Overflow Water coming from the east coast of Greenland and from the Canadian Archipelago.

Deep current directions measured in the Slope Water region support the northern origin for this water. Direct current measurements in the Slope Water off Cape Cod indicate a southwesterly flow from about 1500 m to over 3000 meters (Volkmann, 1962). Measured near-bottom current velocities approach 20 cm/sec. Barrett (1965) measured a deep (from 800 to 2500 m) southwesterly-flowing current of about 20 cm/sec in the Slope Water east of Cape Hatteras.

These measurements suggest that the Slope Water between Cape Cod and Cape Hatteras moves toward the southwest. It also seems likely that the deep southerly-flowing current measured by Swallow and Worthington (1961) in the North Atlantic Deep Water east of the Gulf Stream off Cape Romain (in similar depths and less than 100 miles to the south of Barrett's measurements) is also part of the same southerly-flowing deep current system, the Western Boundary Undercurrent (Swallow and Worthington, 1961), found in the Slope Water region further north. If this is the case, then this deep current must pass beneath or through the northeasterly flowing Gulf Stream.

It seems unlikely that this current is the inherited product of Pleistocene events; more probably it is related to the circulation of an almost fully developed early Tertiary ocean of the Atlantic type. The initiation and maintenance of such a vigorous deep boundary undercurrent requires, however, that the Atlantic be open to northern sources of relatively dense water and this has not always been the case. The southerly-flowing circulation may be one of the most important agents transporting maring organisms southward along the Atlantic margin of the United States.

Water along the European continental slope (Eastern North Atlantic Water) consists of Mediterranean Water (below 600 meters); it moves towards the north, thus perhaps trans-porting benthic organisms from the coast of Spain and Portugal into the region off England, Scotland and Wales.

Western North Atlantic Water and Mediterranean Water

Within the upper thousand meters of the North Atlantic lie two distinguishable water masses: the Mediterranean Water, occupying for the most part the east-central Atlantic, and the Western North Atlantic Water, occupying the west-central Atlantic. The Mediterranean Water is a relatively warm, salty (> 35 ‰) tongue-shaped water mass that is injected into the open Atlantic at the Strait of Gibraltar. Its volume is estimated to be about 22 million km^3 and it comprises about 15% of the total volume of the North Atlantic Ocean. This water actively scours and shapes the sea floor as it flows toward the west and north at depths of up to about 1200 meters (Heezen and Johnson, 1969).

The Western North Atlantic Water lies above the Mediterranean Water in the western basin where the latter is generally colder than 14°C. Western North Atlantic Water comprises about 19 million km^3 or about 38 percent of all of the North Atlantic Water warmer than 4°C (Wright and Worthington, 1970). A thin layer of warm (> 14°C) saline water lies above the Western North Atlantic Water; its volume is estimated to be less than 2 million km.^{3}

The wind stress over the shallower portions of these water masses results in the familiar clockwise gyre pattern of surface circulation in the North Atlantic: the northwesterly Guiana-North Equatorial Current: the northerly to northwesterly Caribbean-Antilles-Florida-Gulf Stream Current; the northeasterly to easterly North Atlantic Drift; and the southerly Portugal-Canaries Current. This circulation pattern is responsible for most of the biogeographic patterns discussed in this paper. An analogous counter-clockwise wind-driven gyre affects and has affected the shallow South Atlantic Water in the South Atlantic Ocean since the initial separation of South America from Africa about 130 million years ago.

As the continents have moved with respect to each other and with respect to the sun's latitude, patterns of surface circulation would, of course, change. The continents while drifting have apparently moved northward and thus the Equatorial divergence would have been, in a Mesozoic ocean, near the present location of the central Atlantic. Even more important changes in surface circulation patterns would result from the opening of the Tethyan seaway or the Isthmus of Panama (figs. 14–19).

With the origin and distribution of the modern-day whole-ocean circulation patterns in mind, it is possible to infer circulation patterns over the past 200 my in an expanding Atlantic Ocean. The basic geologic data upon which our reconstructions of surface and deep ocean circulation patterns for the Mesozoic and Cenozoic of the Atlantic Ocean are inferred include: Initial Reports of the Deep Sea Drilling Project, Legs 1–4, 11–15; Gignoux (1955); Brinkmann (1960); Meyerhoff (1967, 1970a,b); Harrington 1962); in addition to the various sources cited in the section on Paleogeography above. The inferred patterns of circulation also take into account planetary forces such as the Coriolis Force and the wind stress field on a spinning globe upon which continents are moving.

The paleogeographic maps (figs. 12–20) are the reconstructions of Phillips and Forsyth (1972). They have determined the configuration of the Atlantic at various times during the Mesozoic and Cenozoic on the basis of finite rotations of the Atlantic plates about sequential relative motion poles. Sea-floor spreading interpretations of deep-sea drilling results and magnetic anomaly profiles can be used to determine the angular rates of rotation. The position of the latitudes are based upon paleomagnetic poles which were subjected to the same finite rotations as the Atlantic plates. The latitudes for 200 my, 150 my and 97 my represent small circles drawn about a mean pole of the various continents. The latitudes at 130 my, 105 my and 65 my were interpolated. A modified version of the HYPERMAP computer programs of R. Parker (Scripps Institution of Oceanography) was used to plot the data. The maps are drawn on an oblique Lambert azimuthal projection.

In the accompanying figures, which represent Atlantic Ocean reconstructions during various intervals of Mesozoic and Cenozoic time, we have not shown the epicontinental seas which covered the various continents at different times and connected the major oceans. In those cases where major surface current flow is inferred from oceanic region to epicontinental sea we have shown arrows on the margins of the continents to indicate direction of flow.

PALEOCIRCULATION PATTERNS OF THE ATLANTIC AND MEDITERRANEAN (TETHYS)

Late Triassic (200 my ago)

Gondwanaland and Eurasia were essentially contiguous (fig. 12). Marginal and interior evaporite basins developed along the perimeter of the North American Basin and North Africa and possibly the Gulf Coast. No significant marine development occurred in the Atlantic region. Marine Triassic (Muschelkalk) beds were deposited in the Europe-Tethyan region. Circulation was restricted to the shallow saline overflows and to the local development of wind gyre patterns in enclosed basins.

Late Triassic-Middle Jurassic (200–150 my ago)

Sea-floor spreading opened a narrow and relatively shallow North Atlantic Basin, and a sluggish, paleoequatorial surface gyre developed due to the presence of the equator at approximately a central Atlantic position (fig. 13). This North Atlantic gyre (Gulf Stream) flowed northeastwards across the northern Atlantic and into the northern (epicontinental) part of the Tethys Sea and thence eastwards into Himalayan regions. The South Atlantic remained closed. The major circulation in the Tethys Sea was from the east (Indo-Pacific region) to west, similar to the present equatorial currents.

The Gulf of Mexico was probably an evaporite basin with no distinct major circulation pattern connected with world ocean systems. Deep thermohaline Atlantic circulation had not yet developed.

Late Jurassic (150–130 my ago)

The North Atlantic Basin continued to open and a sluggish, widening elliptical clockwise circulation was initiated (fig. 14). Continued flow of a northern branch of this gyre passed through the northern part of Tethys and eastwards toward the Himalayan region. A branch of a proto-Gulf Stream flowed around Newfoundland and along the shallow coastal margin of Newfoundland in response to the increasing fetch of the easterly wind blowing north of the Equator. The modern equivalent is the North Equatorial Current. Northeastward flow of part of this water continued into the narrow, shallow seaway between Greenland and Scandinavia and thence into the Arctic region. A more fully-developed equatorial divergence was developed with concomitant development of upwelling along the Equator, *i.e.* in the central part of the Jurassic Atlantic. The South Atlantic remained essentially closed, although longitudinal rifting in the southern part may have occurred during Late Jurassic-Early Cretaceous. No marine sediments have been reported before Late Aptian and Albian in West Africa (Gabon). Identical fresh water ostracod faunas have been reported in the Late Jurassic-Early Cretaceous of West

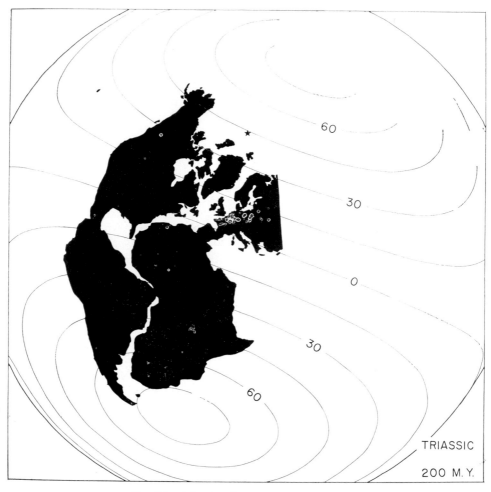

FIG. 12.—Atlantic paleogeography : 200 my ago.

Africa and along the east coast of South America. The rotation of Antarctica and separation from Africa allowed circulation of the Indian Ocean (Agulhas Current) along the SE coast of Africa (Dingle and Klinger, 1971). Westward flow in Tethys was dominant. Subsidence of the Gulf of Mexico may have allowed connection with the world ocean system. Part of the westward flowing Tethys-North Equatorial surface current may then have been deflected northeastward across the Gulf of Mexico and into the epicontinental seaway linking the Gulf with the Arctic via Alaska (Woodring, 1954; Schuchert, 1955); marine connection (at least intermittent) existed between Atlantic and Pacific by means of epicontinental seas in Mexico-Central American region. Deep circulation was not yet developed.

Early Cretaceous (130–105 my ago)

A broad North Atlantic gyre developed in conformity with the changing geometry of the North Atlantic Basin and in response to the relative southward migration of the equator (fig. 15). A branch of the Gulf Stream flowed north around Newfoundland and along the east coast of Labrador (*Orbitolina* reported from Flemish Cap: Sen Gupta and Grant, 1972; tropical planktonic foraminiferal fauna in the Cenomanian on Orphan Knoll: DSDP, Leg 12). Part of this current flowed northeastward into the shallow seaway between Greenland and Scandinavia and into the Arctic region. A branch of the Gulf Stream flowed northeastwards across the Atlantic and across the epicontinental Tethyan Seaway of central and northern Eurasia, thence southwestwards to the Himalayan region and

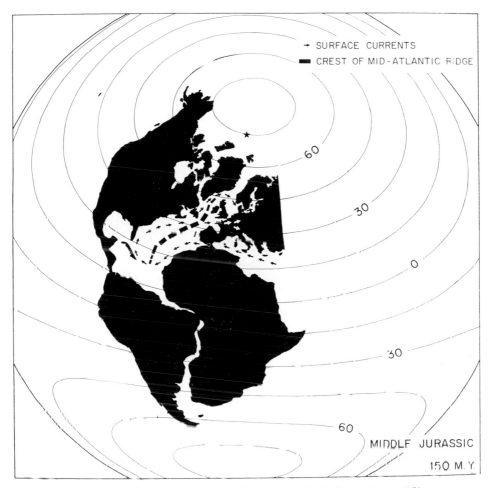

FIG. 13.—Atlantic paleogeography and inferred paleocirculation patterns: 150 my ago.

Indo-Pacific region. Westward flow of the Tethys Sea and its continuation as the North Equatorial Current transported various Tethyan, tropical faunal elements to the Caribbean-Gulf Coast region. Atlantic-Pacific marine connection was maintained across Central America and Mexico allowing Tethyan faunal elements to colonize marginal areas of Central and South America and California. Part of the westward-flowing North Equatorial Current was deflected northwestward across the Gulf of Mexico and into the epicontinental seaway extending to the Arctic region via Alaska (Woodring, 1954; Schuchert, 1955).

At about this time (Early Turonian, ca. 90 my ago) marine communication between the North and South Atlantic was formed by the separation of Africa and South America. The major contribution to South Atlantic circulation was probably derived from the easterly-flowing circumpolar current driven by the Westwind Drift. The deep circulation of N-S Atlantic interchange was still hampered by the topographic barriers of the Walvis Ridge and Rio Grande Rise to the Antarctic Bottom Water and of the Labrador-Greenland-Spitzbergen land bridge across the North Atlantic to the cold Arctic Bottom Waters. There is some evidence in recent deep-sea drilling data for periods of stagnations during the early Cretaceous (Hollister and others, 1972). It is interesting to note here that the circulation pattern we have suggested for this time (130–105 my) is essentially identical to that independently derived by Luyendyk and others (1972) based on experimental studies.

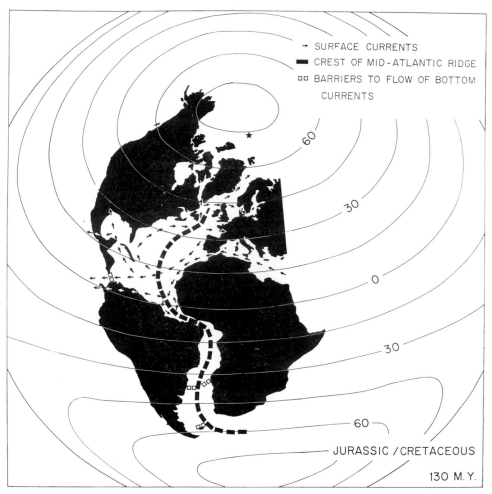

Fig. 14.—Atlantic paleogeography and inferred paleocirculation patterns: 130 my ago.

Late Cretaceous (130–65 my ago)

Continued spreading of North-South Atlantic seafloor resulted in further development of circulation patterns (fig. 16). The Gulf Stream gyre dominated North Atlantic circulation, and a branch continued to flow eastwards across the northern part of epicontinental Tethys Sea to the Himalayan and Indo-Pacific region. Northward a branch flowed into the Labrador Sea, around Greenland and northeastwards towards the Arctic region. The North Atlantic at this time was essentially a subtropical carbonate province with chalks being deposited in the Labrador Sea, coastal Greenland and Denmark. Northward-flowing currents from Tethys along the coastal margin of Europe probably transported tropical elements as far north as Holland-Belgium during the Senonian. The Atlantic and Pacific Oceans were linked via Central

America allowing continued colonization of Central and South America and California by transoceanic migration of Tethyan faunal elements. With reduction of the epicontinental seaway linking the Arctic and Gulf of Mexico by late Cretaceous regression, the Gulf of Mexico developed a roughly clockwise circulation (similar to the present day) in which the inflowing surface water was derived essentially from the wind-driven Antilles Current and the North Equatorial Current and the outflowing water contributed to the generation of the Gulf Stream and the North Atlantic Drift. Greenland was linked with the Alaskan region via a northern seaway around the northern margin of the Canadian Shield.

Paleocene-Eocene (65–35 my ago)

Two main paleogeographic events influenced

current circulation patterns during the early Cenozoic (Paleogene): opening of the northeastern Atlantic and marked reduction in the areal extent of epicontinental seas (particularly in Eurasia) (fig. 17).

Active spreading on the Mid-Atlantic Ridge shifted from the Mid-Labrador Sea Ridge to the Reykjanes Ridge about 60 my ago separating Greenland and Scandinavia and opening up and deepening the Norwegian and Greenland Seas. The final fragmentation of Eurasia was achieved about 50 my ago with the separation of Greenland and Spitsbergen. Abyssal circulation of North Atlantic Deep Water probably began at this time with the development of the Irminger/Labrador/Norwegian/Greenland Seas. Relatively cold Norwegian Overflow Water entered the North Atlantic for the first time, thus significantly modifying the deep circulation of the Atlantic. At the same time, Antarctic Bottom Water started to seep into the North and Equatorial Atlantic via gaps in the Rio Grande Rise. Deep and bottom circulation was probably active in the eastern basins of the North Atlantic due to the eastward leakage of relatively cool Antarctic Bottom Water through fracture zones north of the Eocene equator. Cooler surface water inflow into the North Atlantic from the Arctic region during the Paleogene resulted in the development of a Boreal Faunal Province.

Widespread geographic distribution of planktonic and benthonic foraminiferal elements occurred between Tethys-Caribbean-Gulf Coast regions and between Caribbean-Gulf Coast and northern Europe attesting to the continued efficacy of the North Equatorial Current and Gulf Stream as agents of faunal dispersal. Part of the Gulf of Mexico gyre flowed into the North Atlantic via the Suwanee Channel

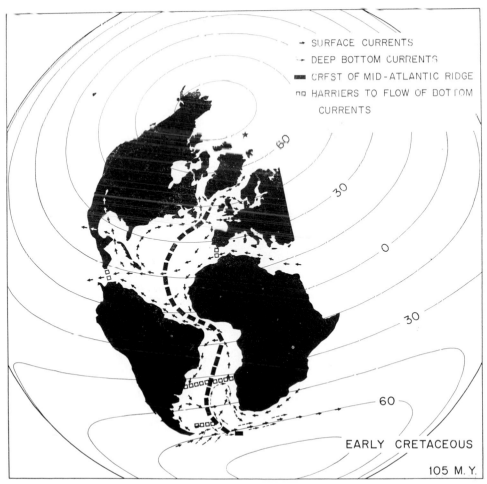

FIG. 15.—Atlantic paleogeography and inferred paleocirculation patterns: 105 my ago.

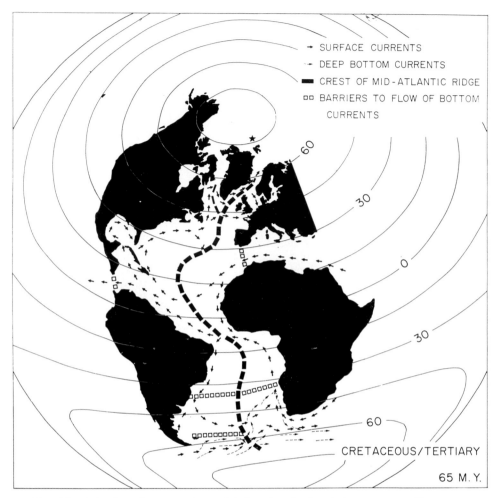

FIG. 16.—Atlantic paleogeography and inferred paleocirculation patterns: 65 my ago.

(northern Florida) during the Paleocene-Middle Eocene but flow into the North Atlantic was wholly by way of the Straits of Florida by the end of the Eocene (Chen, 1965). Subtropical climates extended well into northwestern Europe as *Nummulites* faunas extended as far north as Belgium (Belgian Basin), northwest Germany (North German Basin) and England (Hampshire Basin) in Late Eocene and Early Oligocene time. Atlantic-Pacific marine connection was maintained via Central America.

The presence of sporadic ice-rafted detritus in Subantarctic cores over the past 50 my (Margolis and Kennett, 1970) suggests that the South Atlantic circum-polar circulation, probably initiated in the early Tertiary, may have remained essentially the same during the Cenozoic (with minor modifications as a result of alternate growth and diminution of the ice-cap

during the late Neogene). The subpolar convergence may have been expected to fluctuate with alternate expansions and regressions of the ice cap. This was accentuated in the late Pliocene and Pleistocene in a manner similar to subpolar convergence migration in the North Atlantic.

A widespread seismic reflector—Horizon A— appears to have been formed approximately 45–50 my ago. This Horizon is a prominent and extensive zone of seismic reflecting horizons noted in the North Atlantic basinal sediments. It has been cored several times by the Deep Sea Drilling Project and shown to consist either of radiolarian-diatom chert of latest Early Eocene —early Middle Eocene age (Berggren, 1969a, p. 607; Gartner, 1970, p. 1078), or to be associated with a major early Tertiary unconformity (Hollister and others, 1972).

The origin of Horizon A has puzzled inves-

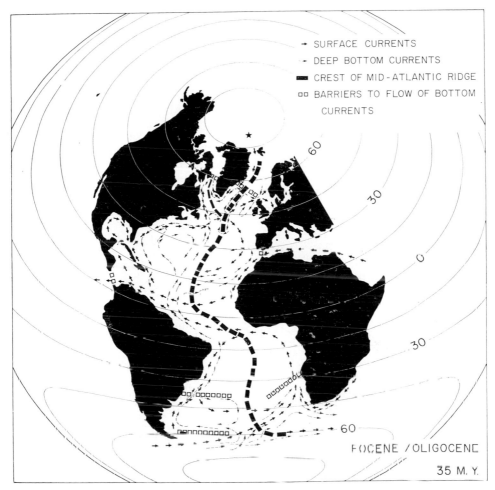

FIG. 17.– Atlantic paleogeography and inferred paleocirculation patterns: 35 my ago.

tigators since it was first penetrated by coring (DSDP, Leg 1) in the western North Atlantic. Berggren and Phillips (1972) suggested that the initiation of cold, deep water circulation in the North Atlantic as a result of the opening of the North Atlantic to the Arctic about 50 million years ago, might have caused the upwelling of nutrients and thus triggered a bloom of siliceous organisms. The authors did not elaborate further at the time on the restricted time interval and the subsequent regional development of Horizon A. Similar ideas were also expressed by Jones and others (1970, p. 1678); Dietz and Holden (1970a, p. 4950); and Ewing and others (1970, p. 5652).

Gibson and Towe (1971) have presented an alternative interpretation of the origin of Horizon A. They suggest that Horizon A is "the result of marine diagenetic alteration of vol-

canic material coupled with an increase in the productivity and preservation of siliceous microplankton in response to an increase in both silica and the nutrient phosphorus that result from the ash alteration process." They indicate that although the changes in oceanic circulation may explain the distribution of the oceanic cherts, they cannot explain the extensive and synchronous nearshore sediments of volcanic origin on the continents nor the relatively restricted time interval involved. Below is an account of the nature and extent of Horizon A; our theory on its development involves aspects of both the ideas suggested initially by Berggren and Phillips (1972)—initiation of deep circulation in the North Atlantic—and by Gibson and Towe (1971)—volcanism.

Volcanism would appear to have been one of the main sources of silica in the sea during the early Cenozoic. In particular volcanism was active in the Caribbean-Antilles region during the Paleocene, and during the Early and Middle Eocene (Bermudez, 1950; Lewis and Straczek, 1955; Taber, 1934; MacGillavry, 1970). The volcanic foundation of at least the northern part of the outer sedimentary arc of the Lesser Antilles was apparently formed during the Middle Eocene (Woodring, 1954). A foundation of andesitic pyroclastics on St. Bartholomew Island is interbedded with Middle Eocene limestones (Christman, 1953). These observations illustrate the fact that Caribbean volcanism was active and probably served as the source of the widespread development of silica in lower-middle Eocene sediments from the Atlantic and eastern Gulf Coast of the United States (Gibson and Towe, 1971) to the deep sea. Associated with an authigenic mineral suite of altered volcanic glass in some deep sea deposits at this time is a rich radiolarian-diatom assemblage (Edgar and others, 1971). The indurated rock of this association is what is commonly known as "Horizon A."

The separation of Europe and Greenland (about 50 my ago) and the formation of the northeastern Atlantic basins would have allowed colder Arctic Bottom Water to flow into the North Atlantic and sink, thereby generating a deep, cold water circulation pattern. The polar water flowing southward into the North Atlantic was certainly not "cold" in comparison to present day conditions. It would have been sufficient for this water to have been merely comparatively cooler than water to the south by virtue of a normal latitudinal gradient established by the opening of Atlantic to the polar regions (i.e., an area of relatively less insolation vis à vis the lower latitudes). With the development of a deep-circulation in the North Atlantic Basin upwelling would develop along zones of convergence and sediment transport and perhaps erosion would be initiated along the basin margins. Upwelling would contribute large amounts of nutrients to the euphotic zone. Another effect of the invasion of the deep basins with relatively cool polar water would be to significantly elevate the carbonate compensation depth. This rapid shift in compensation depth may be related to the deposition of siliceous material forming Horizon A. The corresponding depletion in calcium carbonate in the ocean during this time may, perhaps, be accounted for by the extensive development of the shallow water *Nummulites* deposits along the margins of the Tethys Sea from Indonesia to the western Mediterranean.

Cita (1971) has observed that the distribution of biogenous silica in sediments related to areas of high productivity in the overlying water masses—"clearly indicates that a system of tropical currents was active in the North Atlantic." To account for the observed distribution of biogenous silica in the Atlantic she favored the idea of a strong equatorial current system flowing westwards between the Atlantic and Pacific in the early Cenozoic. She observed that the widespread distribution of siliceous plankton appears to be limited to the Eocene tropical area of the North Atlantic. It can be seen from the reconstruction of the Atlantic Ocean about 65 my ago (fig. 16) that the paleoequator lay on a line from the Tethys to the Caribbean-Panama-Pacific, coincident with the position of a westward flowing equatorial current.

At the present time, a high productivity zone in the Pacific Ocean between 20°N and 20°S is associated with the equatorial current system. Data from the Deep Sea Drilling Project confirm earlier indications that this Pacific equatorial belt of high productivity was already in existence during the Eocene. The most logical explanation for the extensive development of siliceous sediments in the Eocene of the Atlantic (and Pacific) Ocean is the existence of a relatively strong westward flowing equatorial current system through the Isthmus of Panama which, at this time, was open to its maximum extent.

Another significant fact which must be accounted for in any discussion of "Horizon A" is the recent discovery (Hollister and others, 1972) that it represents a major hiatus of 50 to 70 million years between the mid-Tertiary and the mid-Cretaceous along the continental margin of the United States (fig. 18). Here chert is absent; yet the seismic horizon is very well developed. While volcanism and upwelling favored the development of chert in the central deep ocean basins during Eocene, bottom currents were actively scouring the sea floor along the basin edge where, from geostrophic considerations, the highest current velocities would be expected. In fact, the observation of significant early Tertiary hiatuses (fig. 18) in DSDP drill holes along continental margins (Hollister and others, 1972; Laughton and others, 1971, 1972; Hayes and others, 1971) further substantiate the concept of massive sediment erosion (or non-deposition) along the edge of the ocean basins at this time. These hiatuses were probably developed during the early Tertiary in response to the increased bottom currents caused by the opening of the northeastern Atlantic and the initiation of vigorous North Atlantic deep circulation.

Horizon A represents a complex geologic phenomenon. Where present in the Atlantic as a lithologic entity, rich in siliceous plankton, it probably represents the combined effects of volcanism and upwelling. Its areal distribution on the sea-floor would, then, be a direct reflection of the major warm-water gyre. Corroboration of this would seem to come from the fact that traces of late Early Eocene radiolarian-rich chert were found as far north as latitude 54° in the Labrador Sea (Orphan Knoll) on Leg 12 (DSDP). The development of widespread radiolarian cherts of identical age in the equatorial belt in the Pacific (DSDP, Leg 8) can be explained by the westward flow of the Atlantic North Equatorial current into the Pacific through the Panama Straits (the equator lay just south of the Caribbean-Antilles region in the Eocene). Where Horizon A is characterized by a hiatus, however, its areal distribution is a reflection of the erosive action of contour currents flowing along the base of the continental margin. Perhaps the effect of the diminution of volcanic activity combined with the effect of the elevation of the carbonate compensation depth caused by the continued flooding of the deep basins with increasingly colder water during the late Paleogene probably caused the abrupt decrease of siliceous-ooze production, allowing the North Atlantic to come to an equilibrium pattern of organic production similar to what we observe today.

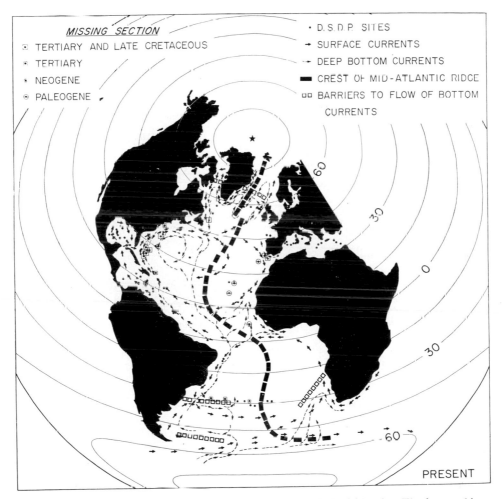

Fig. 18.—Distribution of major hiatuses observed in Atlantic DSDP drill holes. The longest hiatuses (up to 50–70 my of missing section) occur in holes drilled near the axis of relatively strong boundary currents along the base of the continental margin. We suggest that the missing sediment has been eroded during the early Tertiary when strong deep circulation was initiated following the opening of the northeastern Atlantic to sources of relatively dense polar waters that overflow into the North Atlantic basins from the Norwegian Sea.

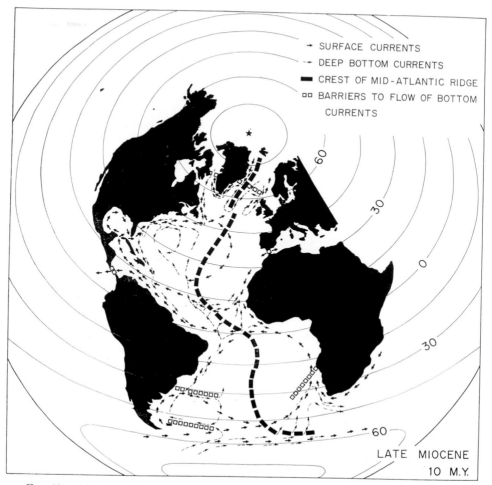

Fig. 19.—Atlantic paleogeography and inferred paleocirculation patterns: 10 my ago.

Early Oligocene-Late Miocene (35–10 my ago)

Three significant events relative to Atlantic-Tethyan circulation patterns occurred during the Miocene (fig. 19).

1) Separation of the eastern and western Tethys by the junction of Africa and Eurasia in the Early Miocene (Burdigalian, *ca.* 18 my ago). The eastern Tethys became constricted by the further rotation of Africa and Arabia relative to Asia and evolved into the Indian Ocean. The western Tethys continued to maintain open connection with the Atlantic and faunal interchange between Tethyan and Caribbean region continued. Flow of warm, salty Mediterranean water into the eastern Atlantic began.

2) Junction of Europe and North Africa at Gibraltar and generation of Gibraltar Sill about 15 my ago. This is suggested by the almost complete cessation in faunal interchange between

western Tethys and Caribbean regions at this time (Berggren, 1969b; 1972; Berggren and Phillips, 1971). Surface circulation was significantly modified to an essentially internal one with unstable currents as western Tethys became further restricted.

Closure of the Tethyan Seaway excluded the Gulf Stream gyre from its former eastward trans-European route towards the Indo-Pacific region. A shallow inland sea (Paratethys) developed in central and southeastern Europe and retained marginal connections with the shrinking Tethys. The Gulf Stream became a self-contained system. A part of the current was deflected northwards to form the North Atlantic Drift. The incursion of warm waters into the northeastern Atlantic probably enhanced circulation in the North Atlantic with the extrusion of a greater volume of Arctic waters into western Atlantic (around the coast of Greenland and Labrador Sea).

3) In the Late Miocene (10–5 my ago) the western Tethys experienced a drastic drop in sea-level concomitant with the widespread deposition of evaporite deposits. The western Tethys was cut off intermittently from communication with the Atlantic Ocean for at least part of the Late Miocene (7–5 my ago). Circulation in the Atlantic remained essentially the same as during the early Neogene, except that the Mediterranean Water ceased to flow into the open Atlantic. At this time bottom circulation appears to have favored high rates of sediment accumulation along the continental margins of the western Atlantic. A warm branch of the Gulf Stream continued to flow along the Newfoundland Coast.

Late Miocene-Recent (10–0 my ago)

Three significant events occurred in the Pliocene which affected the circulation of the Atlantic-Mediterranean region (fig. 20). Because of the proximity of these events to each other and because paleogeographic changes were relatively minor during that interval, only a circulation pattern for the period 3–0 my has been constructed (using the 10 my reconstruction provided by Phillips); no reconstruction is shown for the interval 10–5 my. The three events are enumerated below:

1) Early Pliocene (5 my ago)—Eustatic rise in sea-level led to transgression of the Atlantic Ocean into the Mediterranean region establishing the Mediterranean Sea as we know it today. Circulation in the Mediterranean is sluggish and irregular but greater salinity within the basin relative to the Atlantic results in relatively less dense surface inflow from the Atlantic.

2) Early-Mid-Pliocene (3.5–4 my ago)—Elevation of Isthmus of Panama severed the

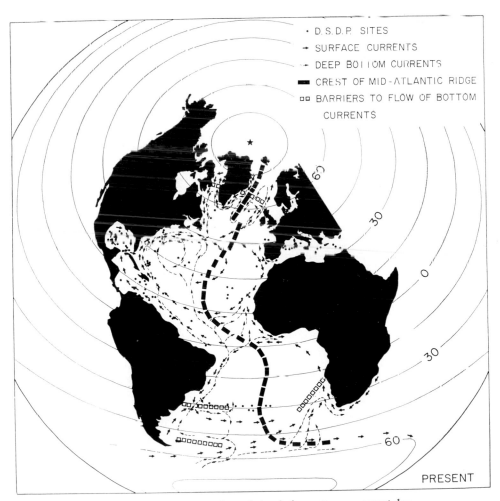

Fig. 20.—Atlantic geography and circulation patterns: present day.

marine connection and faunal interchange between the Atlantic and Pacific oceans. The energy generated in the deflection of the westward flowing North Equatorial Current may be expected to have contributed to a more active Gulf Stream.

3) Mid-Pliocene (~ 3 my ago)—Initiation of glaciation in the Northern Hemisphere and (probable) formation of the Labrador Current as a significant water mass.

The Labrador Current brings subpolar and polar waters southward from Nova Scotia into temperate latitudes (off Newfoundland). The result of the juxtaposition of anomalously cool slope and coastal waters against anomalously warm Gulf waters is the strongest horizontal thermal gradient in the oceans (Ruddiman, 1968). The total temperature range of ocean water in the North Atlantic is about 29°C (− 1°C to 28°C), but over half that difference may be compressed at any moment into a distance of a few hundred miles, and approximately 8°C (30%) into a few thousand meters width of the cold wall of the instantaneous Gulf Stream.

Living planktonic foraminiferal faunas of slope waters are characterized by high standing crops (10,000–100,000 specimens per 1,000 m³) and low diversity (Cifelli and Smith, 1969). About five species of *Globigerina* and a few other forms are recognizable within this water mass, but northwards the fauna is restricted to a few globigerinids and morphologic differentiation between the forms becomes increasingly difficult.

Although there is evidence of a southward displacement of the temperate faunal province along the coastal margin of the Atlantic Coastal Plain during early-middle Miocene time (Gibson, 1967), the fact that tropical faunas occur throughout the mid-late Tertiary (Oligocene and Miocene) on the continental shelf and slope off Nova Scotia (Bartlett, 1968) and were abruptly replaced by subpolar-polar faunas 3 million years ago in the Labrador Sea (Leg 12, DSDP) suggests that the Labrador Current was formed at this time. An earlier coolwater current may well have flowed southwards around Newfoundland and along the east coast of North America during the Neogene, but the intensification of circulation within the Labrador Sea, caused by the development of glaciation in the Northern Hemisphere, is what generated the Labrador Current in its present form. The Labrador Current, in turn, deflected the Gulf Stream southwards and essentially restricted it to latitudes south of 45°N. The Late Pliocene-Pleistocene history of surface circulation in the North Atlantic is essentially one of increasing intensity as a result of climatic deterioration. Although glaciation began in the Northern Hemisphere about 3 my ago, the major cooling which is probably related to the initiation of intense high latitude glaciation (Mindel and younger) occurred between 0.6–0.4 my (mid-Brunhes time). Over the past 250,000 years the polar front has swept back and forth between lat. 60° and 40°N six times—alternately compressing and expanding the tropical-subtropical belt (McIntyre and others, 1971). Cool currents from the north carried North European faunal elements into the Mediterranean near the Pliocene-Pleistocene transition (*ca.* 2 my ago).

SUMMARY AND CONCLUSIONS

In the preceding sections we have presented an historical account of the paleogeography of the Atlantic Ocean and surrounding areas and the effects and restraints which paleogeographic changes have had on paleobiogeography and surface/deep water circulation patterns. The main conclusions of this paper are graphically illustrated in figs. 21 and 22 and are summarized below.

1) Paleobiogeography and the evolution of water mass circulation in the Atlantic and Tethys Oceans is best understood within a paleogeographic framework of continental drift and plate tectonics.

2) The North and South Atlantic have probably had separate and distinct histories. The North Atlantic Basin probably began to form as a result of initial rifting between North America and Africa about 180–200 million years ago. At this time a marine faunal province was established in the Atlantic.

3) Separation of Gondwanaland and Eurasia, about 150 my ago, resulted in marine connections between the Tethys and North Atlantic and faunal exchange between these areas. Jurassic marine and non-marine faunas are relatively cosmopolitan indicating the relative contiguity of land masses and development of extensive continental shelves.

4) Initial rifting in the South Atlantic may have begun in the Early Cretaceous, but South America and Africa were not severed until about 90–95 my ago (Turonian). At this time North and South Atlantic water mass and marine faunal exchange were initiated.

5) The final stages in the fragmentation of Eurasia occurred about 50 my ago with the separation of Scandinavia and Greenland and the rotation of Spitsbergen. The immediate effect of this was the formation of cool surface

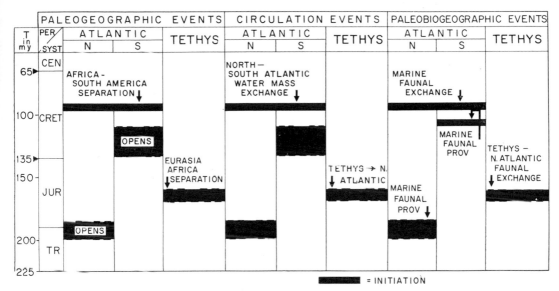

FIG. 21.—Paleogeographic, paleobiogeographic and paleocirculation events in the Atlantic and Tethys Oceans: Mesozoic.

water inflow from polar regions into the North Atlantic and the gradual development of a Boreal Faunal Realm. (Faunal evidence indicates that a Boreal Faunal Province—in the true sense of the word—did not exist in the North Atlantic during the Mesozoic, but is, rather, a Cenozoic phenomenon.) Atlantic deep and bottom water circulation was initiated at this time as well. Widespread hiatuses along basin margins and deposition of siliceous beds in the central basins of both the North Atlantic and Pacific occurred at this time. Seismic

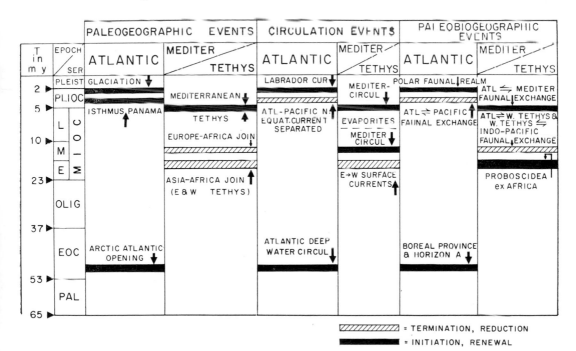

FIG. 22.—Paleogeographic paleobiogeographic and paleocirculation events in the Atlantic and Tethys (Mediterranean) Oceans: Cenozoic.

Horizon A appears to be related to the induration of these siliceous beds and to the abrupt changes in the sediment physical properties at the unconformity and its distribution on the sea-floor thus is a reflection of the combined effects of surface currents and the erosive effects of deep-water circulation.

6) In Miocene time (18 my ago) the Tethys Ocean was first severed in two by the junction of Eurasia and Africa and subsequently (15 my ago) partially isolated from the Atlantic by the junction of Europe and Africa near Gibraltar. The immediate effect of this was the cessation of Indo-Pacific→West Tethys faunal exchange and subsequently of West Tethys→Atlantic faunal exchange—a process which had been going on since Mesozoic time and had been responsible for the enrichment of the Caribbean-West Indies region by tropical faunal elements from more than half way around the world. In many instances Caribbean-West Indian faunas of today are but relicts of the once extensive circum-global Tethyan marine faunal realm.

7) A large drop in sea-level and deposition of extensive evaporites occurred in the western Tethys during the Late Miocene (7–5 my ago). About 5 my ago eastward transgression of the Atlantic resulted in the formation of the Mediterranean Sea as we know it today. The Mediterranean Sea is, thus, a relatively young feature.

8) The Isthmus of Panama emerged about 3.5–4 my ago and formed a barrier to the Atlantic and Pacific water mass and faunal exchange, a process which had been operative since Mesozoic time.

9) The initiation of glaciation in the Northern Hemisphere about 3 my ago was responsible for the formation of the Labrador Current which displaced the warm, northward flowing branch of the Gulf Stream (which had carried tropical faunal and floral elements into the Labrador Sea since mid-Mesozoic time) and the development of a Polar Faunal Realm. At this time the gradual, but inexorable, biogeographic provincialization of the North Atlantic was essentially completed.

ACKNOWLEDGMENTS

We have benefitted greatly from stimulating discussions on regional geology and paleogeography with our colleagues Dr. B. Luyendyk, J. D. Phillips, and E. A. Uchupi, who have reviewed our manuscript. We should also like to thank the various members of the Physical Oceanography Department (in particular Dr. R. W. Wright and Mr. L. V. Worthington) with whom we reviewed our interpretation of the evolution of circulation in the Atlantic in order to test its coherence in terms of present day circulation patterns.

This investigation was supported by the National Science Foundation (Grant GA-16098 and GA-30723) and the Office of Naval Research (Contract N00014-66-C-0241).

This paper is Contribution No. 2717 of the Woods Hole Oceanographic Institution.

REFERENCES

ADAMS, C. G., 1967, Tertiary foraminifera in the Tethyan, American, and Indo-Pacific provinces, *in* ADAMS, C. G., AND AGER, D. V. (eds.), Aspects of Tethyan biogeography: System. Assoc. Pub. 7, p. 195–217.
——, 1970, A reconsideration of the East Indian letter classification of the Tertiary: British Mus. (Nat. History) Bull., v. 19, p. 87–137.
——, AND AGER, D. V. (eds.), 1967, Aspects of Tethyan biogeography: System. Assoc. Pub. 7, vi + 336 p.
ALLARD, G. O. AND HURST, V. J., 1969, Brazil-Gabon geologic link supports continental drift: Science, v. 163, p. 528.
ALLEGRE, C., BOULANGER, D., AND JAVOY, M., 1963, Étude a l'aide des isotopes de l'oxygène de la paléothermométrie du Nummlitique basque: Soc. Géol. Franc., C. R. Somm., no. 8, p. 256–257.
ARKELL, W. J., 1956, Jurassic geology of the world: Edinburgh, Oliver and Boyd, 806 p.
AXELROD, D. I. AND BAILEY, H. P., 1969, Paleotemperature analysis of Tertiary floras: Palaeogeography, Palaeoclimatology, and Palaeoecology, v. 6, p. 163–195
BADEN-POWELL, D. F. W., 1955, The correlation of the Pliocene and Pleistocene marine beds of Britain and the Mediterranean: Geol. Assoc. Proc., v. 66, p. 271–292.
BANNER, F. T., 1970, A synopsis of the Spirocyclinidae: Rev. Espan. Micropaleontol., v. 2, p. 243–290.
BARR, F. T., 1962, Upper Cretaceous planktonic foraminifera from the Isle of Wight, England: Palaeontology, v. 4, p. 522–580.
——, 1966, The foraminiferal genus *Bolivinoides* from the Upper Cretaceous of the British Isles: *ibid.*, v. 9, p. 220–243.
——, 1970, The foraminiferal genus *Bolivinoides* from the Upper Cretaceous of Libya: Jour. Paleontology, v. 44, p. 642–654.
BARRETT, J. R., 1965, Subsurface currents off Cape Hatteras: Deep-Sea Research, v. 12, p. 173–184.
BARTLETT, G. A., 1968, Mid-Tertiary stratigraphy of the continental slope off Nova Scotia: Maritime Sediments, v. 4, p. 22–31.
——, AND SMITH, L., 1971, Mesozoic and Cenozoic history of the Grand Banks of Newfoundland: Canadian Jour. Earth Sci., v. 8, p. 65–84.

BATJES, D. A. J., 1958, Foraminifera of the Oligocene of Belgium: Inst. Roy. Sci. Nat. Belgique, Mém., v. 143, p. 1–188.

BÉ, A. W. H., 1959, Ecology of Recent planktonic Foraminifera, Part 1: Areal distribution in the western North Atlantic: Micropaleontology, v. 5, p. 77–100.

———, 1960a, Some observations on Arctic planktonic Foraminifera: Cushman Found. Foram. Research Contr., v. 11, p. 64–68.

———, 1960b, Ecology of Recent planktonic Foraminifera, Part 2: Bathymetric and seasonal distributions in the Sargasso Sea off Bermuda: Micropaleontology, v. 6, p. 373–392.

BELMONTE, Y., HIRTZ, P., AND WENGER, R., 1965, The salt basins of the Gabon and Congo (Brazzaville). A tentative palaeogeographic interpretation, in Salt basins around Africa: London, Inst. Petroleum, p. 55–74.

BENSON, R. A., 1972, Preliminary report on the ostracodes of holes 117 and 117A, in LAUGHTON, A. S., AND OTHERS, Initial reports of the Deep Sea Drilling Project: Washington, D.C., U.S. Govt. Printing Office, v. 12, p. 427–432.

———, AND SYLVESTER-BRADLEY, P. C., 1971, Deep-sea ostracodes and the transformation of ocean to sea in the Tethys: Centre Rech. Pau, Soc. Natl. Pétroles d'Aquitaine, Bull., Suppl. 5, p. 63–91.

BERGER, W. H., 1970, Biogenic deep-sea sediments: fractionation by deep-sea circulation: Geol. Soc. America Bull., v. 81, p. 1385–1402.

BERGGREN, W. A., 1962, Some planktonic foraminifera from the Maestrichtian and type Danian stages of Denmark and southern Sweden: Stockholm Contr. Geol., v. 9, p. 1–105.

———, 1969a, Biostratigraphy: Cenozoic foraminiferal faunas, in EWING, M., AND OTHERS, Initial reports of the Deep Sea Drilling Project: Washington, D.C., U.S. Govt. Printing Office, v. 1, p. 594–607.

———, 1969b, Biostratigraphy and planktonic foraminiferal zonation of the Tertiary System of the Sirte Basin, Libya, North Africa: 1st Internat. Conf. Planktonic Microfossils, Proc., v. 1, p. 104–120.

———, 1969c, Paleogene biostratigraphy and planktonic foraminifera of northern Europe: ibid., p. 121–160.

———, 1971, Paleogene planktonic foraminifera faunas on Legs I–IV (Atlantic Ocean), JOIDES Deep Sea Drilling Program; a synthesis: 2nd Internat. Conf. Planktonic Microfossils, Proc., v. 1, p. 57–66.

———, 1972, A Cenozoic time-scale: implications for regional paleogeography and paleobiogeography: Lethaia, v. 5, p. 195–215.

———, AND PHILLIPS, J. D., 1971, The influence of continental drift on the distribution of Cenozoic benthonic foraminifera in the Mediterranean and Caribbean-Gulf Coast regions, in Symposium on Geology of Libya (Tripoli, 1969), Proc.: Beirut, Catholic Press, p. 263–299.

BERMUDEZ, P. J., 1950, Contribución al estudio del Cenozoico cubana; Soc. Cubana Hist. Nat., Mem., v. 19, p. 205–375.

BLOW, W.H., 1969, Late middle Eocene to Recent planktonic foraminiferal biostratigraphy: 1st Internat. Conf. Planktonic Microfossils, Proc., v. 1, p. 199–422.

BOLLI, H. M., 1957a, The genera Globigerina and Globorotalia in the Paleocene-lower Eocene Lizard Springs Formation of Trinidad, B.W.I.: U.S. Natl. Mus. Bull. 215, p. 61–81.

———, 1957c, Planktonic foraminifera from the Oligocene-Miocene Cipero and Lengua Formations of Trinidad, B.W.I.: ibid., p. 97–113.

———, 1957c, Planktonic foraminifera from the Eocene Navet and San Fernando Formations of Trinidad, B.W.I.: ibid., p. 155–172.

———, 1959, Planktonic foraminifera from the Cretaceous of Trinidad, B.W.I.: Bull. Am. Paleontology, v. 39, no. 179, p. 257–277.

BOWEN, R. N. C., 1961a, Paleotemperature analyses of Mesozoic Belemnoidea from Germany and Poland: Jour. Geology, v. 69, p. 75–83.

———, 1961b, Oxygen isotope paleotemperature measurements on Cretaceous Belemnoidea from Europe, India and Japan: Jour. Paleontology, v. 35, p. 1077–1084.

———, 1966, Paleotemperature analysis: Elsevier, Amsterdam, 265 p.

BRIGGS, J. C., 1970, A faunal history of the North Atlantic Ocean: Syst. Zool., v. 19, p. 19–34.

BRENNECKE, W., 1921, Die ozeanographischen Arbeiten der deutschen antarktischen Expedition 1911–1912: Deutsche Seewarte, Archiv., v. 39, p. 1–216.

BRINKMAN, R., 1960, Geologic evolution of Europe: New York, Hafner Pub. Co., 161 p.

BROTZEN, F., 1936, Foraminiferen aus dem schwedischen untersten Senon von Eriksdal in Schonen: Sver. Geol. Unders., ser. C, v. 396, arsb. 30, p. 1–206.

———, 1948, The Swedish Paleocene and its foraminiferal fauna: ibid., v. 493, arsb. 42, n. 2, p. 1–140.

BULLARD, E. C., EVERETT, J. E., AND SMITH, A. G., 1965, The fit of the continents around the Atlantic: Roy. Soc. Philos. Trans., v. 258A, p. 41–51.

BUNCE, E. T., EMERY, K. O., GERARD, R. D., KNOTT, S. T., LIDZ, L., SAITO, T., AND SCHLEE, J., 1965, Ocean drilling on the continental margin: Science, v. 150, p. 709–716.

CHANDLER, M. E. J., 1954, Some Upper Cretaceous and Eocene fruits from Egypt: Brit. Mus. (Nat. History) Bull., (a), v. 2, p. 147–187.

CHANEY, R. W., 1940, Tertiary forests and continental history: Geol. Soc. America Bull., v. 51, p. 469–488.

———, 1964, Some observations on climatic relations of Tertiary floras bordering the North Pacific basin, in NAIRN, A. E. M. (ed.), Problems in palaeoclimatology: New York, Interscience, p. 40–43.

CHAPMAN, F., 1892, Microzoa from the phosphatic chalk of Taplow: Geol. Soc. London Quart. Jour., v. 48, p. 514–518.

CHEETHAM, A. H. AND HÅKANSSON, E., 1972, Preliminary report on Bryozoa (site 117), in LAUGHTON, A. S., AND OTHERS, Initial reports of the Deep Sea Drilling Project: Washington, D.C., U.S. Govt. Printing Office, v. 12, p. 432–444.

CHEN, C. S., 1965, The regional lithostratigraphic analysis of Paleocene and Eocene rocks of Florida: Florida Geol. Survey Bull., v. 45, p. 1–105.

CHRISTMAN, R., 1953, Geology of St. Bartholomew, St. Martin and Anguilla, Lesser Antilles: Geol. Soc. America Bull., v. 64, p. 65–96.

CIFELLI, R. AND SMITH, R. K., 1969, Problems in the distribution of Recent North Atlantic planktonic foraminifera and their relationships with water mass boundaries in the North Atlantic: 1st Internat. Conf. Planktonic Microfossils, Proc., v. 1, p. 68–81.

—— AND ——, 1970, Distribution of planktonic foraminifera in the vicinity of the North Atlantic Current: Smithsonian Contr. Paleobiology, no. 4, p. 1–52.

CITA, M. B., 1971, Paleoenvironmental aspects of DSDP Legs I-IV: Planktonic Conf., Proc., no. 2, v. 1, p. 251–275.

CLOUD, P. E., JR., 1961, Paleobiogeography of the marine realm, *in* SEARS, M. (ed.), Oceanography: Am. Assoc. Adv. Sci. Pub. 67, p. 151–200.

COOPER, L. H. N., 1955, Deep water movements in the North Atlantic as a line between climatic changes around Iceland and biological productivity of the English Channel and Celtic Sea: Jour. Marine Research, v. 14, p. 347–362.

CUSHMAN, J. A., 1946, Upper Cretaceous foraminifera of the Gulf Coast region of the United States and adjacent areas: U.S. Geol. Survey Prof. Paper 206, p. 1–261.

——, 1951, Paleocene foraminifera of the Gulf Coastal Region of the United States: U.S. Geol. Surv. Prof. Paper 232, p. 1–75.

DACQUE, E., 1915, Grundlagen und Methoden der Palaeogeographie: Jena, Gustav Fischer, vii + 500 p.

DAVIDS, R. N., 1966, A paleoecologic and paleobiogeographic study of Maestrichtian planktonic foraminifera (Ph.D. thesis): New Jersey, Rutgers Univ., 240 p.

DAVIES, A. M., 1934–1935, Tertiary faunas: the composition of Tertiary faunas: London, Thos. Murby and Co., v. 1: 406 p.; The sequence of Tertiary faunas: v. 2, 252 p.

DAVIS, A. G. AND ELLIOTT, A. F., 1957, The palaeogeography of the London Sea Clay: Geol. Assoc. Proc., v. 68, p. 255–277.

DEROO, G., 1966, Cytheracea (ostracodes) du Maastrichtien de Maastricht (Pays-Bas) et des régions voisines: résultats stratigraphiques et paléontologiques de leur étude: Geol. Sticht. Meded., ser. C, v. 2, no. 2, 239 p.

DEVEREAUX, I., 1967, Oxygen isotope paleotemperature measurements of New Zealand Tertiary fossils: New Zealand Jour. Sci., v. 10, p. 988–1011.

DICKSON, G., 1968, Magnetic anomalies and ocean floor spreading in the South Atlantic: (Ph.D. thesis): New York, Columbia University.

——, PITMAN, W. C., AND HEIRTZLER, J. R., 1968, Magnetic anomalies in the South Atlantic and ocean floor spreading: Jour. Geophys. Research, v. 73, p. 2087–2100.

DIETRICH, G., 1956, Überstromung des Island-Faroer-Rückens in Bodennahe nach Beobachtungen mit dem Forschungsschiff "ANTON DOHRN," 1955–56: Deutsch. Hydrogr. Zeitschr., v. 9, p. 78–89.

——, 1957, Schichtung und Zirkulation der Irminger-See im Juni 1955: Wiss. Kommn. Meeresforsch., Ber., v. 14, p. 255–312.

DIETZ, R. S., 1961, Continent and ocean basin evolution by spreading of the sea floor: Nature, v. 190, p. 854–857.

——, AND HOLDEN, J. C., 1970a, Reconstruction of Pangaea: breakup and dispersion of continents, Permian to present: Jour. Geophys. Research, v. 75, p. 4939–4956.

——, ——, 1970b, The breakup of Pangaea: Sci. American, v. 223, p. 30–41.

——, ——, 1971, Pre-Mesozoic ocean crust in the eastern Indian Ocean (Wharton Basin)?: Nature, v. 229, p. 309–312.

DILLEY, F. C., 1971, Cretaceous foraminiferal biogeography, *in* MIDDLEMISS, F. A., RAUSON, P. F., AND NEWALL, G. (eds.), Faunal provinces in space and time: Liverpool, Seel House Press, Geol. Jour., Special Issue no. 4, p. 169–190.

DINGLE, R. V. AND KLINGER, H. C., 1971, Significance of Upper Jurassic sediments in the Krysna Outlier (Cape Province) for timing of the breakup of Gondwanaland: Science, v. 232, p. 37–38.

DORF, E., 1955, Plants and the geologic time scale: Geol. Soc. America Special Paper 62, p. 575–592.

——, 1964, The use of fossil plants in palaeoclimatic interpretations, *in* NAIRN, A. E. M. (ed.), Problems in palaeoclimatology: New York, Interscience, p. 13–31.

DOUGLAS, R. G., AND RANKIN, C., 1969, Cretaceous planktonic foraminifera from Bornholm and their zoogeographic significance: Lethaia, v. 2, p. 185–217.

——, AND SLITER, W. V., 1966, Regional distribution of some Cretaceous Rotaliporidae and Globotruncanidae (Foraminiferida) within North America: Tulane Studies Geology, v. 4, p. 89–131.

DRAKE, C. L., EWING, J. I., AND STOCKARD, H., 1968, The continental margin off the eastern United States: Canadian Jour. Earth Sci., v. 5, p. 993–1009.

——, EWING, M., AND SUTTON, G. H., 1959, Continental margins and geosynclines: the east coast of North America north of Cape Hatteras, *in* AHRENS, L. H., PRESS, F., RANKAMA, K., AND RUNCORN, S. K. (eds.), Physics and chemistry of the earth: London, Pergamon Press, v. 3, p. 110–198.

——, AND NAFE, J. E., 1968a, Geophysics of the North Atlantic region: UNESCO-IUGS Symposium on continental drift emphasizing the history of the South Atlantic area, Montivideo, Uruguay, October 1967.

——, AND ——, 1968b, The transition from continents to oceans from seismic refraction data, *in* The crust and upper mantle of the Pacific area: Am. Geophys. Union Geophys. Mon. 12, p. 174–186.

DURHAM, J. W., 1950, Cenozoic marine climates of the Pacific Coast: Geol. Soc. America Bull., v. 61, p. 1243–1264.

——, 1952, Early Tertiary marine faunas and continental drift: Am. Jour. Sci., v. 250, p. 320–343.

——, 1959, Palaeoclimates, *in* AHRENS, L. H., PRESS, F., RANKAMA, K., AND RUNCORN, S. K. (eds.), Physics and chemistry of the earth: London, Pergamon Press, p. 1–16.

——, AND McNEIL, F. S., 1967, Cenozoic migrations of marine invertebrates through the Bering Strait region, *in* HOPKINS, D. M. (ed.), The Bering Land Bridge: Palo Alto, California, Stanford Univ. Press, p. 326–347.

DU TOIT, A. L., 1937, Our wandering continents; and hypothesis of continental drifting: London, Oliver and Boyd, 366 p.

——, 1944, Tertiary mammals and continental drift: Am. Jour. Sci., v. 242, p. 145–163.

EAMES, F. E., BANNER, F. T., BLOW, W. H., AND CLARK, W. J., 1962, Fundamentals of mid-Tertiary stratigraphical correlation: Cambridge, England, Cambridge Univ. Press, viii + 163 p.

EDGAR, N. T., AND OTHERS, 1971, Deep Sea Drilling Project, Leg 15: Geotimes, v. 16, no. 4, p. 12–16.

EDGELL, H. S., 1954, The stratigraphical value of *Bolivinoides* in the Upper Cretaceous of north-west Australia: Cushman Found. Foram. Research Contr., v. 5, p. 68–76.

EDWARDS, W. N., 1936, The flora of the London Clay: Geol. Assoc. London Proc., v. 47, p. 22–31.

——, 1955, The geographical distribution of past floras: Adv. Sci., v. 12, p. 165–176.

EMERY, K. O., 1966, Atlantic continental shelf and slope of the United States: geologic background: U.S. Geol. Survey Prof. Paper 529A, 23 p.

——, 1967, The Atlantic continental margin during the past 70 million years, *in* NEALE, E. R. (ed.), Collected papers on the geology of the Atlantic region (Lilly Memorial Vol.): Geol. Assoc. Canada Special Paper 4, 53–70.

——, UCHUPI, E., PHILLIPS, J. D., BOWIN, C. O., BUNCE, E. T., AND KNOTT, S. T., 1970, Continental rise off eastern North America: Am. Assoc. Petroleum Geologists Bull., v. 54, p. 44–108.

EMILIANI, C., 1954, Temperatures of Pacific bottom waters and polar superficial waters during the Tertiary: Science, v. 119, p. 853–855.

——, 1956, Oligocene and Miocene temperatures of the equatorial and subtropical Atlantic Ocean: Jour. Geology, v. 64, p. 281–288.

——, C., 1961a, Cenozoic climatic changes as indicated by the stratigraphy and chronology of deep-sea cores of *Globigerina*-ooze facies. New York Acad. Sci. Ann., v. 95, art. 1, p. 521–536.

——, 1961b, The temperature decrease of surface sea water in high latitudes and of abyssal-hadal water in open oceanic basins during the past 75 million years: Deep-Sea Research, v. 8, p. 144–147.

EWING, J., WINDISCH, C., AND EWING, M., 1970, Correlation of horizon A with JOIDES bore-hole results: Jour. Geophys. Research, v. 75, p. 5645–5653.

——, AND OTHERS, 1970, Deep Sea Drilling Project: Leg 11: Geotimes, v. 15, no. 7, p. 14–16.

FELL, H. B., 1962, West-wind drift dispersal of echinoderms in the southern hemisphere: Nature, v. 193, p. 759–761.

——, 1967, Cretaceous and Tertiary surface currents of the oceans, *in* BARNES, H. (ed.), Oceanogr. Mar. Biol. Ann. Rev. 1967: London, G. Allen and Unwin Ltd., v. 5, p. 317–341.

FISCHER, A. G., 1961, Latitudinal variations in organic diversity: Am. Scientist, v. 49, p. 50–74.

FUGLISTER, F. C., 1960, Atlantic ocean atlas of temperature and salinity profiles and data from the International Geophysical Year of 1957–1958: Woods Hole Massachusetts, Woods Hole Oceanogr. Inst., v. 1, 209 p.

FUNNELL, B. M., 1964, Studies in North Atlantic geology and paleontology; 1, Upper Cretaceous: Geol. Mag., v. 101, p. 421–434.

——, FRIEND, J. K., AND RAMSEY, A. T. S., 1969, Upper Maestrichtian planktonic foraminifera from Galicia Bank, west of Spain: Palaeontology, v. 12, p. 19–41.

——, AND SMITH, A. G., 1968, Opening of the Atlantic Ocean: Nature, v. 219, p. 1328–1333.

GARTNER, S., JR., 1970, Sea-floor spreading, carbonate dissolution level, and the nature of Horizon A: Science, v. 169, p. 1077–1079.

GIBSON, T. G., 1965, Eocene and Miocene rocks off the northeastern coast of the United States: Deep-Sea Research, v. 12, p. 975–981.

——, 1967, Stratigraphy and paleoenvironment of the phosphatic Miocene strata of North Carolina: Geol. Soc. America Bull., v. 78, p. 631–650.

——, 1968, Stratigraphy and paleoenvironment of the phosphatic strata of North Carolina: reply: *ibid.*, v. 79, p. 1437–1448.

——, 1970, Late Mesozoic-Cenozoic tectonic aspects of the Atlantic coastal margin: *ibid.*, v. 81, p. 1813–1822.

——, AND K. M. TOWE, 1971, Eocene volcanism and the origin of Horizon A: Science, v. 172, p. 152–153.

——, HAZEL, J. E., AND MELLO, J. F., 1968, Fossiliferous rocks from submarine canyons off the northeastern United States: U.S. Geol. Survey Prof. Paper 600-D, p. 222–230.

GIGNOUX, M., 1955, Stratigraphic geology: San Francisco, W. H. Freeman and Co., 682 p.

GORDON, W. A., 1970, Biogeography of Jurassic foraminifera: Geol. Soc. America Bull., v. 81, p. 1689–1704.

HALLAM, A., 1967, The bearing of certain palaeozoogeographic data on continental drift: Palaeogeography, Palaeoclimatology, and Palaeoecology, v. 3, p. 201–241.

——, 1969a, Faunal realms and facies in the Jurassic: Palaeontology, v. 12, p. 1–18.

——, 1969b, Tectonism and eustasy in the Jurassic: Earth-Sci. Rev., v. 5, p. 45–68.

——, 1971, Mesozoic geology and the opening of the North Atlantic: Jour. Geology, v. 79, p. 129–157.

HANSEN, H. J., 1970, Danian foraminifera from Nûgssuaq, west Greenland: Grønl. Geol. Unders. Bull. 93, p. 1–132.

HARLAND, W. B., 1967a, Testing a theory of continental drift: Nauchno-Issled. Inst. Geologii Arktiki, Uchennye Zapiski, Regional'naya Geologiya, v. 10, p. 71–98.

——, 1967b, Early history of the North Atlantic Ocean and its margins: Nature, v. 216, p. 464–466.

——, 1969, Contributions of Spitsbergen to understanding of tectonic evolution of North Atlantic region: Am. Assoc. Petroleum Geologists Mem. 12, p. 817–852.

HARRINGTON, H. J., 1962, Paleogeographic development of South America: *ibid.*, Bull., v. 46, p. 1773–1814.

HAYES, D. E., AND OTHERS, 1971, Deep Sea Drilling Project: Leg 14: Geotimes, v. 16, no. 4, p. 14–17.

HAYNES, J., 1955, Pelagic foraminifera in the Thanet Beds, and the use of Thanetian as a stage name: Micropaleontology, v. 1, p. 189.

———, 1956, Certain smaller British Paleocene foraminifera, Part 1, Nonionidae, Chilostomellidae, Epistominidae, Discorbidae, Amphisteginidae, Globigerinidae, Globorotaliidae and Guembelinidae: Cushman Found. Foram. Research, Contr., v. 7, p. 79–101.

———, 1958, Certain smaller British Paleocene foraminifera, Part V, Distribution: ibid., v. 9, p. 83–92.

HAZEL, J. E., 1970, Atlantic continental shelf and slope of the United States—ostracode zoogeography in the southern Nova Scotian and northern Virginian faunal provinces: U.S. Geol. Survey Prof. Paper 529-E, p. 1–21.

HEEZEN, B. C., 1960, The rift in the ocean floor: Sci. American, v. 203, p. 98–110.

———, AND HOLLISTER, C. D., 1964, Deep sea current evidence from abyssal sediments: Marine Geology, v. 2, p. 141–174.

———, ———, AND RUDDIMAN, W. F., 1966, Shaping of the continental rise by geostrophic contour currents: Science, v. 151, p. 502–508.

———, AND JOHNSON, G. L., 1969, Mediterranean undercurrent and microphysiography west of Gibraltar: Monaco, Inst. Océanographique Bull., v. 68, 95 p.

———, AND HOLLISTER, C. D., 1969, Northwest Atlantic Mid-Ocean Canyon: Canadian Jour. Earth Sci., v. 6, p. 1441–1453.

———, SCHNEIDER, E. D., AND PILKEY, O. H., 1966, Sediment transport by the Antarctic Bottom Current on Bermuda Rise: Nature, v. 211, p. 611–612.

HEIRTZLER, J. R., AND HAYES, D. E., 1967, Magnetic boundaries in the North Atlantic Ocean: Science, v. 157, p. 185–187.

———, DICKSON, G. O., HERRON, E. M., PITMAN, W. C., AND LE PICHON, X., 1968, Marine magnetic anomalies, geomagnetic field reversals, and motions of the ocean floor and continents: Jour. Geophys. Research, v. 73, p. 2119–2136.

HESS, H. H., 1962, History of the ocean basins, in ENGEL, A. E. J., JAMES, H. L., AND LEONARD, B. F. (eds.), Petrologic studies, a volume in honor of A. F. Buddington: Geol. Soc. America, p. 599–620.

HILTEN, D. VAN, 1964, Evolution of some geotectonic hypotheses by paleomagnetism: Tectonophysics, v. 1, p. 3–71.

HILTERMANN, H., 1963, Zur Entwicklung der Benthos-Foraminifere Bolivinoides, in KOENIGSWALD, G. H. R. VON, EMEIS, J. D., BUNING, W. L., AND WAGNER, C. W., Evolutionary trends in foraminifera: Amsterdam, Elsevier Pub. Co., p. 198–222.

———, AND KOCH, W., 1950, Taxonomie und Verticalverbreitung von Bolivinoides—Arten im Senon Nordwestdeutschlands: Geol. Jahrb., v. 64, p. 595–632.

HOFKER, J., 1956, Tertiary foraminifera of coastal Ecuador: Part II, Additional notes on the Eocene species: Jour. Paleontology, v. 30, p. 891–958.

———, 1957, Foraminiferen der Oberkreide von Nordwestdeutschland und Holland: Geol. Jahrb., Beih., H. 27, 464 p.

———, 1963, Einige planktonische Foraminiferen aus dem borealen europaischen Oligozan: Neues Jahrb. Geologie u. Palaeontogie, Abh., v. 118, p. 197–206.

———, 1966, Maestrichtian, Danian and Paleocene foraminifera: Palaeontographica Suppl., v. 10, p. 1–376.

———, 1968, Tertiary foraminifera of coastal Ecuador: lower Oligocene and lower Miocene: Palaeontographica, v. 130, pt. A., p. 1059.

HOLLISTER, C. D., AND OTHERS, 1972, Initial reports of the Deep Sea Drilling Project: Washington, D.C., U.S. Govt. Printing Office, v. 11, xii + 1077 p.

———, AND HEEZEN, B. C., 1967, The floor of the Bellingshausen Sea: Johns Hopkins Oceanogr. Studies, v. 3, p. 177–189.

———, AND ———, 1972, Geologic effects of ocean bottom currents, in GORDON, A. L. (ed.), Studies in physical oceanography: New York, Gordon and Breach, v. 2, p. 37–66.

IKEBE, N., TAKAYANAGI, Y., CHIJI, M., AND CHINZEI, K., 1972, Neogene biostratigraphy and radiometric time-scale of Japan—an attempt at intercontinental correlation: Pacific Geology, v. 4, p. 39–78.

IMLAY, R., 1965, Jurassic marine faunal differentiation in North America: Jour. Paleontology, v. 39, p. 1023–1238.

ISELIN, C. O'D., 1936, A study of the circulation of the western North Atlantic: Papers in Phys. Oceanography and Meteorology, v. 4, p. 1–101.

JOHNSON, G. L., AND HEEZEN, B. C., 1967, Morphology and evolution of the Norwegian-Greeland Sea: Deep-Sea Research, v. 14, p. 755–771.

JONES, E. J. W., EWING, M., EWING, J. I., AND EITTREIM, S. L., 1970, Influences of Norwegian Sea overflow water on sedimentation in the northern North Atlantic and Labrador Sea: Jour. Geophys. Research, v. 75, p. 1655–1680.

KAASCHIETER, J. P. H., 1961, Foraminifera of the Eocene of Belgium: Inst. Roy. Sci. Nat. Belgique Mém. 147, p. 1–271.

KANEPS, A. G., 1970, Late Neogene biogeography and depositional history (Ph.D. thesis): New York, Columbia Univ., 185 p.

KAY, M., 1969, Continental drift in the North Atlantic Ocean: Am. Assoc. Petroleum Geologists Mem. 12, p. 965–973.

KLENOVA, M. C. (ed.), 1967, Oceanographic research in the Atlantic: Izd. Akad. Nauk SSSR, Inst. Okeanol., Trudy, v. 56, 1962, 322 p. (translated by Israel Program Sci. Translations).

KNAUSS, J. A., 1965, A technique for measuring deep ocean currents close to the bottom with an unattached current meter and some preliminary results: Jour. Marine Research, v. 23, p. 237–245.

———, 1969, A note on the transport of the Gulf Stream: Deep-Sea Research, v. 16, p. 117–123.

KRÖMMELBEIN, K., 1962, Zur Taxionomie und biochronologic stratigraphisch wichtiger Ostracoden-Arten aus der oberjurassisch?-unterkretazischen Bahia-Serie (Wealden-Fazies) NE Brasiliens: Senck. Lethaia, v. 43, p. 437–537.

———, AND WENGER, R., 1966, Sur quelques analogies remarquables dans les microfaunes Crétacées du Gabon et du Brasil oriental (Bahia et Sergipe), in Bassins sedimentaires du littoral Africain, Part 1: Paris, Union Inst. Sci. Geol. Assoc. Service Geol. Afr., p. 193–196.

KURTÉN, G., 1966, Holarctic land connections in the early Tertiary: Soc. Sci. Fenn. Commentat. Biol., v. 29, p. 1–5.

———, 1967, Continental drift and the palaeogeography of reptiles and mammals: ibid., v. 31, p. 1–8.

———, 1969, Continental drift and evolution: Sci. American, v. 220, p. 54–64.

LANCELOT, Y., HATHAWAY, J. C., AND HOLLISTER, C. D., 1972, Lithology of sediments from the western North Atlantic, in HOLLISTER, C. D., AND OTHERS, Initial reports of the Deep Sea Drilling Project: Washington, D.C., U.S. Govt. Printing Office, v. 11, p. 901–949.

LAUGHTON, A. S., AND OTHERS, 1970, Deep Sea Drilling Project, Leg 12: Geotimes, v. 15, no. 9, p. 10–14.

———, AND OTHERS, 1972, Initial reports of the Deep Sea Drilling Project: Washington, D.C., U.S. Govt. Printing Office, v. 12, xxi + 1243 p.

LE PICHON, X., 1968, Sea-floor spreading and continental drift: Jour. Geophys. Research, v. 73, p. 3661–3697.

———, HYNDMAN, R., AND PAUTOT, G., 1971, Geophysical study of the opening of the Labrador Sea: ibid., v. 76, p. 4724–4743.

LEWIS, G. F, AND STRACZEK, J. A., 1955, Geology of south-central Oriente, Cuba: U.S. Geol. Survey Bull. 975D, p. 175–366.

LORENZ, C., 1969, Contribution a l'étude stratigraphique de l'Oligocène et du Miocène inférieur des confins Liguro-Piemontais (Italie): Univ. Genova Atti del'Inst. Geol., v. 6, p. 253–888.

LOWENSTAM, H. A., 1964, Palaeotemperatures of the Permian and Cretaceous Periods, in NAIRN, A. E. (ed.), Problems in palaeoclimatology, New York, Interscience, p. 277–278.

———, AND EPSTEIN, S., 1954, Paleotemperatures of the post-Aptian Cretaceous as determined by the oxygen isotope method: Jour. Geology, v. 62, p. 207–248.

LUTERBACHER, H., 1972, Foraminifera from the Lower Cretaceous and Upper Jurassic of the northwestern Atlantic (preliminary note), in HOLLISTER, C. D., AND OTHERS, Initial reports of the Deep Sea Drilling Project: Washington, D.C., U.S. Govt. Printing Office, v. 11, p. 561–576.

LUYENDYK, B. P., FORSYTH, D., AND PHILLIPS, J. D., 1972, Experimental approach to the paleocirculation of the oceanic surface waters: Geol. Soc. America Bull., v. 83, p. 2649–2664.

MACGILLAVRY, H. J., 1970, Geological history of the Caribbean: K. Nederl. Akad. Wetensch., ser. B, no. 73, p. 64–96.

McKENNA, M. C., 1971, Fossil mammals and the Eocene demise of the De Geer North Atlantic dispersal route: Geol. Soc. America, Abs. with Programs, v. 3, p. 644.

———, 1972, Eocene final separation of the Eurasian and Greenland-North American land masses: 24th Internat. Geol. Cong., sec. 7, p. 275–281.

McKENZIE, K. G., 1967, The distribution of Caenozoic marine Ostracoda from the Gulf of Mexico to Australia, in ADAMS, C. B., AND AGER, D. V. (eds.), Aspects of Tethyan biogeography: System. Assoc. Pub. 7, p. 219–238.

———, AND HUSSAINY, S. U., 1968, Relevance of a freshwater cytherid (Crustacea, Ostracoda) to the continental drift hypothesis: Nature, v. 220, p. 806–808.

MARGOLIS, S. V., AND KENNETT, J. P., 1970, Antarctic glaciation during the Tertiary recorded in sub-Antarctic deep-sea cores: Science, v. 170, p. 1085–1087.

MAXWELL, A. E., AND OTHERS, 1970, Initial reports of the Deep Sea Drilling Project: Washington, D.C., U.S. Govt. Printing Office, v. 3, xx + 806 p.

MAY, P. R., 1971, Pattern of Triassic-Jurassic diabase dikes around the North Atlantic in the context of predrift position of the continents: Geol. Soc. America Bull., v. 82, p. 1285–1292.

MAYNC, W., 1961, Foraminiferal key biozones in the Lower Cretaceous of the western hemisphere and the Tethys province, 20th Internat. Geol. Cong., Symposium Cretacico, v. 1, p. 85–112.

McINTYRE, A., RUDDIMAN, W. F., AND JANTZEN, R., 1972, Southward penetrations of the North Atlantic polar front: faunal and floral evidence of large scale surface water mass movements over the past 225,000 years: Deep-Sea Research, v. 19, p. 61–77.

MEYERHOFF, A. A., 1967, Future hydrocarbon provinces of Gulf of Mexico-Caribbean region: Gulf Coast Assoc. Geol. Soc. Trans., v. 17, p. 217–260.

———, 1970a, Continental drift: implications of paleomagnetic studies, meteorology, physical oceanography, and climatology: Jour. Geology, v. 78, p. 1–51.

———, 1970b, Continental drift II: high latitude evaporite deposits and geologic history of Arctic and North Atlantic oceans: ibid., p. 406–444.

MOSBY, H., 1934, The waters of the Atlantic Antarctic Ocean: Norwegian Antarctic Exped. 1927–1928, Sci. Results, v. 1, p. 1–131.

NEUMAYR, M., 1883, Über klimatische Zonen während der Jura- und Kreidzeit, Akad. Wiss. Wien, Denkschr., Math. Naturw. Kl., v. 47, p. 277–310.

NEWELL, N. D., Periodicity in invertebrate evolution: Jour. Paleontology, v. 26, p. 371–385.

———, 1956, Catastrophism and the fossil record: Evolution, v. 10, p. 97–101.

———, 1963, Crises in the history of life: Sci. American, v. 208, p. 76–92.

———, 1967, Revolution in the history of life: Geol. Soc. America Special Paper 89, p. 63–91.

OLSSON, R. K., 1960, Foraminifera of latest Cretaceous and earliest Tertiary age in the New Jersey coastal plain: Jour. Paleontology, v. 34, p. 1–59.

———, 1964, Late Cretaceous planktonic foraminifera from New Jersey and Delaware: Micropaleontology, v. 10, p. 157–188.

————, 1970a, Paleocene planktonic foraminiferal biostratigraphy and paleozoogeography of New Jersey: Jour. Paleontology, v. 44, p. 589–597.
————, 1970b, Planktonic foraminifera from the base of the Tertiary, Millers Ferry, Alabama: Jour. Paleontology, v. 44, p. 598–604.
PALMER, K. V. M., 1967, A comparison of certain Eocene molluscs of the Americas with those of the western Tethys, in ADAMS, C. G., AND AGER, D. B. (eds.), Aspects of Tethyan biogeography, System. Assoc. Pub. 7, p. 183–193.
PESSAGNO, E. A., JR., 1967, Upper Cretaceous planktonic foraminifera from the western Gulf Coastal Plain: Paleontogr. Americana, v. 5, p. 249–441.
PHILLIPS, J. D., 1970, Magnetic anomalies in the Red Sea: Roy. Soc. London Philos. Trans., ser. A, v. 267, p. 205–217.
————, AND FORSYTH, D., 1972, Plate tectonics, paleomagnetism and the opening of the Atlantic: Geol. Soc. America Bull., v. 83, p. 1579–1600.
————, AND LUYENDYK, B. C., 1970, Central North Atlantic plate motions over the last 40 million years: Science, v. 170, p. 727–729.
PITMAN, W. C., AND TALWANI, M., 1972, Sea-floor spreading in the North Atlantic: Geol. Soc. America Bull., v. 83, p. 619–646.
PLUMMER, H. J., 1926, Foraminifera of the Midway Formation in Texas: Univ. Texas Bull. 2644, p. 9–198.
POZARYSKA, K., 1965, Foraminifera and biostratigraphy of the Danian and Montian in Poland: Palaeontologia Polonica, no. 14, 154 p.
————, AND SZCZECHURA, J., 1968, Foraminifera from the Paleocene of Poland, their ecological and biostratigraphical meaning: ibid., no. 20, 107 p.
POZARYSKI, W., AND POZARYSKA, K., 1960, On the Danian and lower Paleocene sediments in Poland: 21st Internat. Geol. Cong. Copenhagen, pt. 5, p. 170–180.
RAMSAY, A. T. S., 1970, The pre-Pleistocene stratigraphy and paleontology of the Palmer Ridge area (northeast Atlantic): Marine Geology, v. 9, p. 261–285.
RAVN, J. P. J., 1904, Tertiary fauna at Cape Dalton in east Greenland: Meddel. Grønland, v. 29, p. 93–140.
————, 1918, De marine Kridtaflejringer i Vestgrønland og deres fauna: ibid., v. 56, p. 309–366.
REID, R. E. H., 1967, Tethys and the zoogeography of some modern and Mesozoic Porifera, in ADAMS, C. G., AND AGER, D. V. (eds.), Aspects of Tethyan biogeography: System. Assoc., Pub. 7, p. 171–181.
REID, E. M., AND CHANDLER, M. E. J., 1933, The London Clay flora: British Mus. (Nat. History), 561 p.
REYMENT, R. A., 1969, Ammonite biostratigraphy, continental drift and oscillatory transgressions: Nature, v. 224, p. 137–140.
————, 1971, Experimental studies of Cretaceous transgressions for Africa: Geol. Soc. America Bull., v. 82, p. 1063–1072.
————, 1972, Cretaceous history of the South Atlantic Ocean, in Continental drift, sea-floor spreading and plate tectonics: implications for the Earth Sciences: North Atlantic Treaty Organization Adv. Study Inst. (Newcastle-upon-Tyne, England, April 10–14, 1972), 15 p. (preprint).
————, AND TAIT, E. A., 1972, Biostratigraphical dating of the early history of the South Atlantic Ocean: Roy. Soc. London Philos. Trans., ser. B., Biol. Sci., v. 264, p. 55–95.
ROSENKRANTZ, A., 1970, Marine Upper Cretaceous and lowermost Tertiary deposits in west Greenland: Dansk. Geol. Fören. Meddel, v. 19, p. 406–453.
ROWE, G. T., AND MENZIES, R. J., 1968, Deep bottom currents off the coast of North Carolina: Deep-Sea Research, v. 15, p. 711–719.
RUDDIMAN, W. F., 1968, Historical stability of the Gulf Stream meander belt: foraminiferal evidence: ibid., p. 137–148.
————, 1969, Planktonic foraminifera of the sub-tropical North Atlantic gyre (Ph.D. thesis): New York, Columbia Univ., 291 p.
RYAN, W. B. F., AND OTHERS, 1970, Deep Sea Drilling Project, Leg 13: Geotimes, v. 15, no. 10, p. 12–15.
————, 1973, Initial reports of the Deep Sea Drilling Project: Washington, D.C., U.S. Govt. Printing Office, v. 13, xxiii + 1447 p.
SAITO, T., BURCKLE, L. H., AND HORN, D. K., 1967, Palaeocene core from the Norwegian basin: Nature, v. 216, p. 357–359.
SANDER, N. J., 1970, Structural evolution of the Mediterranean region during the Mesozoic Era, in ALVAREZ, W., AND GOHRBANDT, K. H. A. (eds.), Geology and history of Sicily: Petroleum Explor. Soc. Libya, p. 43–132.
SAVAGE, R. J. G., 1967, Early Miocene mammal faunas of the Tethyan region, in ADAMS, C. G., AND AGER, D. V. (eds.), Aspects of Tethyan biogeography, System. Assoc. Pub. 7, p. 247–282.
SCHEIBNEROVA, V., 1971a, Palaeoecology and palaeogeography of Cretaceous deposits of the Great Artesian Basin (Australia): Geol. Survey New South Wales Rec., v. 13, p. 1–48.
————, 1971b, Foraminifera and the Mesozoic biogeoprovinces: ibid., p. 135–174.
————, 1971c, The Great Artesian Basin, Australia, a type area of the Austral biogeoprovince of the southern hemisphere, equivalent to the Boreal biogeoprovince of the northern hemisphere: 2nd Internat. Conf. Planktonic Microfossils, Proc., v. 2, p. 1129–1138.
SCHNEIDER, E. D., 1969a, The deep-sea—a habitat for petroleum: Undersea Technology, v. 10, p. 32–36.
————, 1969b, The evolution of the continental margins and possible long term economic resources: Houston, Texas, Offshore Technology Conf., p. 257–264.
————, AND JOHNSON, G. L., 1970, Deep-ocean diapir occurrences: Am. Assoc. Petroleum Geologists Bull., v. 54, p. 2151–2169.
SCHUCHERT, C., 1955, Atlas of paleogeographic maps of North America: New York, John Wiley and Sons, xi + 177 p.
SCHWARZBACH, M., 1952, Aus der Klimageschichte des Rheinlandes: Geol. Rundschau, v. 40, p. 128–136.
————, 1961, Das Klima der Vorzeit: Stuttgart, F. Enke Verlag, 275 p.

————, 1963, Climates of the past: London, D. Van Nostrand Co., Ltd., 328 p.

SEN GUPTA, B. K., AND GRANT, A. C., 1972, *Orbitolina*, a Cretaceous larger foraminifer, from Flemish Cap: paleoceanographic implications: Science, v. 173, p. 934–936.

SHAPLEY, H., AND OTHERS, 1953, Climatic change, evidence, causes and effects: Cambridge, Massachusetts, Harvard Univ. Press, 318 p.

SIMPSON, G. G., 1947a, Holarctic mammalian faunas and continental relationships during the Cenozoic: Geol. Soc. America Bull., v. 58, p. 613–687.

————, 1947b, Evolution, interchange and resemblance of the North American and Eurasian Cenozoic mammalian faunas: Evolution, v. 1, p. 218–220.

SITTLER, C., AND MILLOT, G., 1965, Les climates du Paléogène français reconstituées par les argiles néoformées et les microflores: Geol. Rundschau, v. 54, p. 333–343.

SMITH, A. G., AND HALLAM, A., 1970, The fit of southern continents: Nature, v. 225, p. 139–144.

SMITH, L., 1971a, Tertiary and late Mesozoic history of the shelf regions of the eastern Canadian continental margin (abs): Earth Sci. Symposium Offshore Eastern Canada, Ottawa, Feb. 22–24, 1971.

————, 1971b, Continental drift and the Grand Banks—Scotan Shelf salt domes (abs.) *ibid.*

SORGENFREI, T., 1958, Molluscan assemblages from the marine middle Miocene of South Jutland and their environments: Geol. Survey Denmark, ser. 2, v. 79, p. 1–503.

SPAINK, G., 1958, De Nederlandse Eemogen. 1, Algemeen Overzicht: K. Nederl. Natuurhist. Ver., Wetensch. Meded., v. 29, p. 1–44.

SPROLL, W. P., AND DIETZ, R. S., 1969, Morphological continental fit of Australia and Antarctica: Nature, v. 222, p. 345–348.

STAESCHE, K., AND HILTERMANN, H., 1940, Mikrofaunen aus dem Tertiär Nordwestdeutschlands: Reichsanst. Bodenforsch. Abh., new ser., v. 201, 26 p.

STEELE, J. H., BARRETT, J. R., AND WORTHINGTON, L. V., 1962, Deep currents south of Iceland: Deep-Sea Research, v. 9, p. 465–474.

STEVENS, G. K., 1963, Faunal realms in Jurassic and Cretaceous belemnites: Geol. Mag., v. 102, p. 175–178.

STRAUCH, F., 1968, Determination of Cenozoic sea-temperature using *Hiatella arctica* (Linné): Palaeogeography, Palaeoclimatology, and Palaeoecology, v. 5, p. 213–233.

STOMMEL, H., 1960, The Gulf Stream: A physical and dynamical description: Berkeley, Univ. Calif. Press, 202 p.

STRIDE, A. H., CURRAY, J. R., MOORE, D. G., AND BELDERSON, R. H., 1969, Marine geology of the Atlantic continental margin of Europe. Roy. Soc. London Philos. Trans, ser. A, v. 264, p. 31 75.

SWALLOW, J. C., AND WORTHINGTON, L. V., 1961, An observation of a deep countercurrent in the western North Atlantic: Deep-Sea Research, v. 8, p. 1–19.

————, AND ————, 1969, Deep currents in the Labrador Sea: *ibid.*, v. 16, p. 77–84.

SZALAY, F. S., AND MCKENNA, M. C., 1971, Beginning of the age of mammals in Asia: the late Paleocene Gashato fauna, Mongolia: Am. Mus. Nat. History Bull. 144, p. 269–318.

TABER, S., 1934, Sierra Maestra of Cuba, part of the northern rim of the Bartlett Trough: Geol. Soc. America Bull., v. 45, p. 567–619.

TARLING, D. H., 1971, Gondwanaland, palaeomagnetism and continental drift: Nature, v. 229, p. 17–21.

UCHUPI, E. AND EMERY, K. O., 1968, Structure of continental margin off Gulf Coast of United States: Am. Assoc. Petroleum Geologists Bull., v. 52, p. 1162–1193.

UHLIG, B., 1911, Die marinen Reiche des Jura und der Unterkreide: Geol. Gesell. Mitt., Wien., v. 4, p. 329–448.

VALENTINE, J. W., 1967, The influence of climatic fluctuations on species diversity within the Tethyan provincial system, *in* ADAMS, C. G., AND AGER, D. V. (eds.), Aspects of Tethyan biogeography: System. Assoc. Pub. 7, p. 153–166.

————, 1969, Patterns of taxonomic and ecological structure of the shelf benthos during Phanerozoic time: Palaeontology, v. 12, p. 684–709.

————, AND MOORES, E. M., 1970, Plate-tectonic regulation of faunal diversity and sea level—a model: Nature, v. 228, p. 657–659.

VAN COUVERING, J., 1972, Radiometric calibration of the European Neogene, *in* BISHOP, W. W., AND MILLER, J. A. (eds.), Symposium on calibration of hominid evolution: Chicago (Burg Wartenstein Symposium no. 52).

————, AND MILLER, J. A., 1971, Argon isotope age of the Samos Hipparion faunas and late Miocene chronostratigraphy: Nature, v. 230, p. 559–563.

VASSILENKO V. P., 1961, Foraminifery verkhnogo mela poluostrova mangyshlaka: Vses. Neftyan. Nauchno-Issled. Geologo-Razved. Inst. (VNIGRI), Trudy, v. 171, 487 p.

VEEVERS, J. J., JONES, J. G., AND TALENT, J. A., 1971, Indo-Australian stratigraphy and the configuration and dispersal of Gondwanaland: Nature, v. 229, p. 383–388.

VINE, F. J., AND HESS, H. H., 1971, Sea-floor spreading, *in* MAXWELL, A. E. (ed.), The Sea, New York, Interscience, v. 4, p. 587–622.

VOLKMANN, G., 1962, Deep current observations in the western North Atlantic: Deep-Sea Research, v. 9, p. 493–500.

WATSON, J. A. AND JOHNSON, G. L., 1970, Mediterranean diapiric structures: Am. Assoc. Petroleum Geologists Bull., v. 52, p. 2247–2249.

WEGENER, A., 1915, Die Entstehung der Kontinente und Ozeane: Braunschweig, Germany, Vieweg, 94 p.

————, 1924, The origin of continents and oceans: London, Methuen and Co., Ltd., 212 p.

————, 1966, The origin of continents and oceans (translation by John Biram of 4th revised German edition): New York, Dover Pub., Inc., 246 p.

WHITE, E. I., 1931, The vertebrate faunas of the English Eocene: British Mus. (Nat. History), 121 p.

WILLIAMS, C. A., AND MCKENZIE, D., 1971, The evolution of the northeast Atlantic: Nature, v. 232, p. 168–173.

WOODRING, W. P., 1954, Caribbean land and sea through the ages: Geol. Soc. America Bull., v. 65, p. 719–732.

———, 1956, The Panama land bridge as a sea barrier: Am. Philos. Soc. Proc., v. 110, p. 425–433.

WORSLEY, T. R., AND MARTINI, E., 1970, Late Maastrichtian nannoplankton provinces: Nature, v. 225, p. 1242–1243.

WORTHINGTON, L. V., 1971, The Arctic Mediterranean Seas: Oceanus, v. 16, p. 2–7.

———, AND METCALF, W. G., 1961, The relationship between potential temperature and salinity in deep Atlantic water: Rap. Proc. Verb. Reun. Cons. Perm. Int. Expl. Mer., v. 149, p. 122–128.

———, AND VOLKMANN, G. H., 1965, The volume transport of the Norwegian Sea overflor water in the North Atlantic: Deep-Sea Research, v. 12, p. 667–676.

———, AND WRIGHT, W. R., 1970, North Atlantic Ocean atlas of potential temperature and salinity in the deep water: Woods Hole Oceanogr. Inst. Atlas Ser., v. 2, 58 p.

WRIGHT, W. R., AND WORTHINGTON, L. V., 1970, The water masses of the North Atlantic Ocean, a volumetric census of temperature and salinity: Serial Atlas of Marine Environment, Washington, D.C., American Geographical Society, Folio 19.

WÜST, G., 1936, Schichtung und Zirkulation des Atlantischen Ozeans. Das Bodenwasser und die Stratosphäre: Wiss. Erg. Deutsch. Atlant. Exped. METEOR 1925–1927, v. 6, p. 1–228.

———, 1955, Stromgeschwindigkeiten im Tiefen- und Bodenwasser des Atlantischen Ozeans: Deep-Sea Research, v. 3 (suppl.), p. 373–397.

———, 1957, Quantitative Untersuchungen zur Statik und Dynamik des Atlantischen Ozeans: Stromgeschwindigkeiten und Strommengen in den Tiefen des Atlantischen Ozeans: Wiss. Erg. Deutsch. Atlant. Exped. METEOR 1925–1927, v. 6, p. 261–420.

———, AND DEFANT, A., 1936, Atlas zur Schichtung und Zirkulation des Atlantischen Ozeans: *ibid.*, v. 6, p. 103.

ZIMMERMAN, H. B., AND HOLLISTER, C. D., 1970, Contour currents on the continental rise: Am. Geophys. Union Trans., v. 51, p. 336.

MARINE EVAPORITES AND THE COMPOSITION OF SEA WATER DURING THE PHANEROZOIC

HEINRICH D. HOLLAND

Harvard University, Cambridge, Massachusetts

ABSTRACT

The mineralogy and chemistry of marine evaporites sets limits on excursions of the composition of sea water which may have occurred during the Phanerozoic. The permitted volume occupied by Phanerozoic sea water in $\log m_{SO_4^-} - \log m_{Ca^{+2}} - \log m_{HCO_3^-}$ space has roughly the shape of a doubly terminated pyramid. Present-day sea water lies near the center of the permitted volume. The maximum permitted concentration of all the major components in sea water is modest. This is particularly true of Ca^{+2} and HCO_3^-; the oceans have apparently been able to dispose effectively of river alkalinity during the entire Phanerozoic.

INTRODUCTION

Sillén's (1961) paper on the physical chemistry of sea water has had a profound effect on research into the chemistry and chemical evolution of the oceans in the decade since its publication. It stimulated a more thorough analysis of inputs to and outputs from the oceans, and forced a reassessment of the value of the concept of slightly perturbed equilibrium in describing the chemistry of the oceans. The identification of the processes by which sodium, potassium, and magnesium are removed from the oceans has proved unexpectedly difficult (see for instance Russell, 1970). Thermodynamics therefore no longer appears to be as definitive a basis for arguments concerning the history of ocean water, and other sources of data bearing on this problem have become increasingly welcome. Another article in this volume (Garrels and Mackenzie) has suggested that changes in ocean chemistry during the past two billion years have been relatively minor. This paper discusses the limits set on excursions in ocean chemistry by evidence from the mineralogy and chemistry of marine evaporites. Some of these ideas have been presented in Holland (1972).

DISCUSSION

Evaporites are a useful source of data concerning changes in ocean chemistry. Unfortunately, the bulk chemistry of marine evaporites is not related to the chemistry of sea water in a simple way. During the development of marine evaporites, periods of ready access of sea water normally alternate with periods of extensive evaporation and the relative proportions of minerals in evaporites are rarely, if ever, a measure of the relative proportions of their constituents in contemporary sea water. Carbonates and sulfates are typically overrepresented, and chlorides are typically underrepresented in marine evaporites. Furthermore the distribution of minerals in evaporites is frequently modified by

late brines derived from the dehydration of gypsum and by groundwaters completely unrelated to the evaporites themselves. It is therefore impossible to base an accurate assessment of the composition of sea water on the mineralogy and/or the chemistry of marine evaporite sequences.

Nevertheless some interesting limits can be set on possible excursions of the concentration of several major components of sea water during the Phanerozoic. Phanerozoic evaporite sequences typically begin with the formation of a carbonate section; this passes into a gypsum-anhydrite section, which in turn is followed by a halite section. The major differences between marine evaporites begin during the halite section and extend to the crystallization of the final bitterns.

The carbonate-gypsum-halite sequence can be observed in the laboratory by evaporating present-day sea water. Surface ocean waters are saturated or slightly supersaturated with respect to calcite, aragonite, and dolomite. One or both of the $CaCO_3$ polymorphs precipitates on evaporation. As the concentration (m) of calcium in sea water is considerably larger than that of HCO_3^-, (see table 1) the concentration of Ca^{+2} increases and that of HCO_3^- decreases during the initial stages of seawater evaporation. The $SO_4^=$ concentration rises during evaporation, and the product $m_{Ca^{+2}} \cdot m_{SO_4^-}$ gradually approaches the value of this product in NaCl solutions saturated with respect to gypsum. Gypsum saturation is reached after sea water has been reduced to something between 0.25 and 0.20 of its initial volume. Gypsum nucleates relatively easily, and the product $m_{Ca^{+2}} \cdot m_{SO_4^-}$ in naturally occurring brines falls surprisingly close to the gypsum saturation curve in figure 1 (D. J. J. Kinsman, personal communication, 1971). When the volume of sea water has been reduced to approximately one-tenth of its initial volume, halite saturation is reached, and halite

TABLE 1.—THE PRESENT AND THE PROBABLE MINIMUM AND MAXIMUM CONCENTRATION OF THE MAJOR
CONSTITUENTS OF SEA WATER

Cation	Concentrations (m mol/kg)			Anion	Concentrations (m mol/kg)		
	Minimum	Present	Maximum		Minimum	Present	Maximum
Na^+	[230]*	468	950	Cl^-	[270]	545	1100
Mg^{+2}	5	53.3	(200)	$SO_4^=$	2	28.2	300
Ca^{+2}	1	10.3	30	HCO_3^-	0.1	2.3	20
K^+	(5)	9.9	(20)				

* Bracketed figures are quite uncertain.

plus gypsum and/or anhydrite are precipitated.

Since the evaporation of present-day sea water offers an immediate explanation for the early stages of evaporite sequences deposited during the Phanerozoic, the existence of these sequences demands no changes in the composition of sea water during the past 600 million years. They do not, however, prove that the composition of sea water has remained unchanged during the Phanerozoic. This paper sets out to explore just how much the composition of sea water could have varied without giving rise to marine evaporite sequences which differ from those in the geologic record.

The problem consists effectively of mapping out a volume in 7-dimensional space (m_{Na^+}, $m_{Mg^{+2}}$, $m_{Ca^{+2}}$, m_{K^+}, m_{Cl^-}, $m_{SO_4^-}$, $m_{HCO_3^-}$) within which the composition of sea water can move without giving rise to unobserved evaporite sequences. Because we will be dealing mainly with the earlier stages of evaporite formation, m_{K^+} is of no great significance. The major parameters are $m_{Ca^{+2}}$, $m_{SO_4^-}$, $m_{HCO_3^-}$, and m_{NaCl} (which is taken to be roughly the mean of $m_{Na^{+2}}$ and

m_{Cl^-}). $m_{Mg^{+2}}$ is linked to $m_{Ca^{+2}}$ via the requirement that dolomite be made in fair abundance in marine sediments but that magnesite be rare.

Figures 2 through 5 can be regarded as sections through the proposed 7-dimensional volume at constant $m_{SO_4^-}$ and m_{NaCl}. In figure 2 m_{NaCl} and $m_{SO_4^-}$ are set equal to their present value in sea water; the circle indicates the calcium and bicarbonate concentration in ocean water today. If the calcium concentration of the present ocean were tripled, gypsum saturation would be reached, and gypsum would begin to be a constant companion of limestones in slightly evaporative settings. It would also become a constituent of cold water, near surface marine sediments, because the solubility of gypsum decreases with decreasing temperature. Sea water saturation with gypsum seems to be ruled out by the geologic record of the past 2 billion years. The gypsum saturation line is therefore a strong fence against excurions of sea water composition in the direction of high calcium and high sulfate concentrations.

At sulfate concentrations lower than the present value the calcium concentration at the gypsum saturation line is proportionately greater. If sea water ever approached a composition in which $m_{Ca^{+2}} \gg m_{SO_4^-}$, sulfate would be virtually removed during gypsum and/or anhydrite precipitation; the later brines would contain excess Ca^{+2} and would be strongly deficient in $SO_4^=$. This has apparently never happened. Typically Ca^{+2} is strongly depleted, and $SO_4^=$ with Mg^{+2} are concentrated in the later brines. $m_{Ca^{+2}}$ after $CaCO_3$ precipitation has therefore apparently never exceeded $m_{SO_4^-}$, and the boundary

$$m_{Ca^{+2}} = m_{SO_4^-} + \frac{m_{HCO_3^-}}{2} \qquad (1)$$

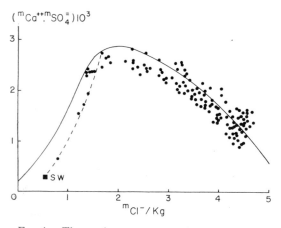

FIG. 1.—The product $m_{Ca^{+2}} \cdot m_{SO_4^-}$ in NaCl solutions saturated with respect to gypsum and in sea water undergoing evaporation. (Courtesy of D. J. J. Kinsman.)

seems to be a second important fence. Figure 3 and particularly figure 4 show that saturation of normal sea water with respect to gypsum becomes progressively more unlikely toward lower sulfate concentrations.

At any given sulfate and NaCl concentration the minimum value of $m_{Ca^{+2}}$ is set by the requirement that gypsum saturation be reached before halite saturation during the evaporation of sea water. In present-day sea water $m_{Ca^{+2}}$ could be as low as 1/30 of the present concentration before halite would begin to precipitate before gypsum. Toward lower sulfate concentrations (figs. 3 and 4) the minimum value of $m_{Ca^{+2}}$ rises progressively toward higher sulfate concentrations (fig. 5), the minimum value of $m_{Ca^{+2}}$ decreases.

The limit of the area defined by the calcium and bicarbonate concentration in Phanerozoic sea water is close to the line

$$m_{Ca^{+2}} = \frac{m_{HCO_3^-}}{2}$$

If $m_{HCO_3^-}$ were to exceed $2m_{Ca^{+2}}$, calcium would be depleted, and the concentration of HCO_3^- would increase in sea water during $CaCO_3$ precipitation. This in turn would lead to the appearance of bicarbonate minerals during the later stages of sea water evaporation. Although minerals such as nahcolite ($NaHCO_3$), and trona ($Na_2CO_3 \cdot NaHCO_3 \cdot 2H_2O$) are common in nonmarine evaporites, they have not been reported from marine evaporites (see for instance Braitsch, 1962; Stewart, 1963), and it is virtually certain that the oceans have never reached the composition of soda lakes during the Phanerozoic.

The eastern boundary is not, however, precisely defined. Dolomite typically accompanies calcite in the carbonate sections of evaporites.

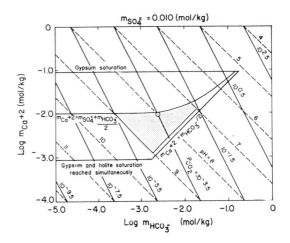

FIG. 3.—Limitations on the Ca^{+2} and HCO_3^- content of Phanerozoic sea water imposed by the mineralogy of evaporites when $m_{SO_4^-}=0.010$ moles/kg and $m_{NaCl}=0.55$ moles/kg.

The number of moles (M) of HCO_3^- removed per kilogram of sea water during carbonate precipitation will therefore be twice the sum of the number of moles of calcium and magnesium precipitated.

$$\Delta M_{HCO_3^-} = 2(\Delta M_{Ca^{+2}} + \Delta M_{Mg^{+2}})?$$

In extreme cases dolomite alone may be deposited, and

$$\Delta M_{HCO_3^-} \cong 4\Delta M_{Ca^{+2}}$$

The concentration of HCO_3^- might therefore be as much as four times that of calcium before

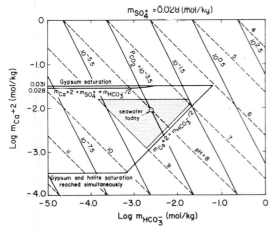

FIG. 2.—Limitations on the Ca^{+2} and HCO_3^- content of Phanerozoic sea water imposed by the mineralogy of evaporites when $m_{SO_4}=0.028$ moles/kg and $m_{NaCl}=0.55$ moles/kg.

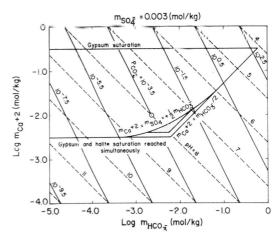

FIG. 4.—Limitations on the Ca^{+2} and HCO_3^- content of Phanerozoic sea water imposed by the mineralogy of evaporites when $m_{SO_4}=0.003$ moles/kg and $m_{NaCl}=0.55$ moles/kg.

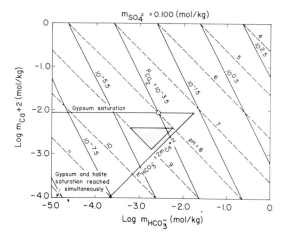

FIG. 5.—Limitations on the Ca^{+2} and HCO$_3^-$ content of Phanerozoic sea water imposed by the mineralogy of evaporites when $m_{SO_4^-} = 0.100$ moles/kg and $m_{NaCl} = 0.55$ moles/kg.

sodium carbonate and/or bicarbonate minerals would necessarily develop during the later stages of sea water evaporation.

On the other hand sulfate competes with bicarbonate for calcium during the simultaneous precipitation of gypsum and calcite. The effect of this competition would be particularly pronounced when sea water is nearly saturated with respect to gypsum. Such competition would lead to calcium depletion during evaporation even when $m_{HCO_3^-}$ is somewhat less than $2m_{Ca^{+2}}$. The opposing effects of the precipitation of dolomite and the precipitation of gypsum are potentially of comparable magnitude. It is likely, therefore, that the HCO$_3^-$ concentration at the eastern boundary for any given evaporative setting probably lies well within a factor of two of the boundaries as drawn.

The absence of brucite and the presence of primary and/or pseudosecondary dolomite in evaporative carbonate sections during the entire Phanerozoic sets rather severe limits to the western extension of the sea water composition field. The activity of Mg^{+2} in sea water today is $10^{-1.8}$. The solubility product (K) of brucite at 25°C is $10^{-11.6\cdot}$ at saturation with respect to brucite

$$K_{Br}^{25°} = 10^{-11.6} = 10^{-1.8} \cdot a_{OH^-}^2;$$

thus the activity (a) can be calculated

$$a_{OH^-} = 10^{-4.9},$$

and the pH equals 9.1. Experiments by Deffeyes and Russell (K. S. Deffeyes, personal communication, 1971) have shown that clays take up Mg(OH)$_2$ rapidly from ocean water at pH's well

below 9.0. A pH of 9.1 is therefore a very strong upper limit to oceanic pH if the magnesium concentration is to remain close to its present value. This is not, however, a requirement for sea water during the entire Phanerozoic. What does seem to be required is (1) that the ratio $m_{Mg^{+2}}/m_{Ca^{+2}}$ be large enough so that dolomite is a common component of carbonate sections in evaporative settings, (2) that this ratio be small enough to prevent the large scale deposition of magnesite, MgCO$_3$, nesquehonite, MgCO$_3$·3H$_2$O, or hydromagnesite, Mg$_4$(CO$_3$)$_3$(OH)$_2$·3H$_2$O, and (3) that enough magnesium be available during the later stages of evaporation for the deposition of minerals such as polyhalite, Ca$_2$K$_2$Mg(SO$_4$)$_4$·2H$_2$O, kainite, KMgClSO$_4$·3H$_2$O, and kieserite, MgSO$_4$·H$_2$O.

At present the ratio $a_{Mg^{+2}}/a_{Ca^{+2}}$ in sea water is nearly 5. In sea water at equilibrium with both calcite and dolomite the value of this ratio is probably close to unity; the importance of primary and/or pseudosecondary dolomites in Phanerozoic carbonates implies that $m_{Mg^{+2}}/m_{Ca^{+2}}$ has always been in excess of unity, and that it may well have been in excess of its present value during much of the Phanerozoic era.

In sea water saturated with respect to calcite, the pH and the CO$_2$ pressure (P_{CO_2}) of an atmosphere equilibrated with sea water are related to the activity of calcium and bicarbonate via the relations

$$CaCO_3 + H^+ \rightleftharpoons Ca^{+2} + HCO_3^- \qquad (2)$$

$$K_2^{25°} = \frac{a_{Ca^{+2}} \cdot a_{HCO_3^-}}{a_{H^+}} = 10^{+2\cdot}$$

and

$$CaCO_3 + CO_2 + H_2O \rightleftharpoons Ca^{+2} + 2HCO_3^- \qquad (3)$$

$$K_3^{25°} = \frac{a_{Ca^{+2}} \cdot a_{HCO_3^-}^o}{P_{CO_2}} = 10^{-5.8}$$

Lines of constant pH therefore have a slope of -1 in figures 2 through 6, and lines of constant P_{CO_2} have a slope of -2. In sea water saturated with respect to calcite and brucite, and with a $m_{Mg^{+2}}/m_{Ca^{+2}}$ ratio of 5

$$m_{Mg^{+2}} = \frac{5K_2 a_{H^+}}{a_{HCO_3^-} \gamma_{Ca^{+2}}} = \frac{K_{Br}}{a_{OH^-}^2 \gamma_{Mg^{+2}}} \qquad (4)$$

Equation 4 can be rearranged to yield

$$\frac{5K_2 K_w^2}{a_{H^+} \cdot a_{HCO_3^-}} = K_{Br} \frac{\gamma_{Ca^{+2}}}{\gamma_{Mg^{+2}}} \cong K_{Br} \qquad (5)$$

The product $a_{H^+} \cdot a_{HCO_3^-}$ is related to the first ionization constant of carbonic acid, k_1, and to the Henry's Law constant, B, for CO$_2$ in water by the expression

$$\frac{a_{H^+} \cdot a_{HCO_3^-}}{P_{CO}} = B^{25°} \cdot k_1^{25°} = 10^{-7.8} \qquad (6)$$

thus P_{CO2} will be constant and at 25°C equal to

$$P_{CO_2} \cong \frac{5K_2K_w^{\frac{2}{3}}}{BK_{Br}k_1} = 10^{-5.9}$$

in sea water with the present Mg^{+2}/Ca^{+2} ratio and saturated with respect to calcite and brucite. This is such a very low value of P_{CO_2} compared to the present value, that non-appearance of brucite in evaporites is hardly surprising. It is unlikely that the atmosphere has approached the boundary $P_{CO_2} = 10^{-5.9}$ during the Phanerozoic, and it is likely that even the boundary pH = 9 chosen for the edge of the sea water composition area is generously high.

The permitted areas defined by the various boundaries described above vary in size and position with the $SO_4^=$ content of sea water. Toward lower $SO_4^=$ concentrations the permitted area stays reasonably constant down to $m_{SO_4^-} = 0.010$ moles/kg (see fig. 3). When $m_{SO_4^-} = 0.003$ moles/kg (see fig. 4), the permitted area has become very small, and disappears completely at slightly lower sulfate concentrations. Toward $SO_4^=$ concentrations higher than at present the permitted area decreases rapidly and is already much reduced in size when $m_{SO_4^-} = 0.100$ (see fig. 5). The permitted areas at various sulfate concentrations are super-imposed in figure 6. The permitted volume in log $m_{SO_4^-}$ − log $m_{Ca^{+2}}$ − log $m_{HCO_3^-}$ space has roughly the shape of a doubly terminated pyramid with apices near 0.30 and slightly below 0.003 moles/kg $SO_4^=$, and with the indicated range of $m_{HCO_3^-}$, $m_{Ca^{+2}}$, pH, and P_{CO_2}.

Similar diagrams have been constructed for NaCl concentrations one half and twice the present value. The shape, size, and position of the permitted volumes are nearly identical. Variations of m_{NaCl} in excess of a factor of two during the Phanerozoic are unlikely. It seems likely that the quantity of salt in evaporites is approximately equal to that in sea water. Doubling the NaCl concentration seems possible only if virtually no NaCl was stored in sediments at some time during the Phanerozoic. This possibility is essentially ruled out by the existence of evaporites in all periods in the Phanerozoic. A reduction of m_{NaCl} in sea water by a factor of two demands an unusual intensity of evaporite deposition during an extended period of time. The existence of such a period seems unlikely but cannot be ruled out at present.

CONCLUSIONS

The limits set on variations in the composition of sea water during the Phanerozoic by the

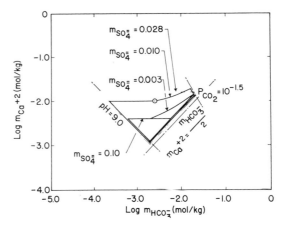

FIG. 6.—Permitted ranges of $m_{Ca^{+2}}$ and $m_{HCO_3^-}$ in sea water at sulfate concentrations between 0.003 and 0.100 moles/kg; $m_{NaCl} = 0.55$ moles/kg.

mineralogy and chemistry of evaporites are nontrivial but not highly restrictive. The permitted values of $m_{Ca^{+2}}$, $m_{HCO_3^-}$ and $m_{SO_4^-}$ lie within a volume which approximates a doubly terminated pyramid. The upper and lower limits of $m_{SO_4^-}$ are near 0.30 and 0.002 moles/kg; the maximum and minimum values of $m_{Ca^{+2}}$ are 0.030 and 0.001 moles/kg; those of $m_{HCO_3^-}$ are 0.020 and 0.0001 moles/kg (see Table 1). The composition of sea water is presently near the center of the double pyramid, and changes by a factor of 2 in the concentration of $SO_4^=$, Ca^{+2}, and HCO_3^- either singly, in pairs, or simultaneously would still keep the composition of sea water within the confines of the permitted volume.

The total mass of salt in evaporites sets a strong upper limit near 1.0 moles/kg for the NaCl concentration in sea water. The concentration of Mg^{+2} must always have been greater than that of Ca^{+2} and was probably at least 5 times greater during much of the Phanerozoic. The late appearance of potassium salts in marine evaporites shows that the concentration of potassium has been small compared to that of sodium during the Phanerozoic; it seems likely that the ratio m_{K^+}/m_{Na^+} has been at least roughly equal to its present value; the estimated minimum and maximum concentration of potassium are based on this likelihood.

Perhaps the most interesting aspect of table 1 is the modesty of the maximum concentration of the major components of sea water. This is particularly striking for Ca^{+2} and HCO_3^-. The residence time of HCO_3^- in the oceans is currently 10^5 years. If the HCO_3^- concentration were equal to the maximum value cited in table 1, the residence time of HCO_3^- would be 10^6

years. This is still a very short part of geologic time, and shows that the oceans have been able to dispose effectively of river akalinity during the entire Phanerozoic.

ACKNOWLEDGMENTS

The author wishes to thank his colleagues Professors D. J. J. Kinsman, A. G. Fischer, K. E. Deffeyes, and R. Moberly for helpful discussions. The National Science Foundation provided financial assistance under Grant GA 985. The University of Hawaii provided the setting in which many of the ideas for this paper were developed.

REFERENCES

BRAITSCH, O., 1962, Entstehung und Stoffbestand der Salzlagerstätten: Heidelberg, Springer-Verlag, v. 3, 232 p.

HOLLAND, H. D., 1972, The geologic history of sea water—an attempt to solve the problem: Geochimica et Cosmochimica Acta, v. 36, p. 637–651.

RUSSELL, K. L., 1970, Geochemistry and halmyrolysis of clay minerals, Rio Ameco, Mexico: *ibid.*, v. 34, p. 893–907.

SILLÉN, L. G., 1961, The physical chemistry of sea water, *in* SEARS, M. (ed.), Oceanography: Washington, D.C., Am. Assoc. Adv. Sci. Pub. 67, p. 549–581.

STEWART, F. H., 1963, Marine evaporites: U.S. Geol. Survey Prof. Paper 440, Chap. K, p. Y1–Y53.

CHEMICAL HISTORY OF THE OCEANS DEDUCED FROM POST-DEPOSITIONAL CHANGES IN SEDIMENTARY ROCKS

ROBERT M. GARRELS[1] AND FRED T. MACKENZIE
Scripps Institution of Oceanography, LaJolla, California, and
Northwestern University, Evanston, Illinois

ABSTRACT

The materials entering the ocean today are similar in their heterogeneity, chemical and mineralogic composition, and rates of addition to those of the past two billion years of Earth history. Major differences between modern sediments and those of the past are largely the result of post-depositional changes.

Trends in the chemistry and mineralogy of shales with geologic age are shown to be similar to well-documented, short-term, post-depositional changes in Gulf Coast shales undergoing burial diagenesis. Mixed-layer clays are converted to illite, and Ca, Mg, Na, and Si are lost from the sediment system but K is fixed in both cases. The Ca, Na, and Si enter the ground water system and eventually return to the dissolved load of streams whereas Mg is transferred to carbonate rocks.

Sediments initially contain a variety of phases, many of which are lost during diagenesis as internal equilibrium is approached in the rocks. The rate of diagenetic change increases with increasing temperatures and pressures of burial; on the average 200–250 million years are required for compositional stabilization.

Because the particulate and dissolved feed of streams to the ocean has remained practically constant when on a long-term basis, it is likely that seawater composition of today is much like that of at least one-half of geologic time. Owing to their long residence times and significant oceanic masses, chloride, sulfate, sodium, and magnesium, may have varied in oceanic concentration in the past by 10% or more from their present values. No data, however, are available to prove such changes have occurred.

INTRODUCTION

There are no compelling reasons to believe that important changes in ocean chemistry have occurred during the last 2 billion years. The current rate of fresh water input is such that the water of the oceans would be completely renewed about 50,000 times in 2 billion years and the circulation rate is such that it would be "stirred" a million times or more. The total amount of material that has gone through the ocean is estimated at a mass about 2/3 that of the total crust; that is, a mass equal to that of the ocean every 200 million years. When viewed in this perspective the ocean is hardly a storage place. It is more like a capacitor in an electrical system in that it can accumulate and discharge part of the continuous material flow into it from time to time. The residence times of the various elements in the ocean—the time required to add an amount of the element equal to the amount currently in the sea—range from very short times measured in hundreds of years to relatively long ones of the order of 100 million years, but most lie in the range from a few hundred to a few tens of millions of years. It follows that accumulation of most elements in the sea could not continue for more than a few tens of millions of years without affecting all marine organisms. Their ranges of elemental tolerance would soon be exceeded by the amounts added at rates that could overwhelm the adaptability of even the most rapidly evolving forms.

In view of the rapid turnover of oceanic constituents, it seems reasonable that any important long-term continuous trends in seawater composition would have to be the result of comparable trends in the particulate and dissolved feed from streams. Streams contribute 80% or more of all the material that enters the ocean each year. If it can be shown that the feed into the oceans has not changed with time, then oceanic composition should not change significantly either. Most of the arguments concerning changes in ocean chemistry are based on differences in the compositions of the minerals eroded from the land at different times. For example, it has been suggested that the coming of land plants would change the relative rates of erosion of constituents from the land and thus change ocean water composition. Major arguments have been based on the fact that the ratio of sedimentary rock types of a given age may differ from ratios in Recent sediments, or from those of other ages. Precambrian rocks contain a relatively small proportion of carbo-

[1] Present address: Northwestern University, Evanston, Illinois.

nate rocks and those that do remain are high in magnesium relative to present-day carbonate sediments. These differences between Precambrian and Recent carbonates have been interpreted as requiring a change in the Ca-Mg ratio in the waters of the ancient seas, or a change in the CO_2 content of the atmosphere. The clay fraction of Paleozoic and older shales is made up almost entirely of the minerals chlorite, illite, and quartz, whereas younger shales have a much greater variety of clay minerals, including an abundance of mixed-layer and kaolinitic clays. These differences have been interpreted as requiring a difference in the composition of seawater and/or a difference in the chemical and mineralogical composition of the land areas being eroded.

COMPARISON OF THE COMPOSITION OF MISSISSIPPI
DELTA SEDIMENTS AND AVERAGE SHALY ROCKS

The Mississippi Delta and the near-shore sediments of the Gulf of Mexico have been studied in great detail by many geologists and have been used as a natural laboratory to test a variety of concepts. The accumulation of tens of thousands of feet of sediments within tens of millions of year makes it possible to examine fresh material and also to look at its counterpart buried fifteen thousand feet and raised to a temperature of 150°C (Perry and Hower, 1970). The battle of provenance versus environment has been waged through the years in studies concerned with the origin of the Delta sediments, particularly the fine-grained clay minerals, as deduced from clay-mineral distribution patterns (c.f. Grim, 1968). At times vertical variations in mineralogy have been attributed almost entirely to post-depositional changes. At other times, they have been explained on the basis of differential setling rates of the clay minerals or changes in the mineralogic species brought down the river. Several recent studies (Burst, 1969; Perry and Hower, 1970; Weaver and Wampler, 1970), based firmly on a monumental amount of earlier work, have managed to separate variations in initial composition from those that have taken place after deposition.

Perry and Hower performed detailed mineralogic and chemical investigations on five wells in the Gulf Coast region down to depths of 12,000–15,000 feet. These wells contained sections in which the initial bulk chemistry was essentially identical from bottom to top and for which they could determine post-depositional mineralogic changes. Their conclusions are as follows: 1) The percentage of expandable mixed-layer minerals diminishes downward.

2) The mixed-layer clays take potassium into the interlayer positions while gaining aluminum and losing silica. The change goes on progressively until an illite is created that has a total lattice charge of about 0.80 at a depth of the order of about 2 miles and does not change further with deep burial. 3) The potassium for the formation of the illite is derived from the destruction of detrital mica and potassium feldspar. The potassium content of the whole rock changes little, if at all, but that of the clay fraction rises markedly.

Weaver and Wampler (1970), in a complementary study, determined the potassium-argon ages of Mississippi Delta sediments as a function of depth. Bulk sample ages of the sediments at 4,000 feet were about 325 million years, and decreased by about 100 million years progressively downward to a depth of about 3 miles. The deepest samples were of Miocene age, so the interval between deposition of the deeper sediments and the shallow ones is not an important contribution to the age change. Their interpretation is straightforward: the potassium-argon ages of recent sediments are a composite of the K-Ar ages of the detrital clays brought down by the Mississippi, and because of translocation of K from micas and feldspars to illite, the age of the bulk samples becomes a composite of these initial detrital ages plus those of newly formed illitic material.

Perry and Hower (1970) noted some changes in the bulk composition of the sediments with depth, such as a decrease of MgO and Na_2O downward. Figure 1A is a plot of the composition of the sediments at three levels in their well E, in Oligocene sediments of Galveston County, Texas. A composite of 4 samples from 7,023 to 7,514 feet (average ~7,250 feet) is used as a standard for comparison. The differences in the ratios of the various metal oxides to alumina relative to the ratio at 7,023–7,514 (7,250) feet are plotted as percentage differences. Fe_2O_3, K_2O, and SiO_2 change little with depth. The differences shown are probably within the limits of original compositional variation of the sediments. However, CaO, MgO, and Na_2O diminish markedly with depth. The values at 11,718–11,969 (~12,000) feet average about 50% less than those at 7,023–7,514 feet. The constancy of the ratios of iron, potassium, and silica to alumina suggests that there were no differences in the initial bulk compositions of the sediments, and, by implication, that MgO, CaO, and Na_2O have been lost from the sediment system. For comparison, figure 1B plots changes in the same oxides in average shales as a function of their ages. The similarity be-

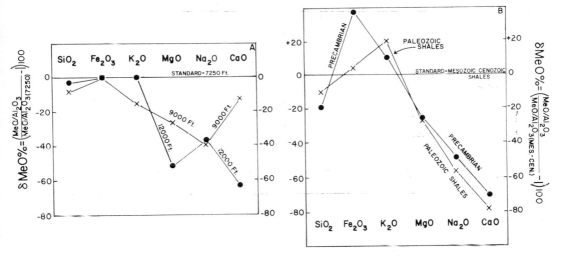

FIG. 1A, B —Comparison of chemical changes with depth in Gulf Coast sediments with changes with age for average shales. A. Changes with depth shown as differences from the average composition at 7000-7500 feet. Data from Perry and Hower (1970). B. Changes with depth shown as differences from the composition of the average Mesozoic-Cenozoic shale. Data from Garrels and Mackenzie (1971). MeO = metallic oxides.

tween the chemical differences in shales as a function of their ages and the differences in Delta sediment as a function of depth are obvious. The increase in the ratio of K_2O to Al_2O_3 as a function of increasing age is large enough to suggest either an addition of potassium to the system, or even a small loss of aluminum.

If it is assumed that the bulk composition of the sediments at a depth of 7,023–7,514 feet in the Gulf and those at greater depths were initially the same, the loss in mass between these depths, exclusive of water, is about 10%; the corresponding loss of mass for Paleozoic shales relative to Mesozoic-Cenozoic shales is about 20%. The mechanisms by which the sodium, magnesium, and calcium are lost are not obvious, but subsurface brines are commonly enriched in these constituents. Furthermore, the observation that brines in shales are much fresher than those in accompanying sandstones implies that pore waters can migrate and change their initial compositions as well (Schmidt, 1971; K. L. Russell, personal communication, 1971). The dissolved load of streams whose channels intersect such a subsurface water system would have Ca, Na, Mg, and Si as their major constituents.

In the stratigraphic section of the Delta, deep burial accompanied by relatively high temperatures has accelerated processes that usually take much longer. Figure 2 shows K-Ar ages of illites and glauconites plotted as a function of their ages. K-Ar age relations of illites show

the same relation with age as that described by Weaver and Wampler (1970) as a function of depth in Delta sediments. Hurley (1966, p. 148)

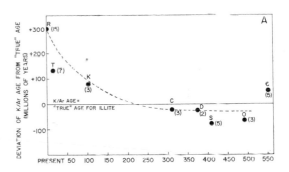

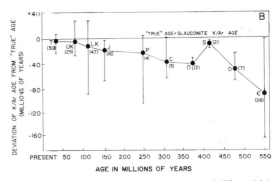

FIG. 2A, B.—Relation of K/Ar ages of illites (A) and of glauconites (B) relative to the "true" age of shaly rocks. Numbers in parentheses refer to the number of samples averaged for a given point. Data from Hurley (1966).

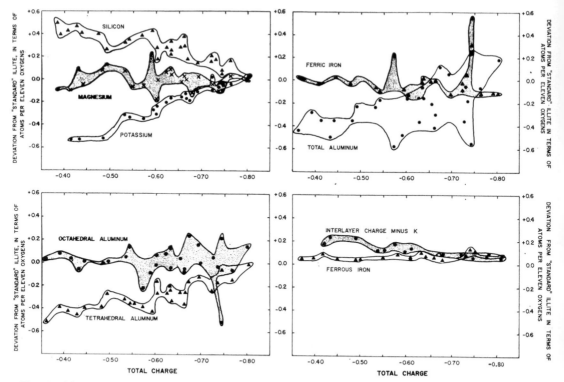

Fig. 3.—Variations in the composition of minerals in the mixed-layer clay-illite solid-solution series as a function of total charge. Compositions are shown as deviations from the composition of an hypothesized end-member illite with a charge of −0.80. Data from Hower and Mowatt (1966).

has observed: "It appears from these studies that there is no zero-age, fine-size, illitic material deposited in sediments at the outset, but that the detrital age is gradually wiped out during burial and argon starts to accumulate at the same time in reordered material. The aggregate age of the clay-size fraction gradually decreases from an excess age in young sedimentary rocks to a deficiency in age that is commonly about 15 percent too young in older sedimentary rocks. Superimposed on this is a resistant detritus that is made up of 2M muscovite (and probably other K-bearing igneous materials), which adds an excess age value to the shale aggregate as a whole. Frequently, the sum of the two components, older 2M muscovite and younger and 1Md illite, is nearly balanced out and the apparent K-Ar age on the total shale turns out to be quite close to the time age of the sedimentation. However, this is fortuitous and not to be relied upon." Whereas the "half-life" for the development of new illite and the attainment of a constant age in the average shale is apparently about 50 million years, that in the Gulf Coast, accelerated by rapid burial and increased temperatures, is far less.

The glauconite ages tell the same story except that, in general, the initial age of the glauconites is very nearly the same as that of the enclosing shale. The glauconites take on new potassium through time so that their apparent ages become steadily younger, yet the upper limit of the age range is nearly equal to the true age and is independent of time, demonstrating that the deviation of glauconite ages from true age with time is a highly statistical matter. Some sediments have remained so shallow and cool that even 500 million years has not been enough time for potassium to enter the glauconite structure. Tentatively, it appears that addition of potassium to glauconites is a slower process than the collapsing of mixed-layer clays by the addition of potassium to form illites.

Details of the chemical changes that occur when mixed-layer clays are converted to illites can be illustrated graphically by plotting the compositions of the montmorillonites and illites provided by Hower and Mowatt (1966) in their classical paper on this subject. The compositional plots of figure 3 add little to what Hower and Mowatt deduced but they clearly show two relations that need emphasis. First, as the total charge on the lattice increases, all of the analyses of montmorillonites and illites converge to a narrow range of composition. The illite composition given below is approximately that upon which all of the clays converge independent of the geology or the age of their sources:

$$X_{0.05}^{+}K_{0.75}[(Mg_{0.34}Fe_{0.17}^{+3}Fe_{0.04}^{+2}Al_{1.50})(Al_{0.57}Si_{3.43})O_{10}(OH)_2].$$

It is used henceforth as the end member composition of the montmorillonite-illite solid-solution series. The second conclusion that can be drawn from figure 3 is that the octahedral composition of montmorillonite-illite does not change with increase in charge. The conversion is simply substitution of aluminum for silicon in the tetrahedral layer and uptake of potassium to balance the increasing charge. A little potassium, in addition to that moving into interlayer position to balance the increased charge, seems to displace other interlayer cations (fig. 3). The interlayer cations displaced are Ca and Na in roughly equivalent amounts. This displacement may account for a small part of the Ca and Na lost from shales with burial and/or age. The chemical reaction for the conversion of typical montmorillonite to end-member illite is

$$2.5X_{0.05}^{+}K_{0.35}[(Mg_{0.34}Fe_{0.17}^{+3}Fe_{0.04}^{+2}Al_{1.50})$$
$$\cdot(Al_{0.17}Si_{3.83})O_{10}(OH)_2] + K^{+} + AlO_{2}^{-}$$
$$= 2.5X_{0.05}^{+}K_{0.75}[(Mg_{0.34}Fe_{0.17}^{+3}Fe_{0.04}^{+2}Al_{1.50})$$
$$\cdot(Al_{0.57}Si_{3.43})O_{10}(OH)_2] + SiO_2.$$

The chemical basis for the formation of illite from mixed-layer clay by the destruction of detrital mica and K-feldspar as shown by Perry and Hower (1970) is implicit in figure 4. Because the magnesium and iron content remain constant during the conversion of mixed-layer clay to illite, the compositional change with reference to other minerals in the system can be shown in the three component diagram Al_2SiO_5–SiO_2–K_2SiO_4 (or Al_2O_3–SiO_2–K_2O). End-member illite appears as a phase almost exactly intermediate between kaolinite and K-spar on the one hand and mica and quartz on the other. The dashed lines show the metastable pairs that react with depth and/or age to change mixed-layer clay toward end-member illite. The chemical reactions are

    5 montmorillonite + 2 mica + 4 water =
    5 illite + 4 kaolinite + 4 quartz

and

    5 montmorillonite + 2 K-spar + 2 water =
    5 illite + 8 quartz.

The conversion of mixed-layer clay to illite

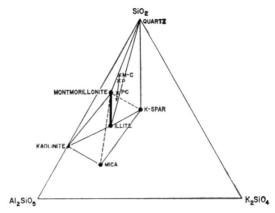

FIG. 4.—Composition and stability relations among some of the phases of shaly rocks. The compositional continuum between montmorillonite and illite is that shown on fig. 3. The crosses are for the K_2SiO_4, Al_2SiO_5, and SiO_2 content of average Mesozoic-Cenozoic (MC), average Paleozoic (P), and average Precambrian (PC) shales. Solid lines represent stable associations, dashed lines are metastable associations. Data from Hower and Mowatt (1966) and from Garrels and Mackenzie (1971).

may well be driven by the crystallization of quartz. Pore waters are usually highly supersaturated with respect to quartz and seem to remain supersaturated for as long as 60 million years. Interstitial waters in deep sea sediments of ages from Eocene to Recent commonly have SiO_2 contents far in excess of quartz solubility (c.f. Manheim and others, 1970). Under these circumstances montmorillonite and other high silica compounds can persist metastably with detrital silicates such as kaolinite, K-mica and K-feldspar. When quartz crystallizes the silica content of the interstitial waters diminishes and the reactions are driven toward end-member illite. The overall picture then, with respect to illite, is that modern illites are detrital, inherited from ancient rocks without change in K/Ar age. Mixed-layer clays may be either detrital or pedogenic. In either case, they are destroyed by burial and/or time along with some detrital mica and K-spar. The high illite content of Paleozoic and older sediments does not reflect unusual conditions in Paleozoic seas or land areas. The K-Ar age relations are evidence of the former presence of abundant mixed-layer clays in Paleozoic shales.

The increased chlorite content of Paleozoic and older shales over Mesozoic and Cenozoic shales may be derived by comparable diagenetic reactions (c.f. Dunoyer de Segonzac, 1955) but data on sedimentary chlorite compositions are few.

Figure 5 is drawn to suggest the complicated

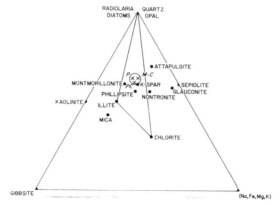

FIG. 5.—Schematic diagram to illustrate variety of phases and compositions of newly deposited muddy sediments, plotted as a function of the atomic percents of Al, Si, and Na + Fe + Mg + K. Circled area contains the compositions of average Mesozoic-Cenozoic (M-C), Paleozoic (P), and Precambrian (PC) shales. The triangle indicates that the 3-phase assemblage illite-chlorite-quartz tends to be the final product of post-depositional change of initial multiphase assemblages.

set of changes that may result in the elimination of many of the minerals found in recent sediments. The list of chemical species that are found at least locally in modern fine-grained sediments in important percentages is growing rapidly. Among them are volcanic glasses of a wide range of composition, opaline silica, gibbsite, sepiolite, attapulgite, a variety of zeolites, most of which have silica to alumina ratios near K-feldspar, aragonite, magnesian calcite, calcite, and dolomite. Of these, glass, opal, sepiolite, attapulgite, aragonite, magnesian calcite, and a number of zeolites are unknown in sedimentary rocks older than Triassic. Kaolinite and montmorillonite occur in much smaller percentages in pre-Triassic than in post-Triassic rocks. Many of the phases that are, according to us, "eliminated," are high in silica relative to the bulk composition of the sediments. Their elimination by reaction with highly aluminous phases such as gibbsite or kaolinite may also be driven by the crystallization of quartz. Like montmorillonite, zeolites, sepiolite, and attapulgite are stable only in solutions supersaturated with respect to quartz. With the exception of kaolinite, most of the siliceous phases listed are relatively minor constituents of sediments on a global scale so that they can all be destroyed by reaction with the relatively abundant kaolinite.

The bulk compositions of Mesozoic-Cenozoic, Paleozoic, and Precambrian shales in terms of the components K_2O, Al_2O_3, SiO_2, are shown by X's on figure 4. The trend with age toward

illite is obvious. There is some indication that with increasing age and/or metamorphism the iron and magnesium are lost from the illites and are presumably taken up in chlorite, although the process tends to be nearly isochemical as far as bulk composition is concerned. Thus, at higher temperatures, illite disproportionates back to mica and quartz.

SOME OTHER EVIDENCES OF POST-DEPOSITIONAL CHANGES

The ratio of O^{18} to O^{16} in carbonate rocks and in cherts diminishes with age (fig. 6). For limestones, the change is from a modern δO^{18} of about +30 to a value of about +21 for Cambrian rocks. There are various interpretations of this change, but the prevalent view is that the limestones and cherts have encountered "light ground waters" after deposition. The degree of change implies a substantial water circulation through the rocks; on a statistical basis, the volume of water passing through the rocks increases with the length of time the rocks have been in existence and hence the opportunity for contact with ground waters. A correlation can be made between the O^{18}/O^{16} changes with age and the Ca/Mg ratio of carbonate rocks (fig. 7). Present-day primary dolomite is miniscule in amount compared to calcite and aragonite, and most geologists agree that the dolomites of the rock record are overwhelmingly the result of post-depositional processes. The timing of such dolomitization is extremely variable, ranging from instances in which dolomitization may have taken place

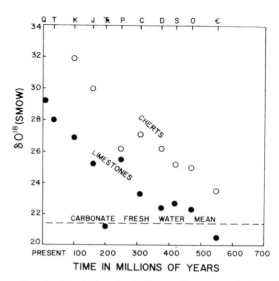

FIG. 6.—Variations in δO^{18} in carbonates and cherts as a function of geologic age. Data from Degens and Epstein (1962).

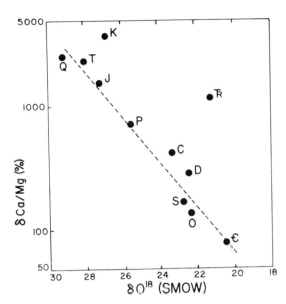

FIG. 7.—δCa/Mg in carbonate rocks as a percentage difference from the composition of dolomite

$$\left[\delta Ca/Mg\ (\%) = \frac{Ca/Mg\ in\ sample}{Ca/Mg\ in\ dolomite} - 1 \cdot 100 \right]$$

versus δO¹⁸%. Data for Ca/Mg from Garrels and Mackenzie (1971); for δO¹⁸ from Degens and Epstein (1962).

prior to the deposition of a succeeding unit to those instances in which dolomitization is related to tectonic events hundreds of millions of years after initial sedimentation. As illustrated in figure 7, the sporadic events that caused dolomitization are strongly correlated with the sporadic events that result in oxygen isotope exchange. There is no necessary direct causal relation between the two—merely, they are the results of the same kinds of processes—processes that go on continuously through time and thus have effects that become greater and greater with increasing rock age.

It is likely that magnesium loss from shaly rocks is related to magnesium uptake by carbonate rocks. This process is specifically documented in a recent publication by Murata and others (1969). Thin layers in Miocene shales of California which were originally calcitic lime-stone are now largely dolomite. In some instances part of a layer a foot or two thick is still calcite, whereas the rest is dolomitized.

Other aspects of the complex cycling and exchange of elements can best be followed by reference to figure 8. In this schematic diagram, the three major reservoirs are shown as the ocean, as new sedimentary rocks, and as old sedimentary rocks. New sediment includes rocks

with ages up to about 250 million years, old sediments all the rest. The division is arbitrary, because the rate of change from new to old diminishes continuously and logarithmically, but on the average, major diagenetic changes are complete at the end of 200–250 million years. Thus new sediment includes Cenozoic and Mesozoic rocks; old sediment comprises Paleozoic rocks and all older sediments and meta-sediments.

Our best estimates of the percentage of the major elements are given for each reservoir. The data should not be regarded as final; there are still inconsistencies between these estimates and those of other investigators. Ronov (1968), for example, has almost twice as much calcium in his average sedimentary rock as we show. On the other hand, the relations of the numbers for the elements in the various reservoirs indicate the qualitative differences between them. The overall percentage figures approximate the relative masses of material in the three reservoirs. The numbers on the arrows between reservoirs are estimates of the relative fluxes from one to the other.

In the following discussion, the inadequacy of the current estimates should become clear, as well as the status of the diagram as a preliminary working model of the real system. First of all, the model is entirely cannibalistic; that is, it is a closed system with respect to sedimentary rocks, and does not include the cycling of sediments into igneous rocks and back into sediments again. The relative mass distribution between ocean and sediments indicates the inadequacy of the ocean as a storage place, especially when it is considered that the total mass of sediments that has been cycled is more than 5 times the total of all reservoirs (Garrels and Mackenzie, 1971).

Long-term diagenetic loss of the mobile elements Ca, Si, and Na is illustrated by their percentage changes between new and old sediment; it is presumed that they are expelled in ground waters and enter streams. The absolute increase in Si from new to old is actually a decrease relative to Al, and represents a net loss from new sediment. Magnesium also may be lost to streams, but it is also likely that much magnesium is simply transferred from the shale component of new sediments to the carbonate component of old ones. During diagenesis potassium remains in the sediments and may even be removed by the sediments from ground waters, for the K/Al ratio in old sediments is higher than that in new.

Both weathering and diagenesis of new sediment produce waters of similar composition,

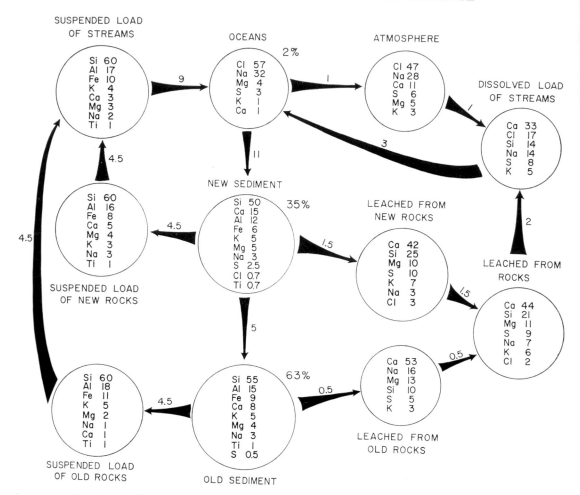

Fig. 8.—Cycling of some elements in the atmosphere-ocean-sedimentary rock system.

dominated by calcium and silicon. Because old shales are well-leached by diagenetic processes, it can be deduced that the soluble components of old sediments are derived chiefly from carbonate rocks, hence the importance of Ca and Mg as constituents in the solutions resulting from the weathering of old sediments. This contention is supported somewhat by the predominance of illite in the clay fraction of old shales, for illite goes through weathering and erosion without significant change in its potassium-argon age, indicating resistance of chemical attack as well.

As shown, the relative fluxes of suspended and dissolved material into the ocean are 9/3. The average sedimentary rock, both new and old, could be constituted by mixing suspended and dissolved load in a ratio of about 4 or 5 to 1. Our view is that the ratio of suspended to solution load fluctuates between 5/1 and 1/1 as

a function of time, with the solution load remaining relatively constant. The ratio of 4.5/1 today with the continents high and the oceanic area at a minimum perhaps is an extreme in the ratio of suspended to solution load. Therefore, on the average, the constituents of carbonate rocks and evaporites turn over more rapidly than those of sandstones and shales. The aluminum, iron, and titanium of the sedimentary mass turn over about every 500–600 million years, for they are restricted to the suspended load of streams. Calcium, sulfur, and chlorine, which are transported chiefly in the dissolved load, cycle two or three times as fast. Silicon has a significant content in the dissolved load of streams relative to the suspended load, which speeds up its cycling appreciably over insoluble iron, aluminum, and titanium, but it is far slower than calcium, sulfur, and chlorine. Potassium and magnesium also cycle at intermediate rates, with magnesium probably turning over faster than potassium. Both have significant transport in the dissolved load of streams. Figure 9 shows the difference in age and depth behavior of the immobile elements Al, Fe, and K versus fugitive Ca, Na, and Mg.

One of the major sources of uncertainty in the overall system is the rate of transfer of elements from the ocean through the atmosphere into the streams. The cycling of Cl and S, in particular, are in a confused state. The numbers given for the elements in the atmosphere are those for a presumed average rain, and do not take cognizance of dry fallout. Large changes in the percentages of the elements transported through the atmosphere could cause marked changes in their calculated cycling times through the sediment system.

The flux of suspended and dissolved material from new sediments is shown as being higher than that from old sediments, even though the mass of new sediments is less. New sediments are more susceptible to destruction than old ones, both because of their high content of "soluble" materials and because they tend to be placed in greater erosional jeopardy (Garrels and Mackenzie, 1971) than the older ones. The numbers given for the relative fluxes should be treated more as illustrating the general situation than as being usable for mass calculations. The life of new sediments is short. Less than half of new sediments deposited manage to become old sediments by reaching the age of 200–250 million years, but every year they survive increases their life expectancy.

The suspended materials from new sediments are higher in Na, Ca, and Mg than those from old sediments because diagenetic changes are not complete. They are more distinctive mineralogically than chemically, because of their greater mineral diversity, as opposed to the small number of minerals in old sediments. The relations of Na are particularly difficult to define. New sediments contain 2–3 weight percent of Na (not balanced by Cl) in silicates; old sediments are slightly lower. Thus there is some Na obtained from silicate minerals that cycles through the system in the dissolved load of streams. There is also Na in the dissolved load of streams derived from Na balanced by Cl in the new sediments, and Na cycled into the dissolved load from the atmosphere. Because the Na associated with silicates is a small percentage of a large mass of rock, it is difficult to get sufficiently representative analyses of the sediments to determine the amount of Na contributed to the cycle that is not moving in balance with Cl.

A by-pass for suspended sediment has been drawn through the ocean to suggest that it passes through the marine environment with little change, and to emphasize that the composition of the oceans is heavily dependent on the cycling among ocean, atmosphere, and the dissolved load of streams. Because the long-term situation is clear—the contributions from streams pass through the oceans quickly and little of their total mass is there—the most important oceanic fluctuations would be expected to involve the four elements with a significant part of their mass in the oceans, Na, Cl, Mg, and S. More than half the total Cl, about half the total Na, 10% of total S, and about 2% of the total Mg are in the ocean reservoir. It is

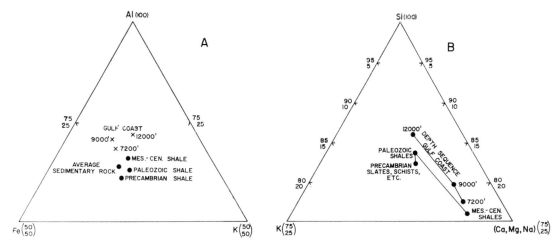

FIG. 9A, B.—Compositions of some sedimentary rocks as a function of their ages, showing the constancy of ratios of Al, Fe, and K (A), and the marked changes involving Ca, Na, Mg, and Si (B). Compositions are expressed in atomic percents. Data from Perry and Hower (1970) and from Garrels and Mackenzie (1971).

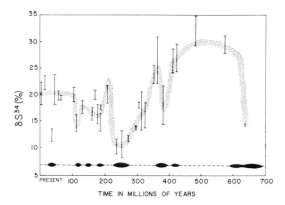

TIME IN MILLIONS OF YEARS

FIG. 10.—Sulfur isotope ratio variation in evaporites as a function of age (Holser and Kaplan, 1966). Dark areas represent times of major evaporite formation (Lotze, 1964).

conceivable that oceanic chlorinity could have ranged tens of percents above and below the present value, depending upon the amount of NaCl storage in rocks, but we know of no consequences of such changes that could be read from the inorganic rock record.

On the other hand, work on the isotopes of sulfur in evaporite deposits by Holser and Kaplan (1966) shows striking fluctuations of the S^{34}/S^{32} ratio as a function of rock age (fig. 10). Furthermore, they present convincing arguments that the isotope ratios measured are primary features of the rock and are close to the ratios in the seawater from which they precipitated. It would be possible for the sulfur content of seawater to increase several times without precipitating calcium sulfate from the open ocean, but accumulation of the present-day feed of sulfur in the ocean would cause the isotope ratio to be lowered markedly, if the sparse data on S^{34}/S^{32} ratios in streams are accepted as representative. Accumulation of sulfur, however, is not the only way to change the S^{34}/S^{32} ratio in the oceans. It can also be done, as shown by Rees (1970), by varying ratios in the input and output while maintaining total dissolved sulfur constant.

The sulfur of shales is largely sufide sulfur, and has a low S^{34}/S^{32} ratio, whereas that of evaporites, while variable, has a much higher ratio. The total sulfur in each reservoir is about the same. If the sulfur in the ocean remained constant, and if the feed were removed chiefly as calcium sulfate in evaporites, the S^{34}/S^{32} ratio in the ocean would diminish. On the other hand, if the feed were removed as sulfide sulfur, largely in pyrite in reducing environments, the isotopic ratio of the oceans would increase.

Detailed calculations (McKenzie, 1971) show that the secular variations in the S^{34}/S^{32} ratio in evaporites could have resulted from moderate variations in the type of output, assuming a uniform feed equally from the evaporite and the reduced sulfur reservoirs. Some evidence to support this conclusion is provided by the fact that ages of isotopically light evaporites are approximately coincident with times of major evaporite formation (fig. 10).

Despite the lack of a unique interpretation of the S^{34}/S^{32} data, it is obvious that sulfur behavior deviates markedly from that expected from an extreme concept of a steady state ocean. In such a view the amount present in the ocean would be constant, its partition into the reduced and oxidized reservoirs would be at a fixed ratio, and the feed would be constantly the same, being derived with a fixed ratio from the two chief reservoirs.

The variations in S^{34}/S^{32} ratio of evaporites hold promise of telling much more about oceanic and atmospheric history than they have so far. If the total reservoir of oxidized sulfur increases at the expense of that of reduced sulfur, no matter how oxidized and reduced sulfur are partitioned among shales, evaporites, and the ocean, oxygen would be fixed by the process, and if the atmosphere were not depleted, it would have to be given up by some other process, such as an increase of CO_2 fixation by photosynthesis relative to oxidative release. Eventually data on rock compositions should be adequate to see if the oxidized sulfur and carbon content of sedimentary rocks vary antithetically.

Magnesium has been a difficult element for the geochemists. It is an important part of the dissolved load of streams, and is derived largely from the solution of carbonate rocks, especially old ones. Modern carbonates are much lower in Mg than old ones, so at present no adequate oceanic sinks for Mg are known. The reversal of the Ca/Mg ratio in the ocean from that in streams indicates the tendency of Mg to accumulate in the oceans, but its oceanic mass is insignificant relative to that stored in sediments. Presumably it is removed from the oceans today by some mechanism involving clay minerals. Drever (1971) demonstrated that clays in anoxic environments take up Mg when their Fe is removed by H_2S to form pyrite, but there is probably not enough oxygen-deficient ocean bottom to take care of the current Mg influx. Magnesium concentration might well fluctuate with time. A possible upper limit would be a concentration several times the present one, at which sepiolite, magnesium hydroxysilicate, could precipitate. Sepiolite does occur locally in thick beds, but is not formed in an open-ocean environment. Whatever the details of Mg removal from the ocean, its pathway as a dissolved species is into streams from the diagenesis and weathering of shales, and from the dissolution of Mg-enriched carbonate rocks, and out of the oceans associated with shales.

Today the Si that comes down the streams to the oceans is removed as opaline tests of microorganisms. These may eventually recrystallize to fine-grained quartz (chert), or react with various aluminosilicates to make more siliceous aluminosilicates. The Si content of the interstitial waters of sedimentary rocks is higher than that of bottom seawater, so there is a postdepositional flux of silica back into the oceans, but its magnitude cannot yet be assessed. The fundamental problem of silica cycling remains unanswered; the molecular SiO_2 deposited by organisms is derived from silicate minerals. If it is not eventually reincorporated into silicate minerals—if there is a continuous accumulation of Si as SiO_2—the flux through the oceans is so rapid that 2 billion years of sedimentary cycling would yield a sedimentary mass consisting of about 30% cherts. Also, important changes in oceanic chemistry could be anticipated if SiO_2 were to accumulate (Garrels and Mackenzie, 1971, p. 283).

This discussion serves to emphasize our ignorance of the sedimentary sinks for the elements. Calcium is the only major element in sea water for which there is reasonable documentation of depositional rate currently equivalent to input rate.

CONCLUSIONS

It is suggested that the present-day compositions of sedimentary rocks are grossly consistent with a model in which the material initially deposited has not differed significantly in bulk composition during the last 2 billion years. After deposition, compositional change begins, dominated chemically by expulsion of Ca, Na,

Si, and Mg from shaly rocks. The Ca, Na, and Si are believed to be returned to the dissolved load of the surface circulation system, whereas much of the Mg is transferred from shaly to carbonate rocks. The elements Al, Fe, Ti, and K remain, and are cycled by mechanical erosion. Because of the selective expulsion of Ca and Na, during diagenetic change, plus selective removal of these elements and of Mg during weathering, the rocks dominated by these elements (carbonate rocks and evaporites) cycle faster than those dominated by Al, Fe, Ti, and K (shales and sandstones). Post-depositional chemical change is reflected in marked mineralogical changes. Sediments initially contain many phases, most of which are incompatible in a system at chemical equilibrium; with time, excess phases are eliminated, and internal equilibrium is approached in the rocks. The rate of diagenetic change increases with depth of burial and the accompanying high temperatures and pressures. With rapid burial, change may be essentially complete in a few millions of years, but on the average, about 200–250 million years are required. Thus the degree of change observed in a given rock, even if it is very old, may range from barely detectable to complete.

It is concluded that time variations in ocean chemistry are most likely for those elements that have long residence times and an oceanic mass that is a significant fraction of their total ocean plus sediment content. Chloride, sulfate, sodium, and magnesium are chosen as those whose oceanic concentrations may well have varied by 10% or more from present values, but there are still no data that prove that such changes have taken place.

ACKNOWLEDGMENTS

We gratefully acknowledge support from the National Science Foundation and the Petroleum Research Fund of the American Chemical Society. Our thanks go to many colleagues for their comments and criticisms.

REFERENCES

BURST, J. F., 1969, Diagenesis of Gulf Coast clayey sediments and its possible relation to petroleum migration: Am. Assoc. Petroleum Geologists Bull., v. 53, p. 73–93.
DEGENS, E. T., AND EPSTEIN, S., 1962, Relationship between O^{18}/O^{16} ratio in co-existing carbonates, cherts, and diatomites: ibid., v. 46, p. 534–542.
DREVER, J. I., 1971, Magnesium-iron replacement of clay minerals in anoxic marine sediments: Science, v. 172, p. 1334–1336.
DUNOYER, DE SEGONZAC, D., 1965, Les argiles du Crétacé supérieur dans le bassin de Douala (Cameroun): problèmes de diagenèse: Service Carte Géol. Als. Lorraine Bull., T. 17, v. 4, p. 287–310.
GARRELS, R. M., AND MACKENZIE, F. T., 1971, Evolution of sedimentary rocks: New York, W. W. Norton & Co., 397 p.
GRIM, R. E., 1968, Clay mineralogy: New York, McGraw-Hill Book Co., 2nd ed., 596 p.
HOLSER, W. T., AND KAPLAN, I. R., 1966, Isotopic geochemistry of sedimentary sulfates: Chem. Geol., v. 1, p. 93–135.

HOWER, J., AND MOWATT, T. C., 1966, The mineralogy of illites and mixed-layer illite/montmorillonites:
  Am. Mineralogist, v. 51, p. 825–854.
HURLEY, P. M., 1966, Dating of sediments, *in* SCHAEFFER, O. A., AND ZAHRINGER, J. (eds.), Potassium-
  argon dating: New York, Springer-Verlag, p. 134–151.
LOTZE, F., 1964, The distribution of evaporites in space and time, *in* NAIRN, A. E. M. (ed.), Problems in
  paleoclimatology: New York, Interscience, p. 491–509.
McKENZIE, J., 1971, Unpublished report on sulfur cycling: La Jolla, California, Scripps Inst. Oceanography.
MANHEIM, F. T., CHAN, K. M., KERR, D., AND SUNDA, W., 1970, Interstitial water studies on small core
  samples, *in* MAXWELL, A. E., AND OTHERS, Initial reports of the Deep Sea Drilling Project: Washing-
  ton, D.C., U.S. Govt. Printing Office, v. 3, p. 663–666.
MURATA, K. J., FRIEDMAN, K., AND MADSEN, B. M., 1969, Isotopic composition of marine Miocene forma-
  tions of California and Oregon: U.S. Geol. Survey Prof. Paper 614-B, p. 1–24.
PERRY, E., AND HOWER, JR., 1970, Burial diagenesis in Gulf Coast pelitic sediments: Clays and clay minerals,
  v. 18, p. 167–177.
REES, C. E., 1970, The sulphur isotope balance of the ocean: an improved model: Earth and Planet. Sci.
  Letters, v. 7, p. 366–370.
RONOV, A. B., 1968, Probable changes in the composition of sea water during the course of geological time:
  Sedimentology, v. 10, p. 25–43.
SCHMIDT, G. W., 1971, Interstitial water composition and geochemistry of Gulf Coast deep shales and sand-
  stones: Am. Assoc. Petroleum Geologists Bull., v. 55, p. 363.
WEAVER, C. E., AND WAMPLER, J. M., 1970, K, Ar, illite burial: Geol. Soc. America Bull., v. 81, p. 3423–
  3430.

EARLY EVOLUTION OF THE OCEANS—A WEATHERING MODEL

G. MICHEL LAFON[1] AND FRED T. MACKENZIE
State University of New York, Binghamton, and Northwestern University,
Evanston, Illinois

ABSTRACT

The long-term chemical composition of sea water is controlled by the generalized reaction: primary igneous rock minerals + water + acid volatiles = sediments + oceans + atmosphere. Unstable crustal minerals are weathered by water and acid volatiles, and local equilibrium between the products of the reaction—oceanic sediments, sea water and the atmosphere—is closely approached.

To obtain a better picture of the evolution of the oceans as this reaction proceeds (minerals formed, mass transfers involved, changes in sea water composition), we simulated with a model calculation on a high-speed computer the irreversible attack of "average igneous rock" by water and acid volatiles. We assumed a single-stage degassing process under reducing conditions at 25°C and 1 atm. The predicted final solid products ranked according to decreasing mass are clays and amorphous silica (= chert in the geologic record), then feldspars and carbonates. The predicted composition of the early ocean resembles that of present sea water except that (1) the dissolved sulfur is in reduced form, (2) the solution is saturated with amorphous silica, and (3) the salinity is about twice that of today because of non-removal of NaCl in evaporites.

Extension of these results to more realistic systems can at best be semiquantitative because of lack of sufficient thermochemical data. Furthermore, the recycling of sediments makes it very difficult to estimate early environmental conditions from present remnants of Precambrian sediments. Some generalizations can nevertheless be made with confidence.

A more basic initial crustal material such as oceanic basalt would lead to larger amounts of clays and carbonates in the sediments at the expense of chert and to a large concentration of dissolved ferrous iron in the ocean. Degassing of water preferentially to other volatiles would not affect the outcome of the weathering process unless the escape rates of the volatiles differed by several orders of magnitude. Although our model clearly represents an extreme case, rapid degassing, the available geologic evidence does not preclude its having taken place.

INTRODUCTION

The composition of sea water is continuously affected by active processes such as river discharge, ion-exchange, diffusion of dissolved material, reactions with the suspended load and sediments, and so forth. Compositional changes continue in waters trapped as pore fluids in marine sediments and, therefore, there is little hope of ever finding direct evidence bearing on the evolution of the oceans. At the present time, one of the best avenues of investigation still appears to be the comparison of the composition of primary igneous rocks with those of sediments, sea water and the atmosphere, a method used often in the past (Clarke, 1924; Goldschmidt, 1933; Kuenen, 1946; Rubey, 1951; Garrels and Mackenzie, 1971). This method of geochemical balances expresses the fact that sedimentary rocks are the product of a long-term titration of the primary igneous rock minerals by acids contained in "excess volatiles" degassed out of the earth's interior through geologic time; a reaction summarized by the equation:

$$\text{Primary Igneous Rock Minerals + Excess Volatiles} = \text{Sedimentary Rocks + Oceans + Atmosphere.} \quad (1)$$
(Composition and Mass)

The volatiles (principally H and O as combined in H_2O, C, Cl, N, S, B, Br, F, As) are particularly abundant in the present atmosphere and oceans, and must have been brought to the earth's surface primarily by hot springs and volcanic activity (Rubey, 1951).

This reaction can be used in two ways: (1) balancing elemental abundances permits an evaluation of the mass of the excess volatiles; (2) physicochemical modeling of the reaction permits prediction of the kinds and amounts of sedimentary material derived from interactions between chosen initial reactants. Comparison of these results with the known sedimentary record may impose restrictions on the possible reactants and provide some information about the early history of the earth's surface.

The purpose of this paper is to present the results of a simulation by high-speed computer of the generalized reaction represented by Equation (1). Various models for sea water composition have previously been proposed (e.g. Sillén, 1961, 1967; Holland, 1965; Mackenzie and Garrels, 1966; Pytkowicz, 1967, 1971;

[1] Present address: The Johns Hopkins University, Baltimore, Maryland.

Broecker, 1971; Helgeson and Mackenzie, 1970). The calculations reported here are based on quantification of Sillén's (1961) original chemical-equilibrium model of sea water and are fundamentally an expansion and modification of the work of Rubey (1951, 1955).

Chemical equilibrium models have been used with success in the study of natural waters (e.g. Sillén, 1961, 1967; Stumm, 1964; Kramer, 1965, 1967; Holland, 1965; Helgeson and others, 1969; Helgeson and Mackenzie, 1970) and their general characteristics have been discussed by Stumm and Morgan (1970). These models, however, have also been the subject of much criticism from workers focusing their attention on relatively localized and short-term phenomena. For example, it can be shown that equilibrium is not attained between much of the detrital material that passes through the oceans and sea water. Other examples of disequilibrium and/or metastable configurations can be observed in nature: absence of precipitation of dolomite or magnesite from sea water, supersaturation of pore fluids of marine sediments with respect to quartz, biogenic precipitation of aragonite and magnesian calcite, and so forth. Chemical equilibrium is here considered to be a valid first approximation of the natural processes; presented below are some general features of equilibrium modeling, its limitations, and its applicability to sea water systems.

EQUILIBRIUM MODELS IN GEOLOGY

Equilibrium modeling is not an attempt at closely reproducing all observed natural relations; rather, the approach reflects inability to describe complex natural systems in their entirety by specifying all fluxes of matter as functions of time and location. An equilibrium model allows the time-invariant state of a system to be estimated from the thermodynamic properties of its constituent phases without necessitating knowledge of these fluxes. The various kinds of information that can be obtained from the model have been summarized by Stumm and Morgan (1970). Two of these aspects of equilibrium modeling are especially relevant: (i) the ability to predict the compositions and relative abundances of the various phases, and (ii) the ability to discriminate between alternative choices of equilibria considered, based on comparison between the end results of the model calculations (nature and abundances of the various phases) and observational chemical and physical data.

The ability of a chemical-equilibrium model to provide meaningful answers to a geologic problem depends to a large extent on the scaling of the model in time and space relative to the system investigated. This point is well illustrated by the precipitation and dissolution of calcium carbonate in the oceans, essentially a steady state process (Turekian, 1965). *In situ* dissolution experiments (Peterson, 1966; Berger, 1967) and calculations (Berner, 1965, and elsewhere in this volume; Culberson and Pytkowicz, 1969; Li and others, 1969; Broecker, elsewhere in this volume), show that sea water is supersaturated with calcite and aragonite at the surface and undersaturated at moderate depths (a few hundreds of meters to perhaps two thousand meters). Departure from equilibrium of sea water with respect to calcite is usually less than a factor of two (Lafon, 1969). Thus, an equilibrium model comprising an aqueous phase, a gas phase, and calcite is clearly appropriate for describing within this margin of uncertainty the interactions between sea water and carbonates, if we consider the oceans as a whole over intervals of time longer than a few thousands of years and assume that dolomite formation can be neglected. In contrast, the composition of a deep oceanic watermass considered over periods of time much shorter than the mixing time of the oceans cannot be modeled accurately by assuming equilibrium with calcite. In the first case, the model provides a useful approximation and deviations from it can be treated as disturbances which average out when integrated in space and time. In the second case, although departure from equilibrium is no larger than formerly, it is systematic and cannot be considered as a minor null-averaging perturbation.

In general, equilibrium models appear best suited to the representation of large natural systems where time and space averaging tend to smooth out local variations. This limitation in turn entails some lack of definition and the necessary neglect of phenomena that have at the scale of the system only localized and/or short-lived existence.

Sea Water and Equilibrium

Present-day sea water is essentially an aqueous solution of ten inorganic components (Culkin, 1965), six of which constitute more than 99% of the total dissolved load (NaCl, KCl, $MgCl_2$, $CaCl_2$, H_2SO_4 and CO_2). The relative proportions of major components other than CO_2 are nearly constant except in areas of major river runoff or in semi-enclosed basins, and variations of the total concentration of dissolved carbon are small (less than 10%;

Koczy, 1956). The pH of sea water ranges from about 7.5 to 8.5. These conditions must have existed for at least a few thousands of years, the age of the oldest water found in the oceans. Arguments based on the residence times of dissolved constituents (Garrels and Mackenzie, 1971), the sedimentary and paleontologic records, paleosalinity indicators (Reynolds, 1965; but see Perry, 1972), carbon isotope ratios (Becker and Clayton, 1970), all suggest that little change of the chemistry of sea water has taken place over extended periods of geologic time. Possible excursions from the present composition are severely constrained by the likely precipitation of minerals such as gypsum, brucite, sepiolite and others, and most geologists agree that the oceanic system is nearly steady state.

To explain the constant composition of sea water, Sillén (1961, 1967) proposed a multi-phase equilibrium model in which the composition of the aqueous solution closely resembled that of sea water and was determined by the choice of temperature, chlorinity, and of seven solid phases, mostly aluminosilicates, chosen among minerals that are commonly found in deep-sea sediments. He emphasized that although chemical equilibrium is obviously not attained in the oceans, the equilibrium model provides a useful *approximation* to the real system and stressed more particularly that reactions with fine-grained silicates may be an important control of sea water composition.

Further refinements of Sillén's model (Helgeson, and others, 1969; Helgeson and Mackenzie, 1970) led to additional distinctions among the dissolved constituents of sea water. If we confine our attention to substances and components of major geological interest, phase relations between sedimentary minerals coexisting with sea water can be expressed in terms of T, P, pH, log $a_{H_4SiO_4}$ and log a_{CO_2}. Figure 1, taken from Helgeson and Mackenzie (1970), portrays these relations at 25°C and 1 atmosphere total pressure, assuming equilibrium with calcite. It is readily seen that the compositions of sea water and marine pore fluids are consistent with various equilibrium assemblages of common sedimentary minerals.

From the discussion above and for the system investigated here (the early oceans as a whole over a few hundreds of millions of years), we believe that a model built on the assumption that equilibrium is maintained between sea water and sediments is a good first approximation to the real system. Because of the geological reactivity of almost all sedimentary particles, including carbonates and alumi-

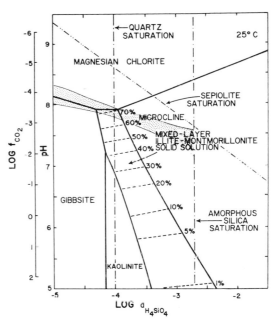

Fig. 1.—Logarithmic activity diagram depicting equilibrium phase relations in the system HCl–NaCl–KCl–MgCl$_2$–CaCl$_2$–SiO$_2$–Al$_2$O$_3$–CO$_2$–H$_2$O. The activities of Na$^+$, K$^+$, Ca^{++} and Mg^{++} are fixed at $10^{-0.50}$, $10^{-2.21}$, $10^{-2.64}$ and $10^{-1.79}$ respectively. The scale to the left of the diagram indicates the equilibrium fugacity of CO$_2$ in the system saturated with calcite, and the dot-dash lines correspond to saturation with quartz, amorphous silica and sepiolite. The stippled area represents the approximate compositional range of sea water at this temperature and pressure. The dashed contours show the calculated composition (in per cent illite) of an idealized mixed-layer illite-montmorillonite solid-solution at equilibrium with the aqueous phase. (After Helgeson and Mackenzie, 1970.)

nosilicates, the model should yield useful information about the composition and relative abundances of early sea water and sediments.

CONDITIONS ON THE EARLY EARTH

It is likely that the early atmosphere was in a comparatively reduced state, no free oxygen being present. Volcanic gases do not at present contain free oxygen and there is no evidence of a progressive change in their composition over considerable periods of geologic time (Holland, 1964). Equilibrium models involving basalt melts and volcanic gases (Holland, 1962, 1964) also suggest that the fugacity of oxygen must have been very small. The state of oxidation of very old sedimentary rocks suggests deposition in reducing environments (Rutten, 1962). Finally, the inorganic synthesis of primitive life apparently requires the absence of oxygen. However, volatile elements were not necessarily present in their most reduced state. Calculations based on widely differing equilibrium models (Rubey, 1955; Holland, 1962, 1964; French, 1966) and considerations involving the physics and photochemistry of the early atmosphere (see for example Abelson, 1966) strongly suggest that carbon was degassed mostly as CO_2 rather than methane and nitrogen mostly as N_2 gas rather than ammonia.

There is little agreement, however, about the history and growth of the oceans (Mason, 1966). We have no firm method of estimating the rate of earth's degassing as a function of time, and widely differing models have been proposed by various investigators. As was pointed out by Rubey (1951), one school of thought prefers rapid degassing followed by large-scale reaction between a primordial ocean and the juvenile crust whereas the other advocates slow and progressive degassing, stretching the generation of the hydrosphere over most of the history of the earth.

The rate of production of free oxygen at the surface of the earth is another source of disagreement. Berkner and Marshall (1964, 1965, 1966) proposed that photodissociation of water vapor by solar radiation was a negligible source of O_2 because of the absorption of ultraviolet photons by O_2 itself in the upper atmosphere. In their model, establishment of a significant amount of O_2 in the atmosphere had to await the development of large-scale photosynthesis. Brinkmann (1969), however, showed that more precise calculations based on a similar physical model for the structure of the present atmosphere can lead to production of significant amounts of free O_2 by the photodissociation mechanism over times of a few hundred million years.

THE MODEL

We chose to represent the generalized reaction given by equation (1) by an isothermal, isobaric thermodynamic model. Compositional changes and mass transfers were calculated on a high-speed computer using the mathematics of equilibrium thermodynamics (cf. Helgeson, 1968).

Figure 2 is a schematic graphic representation of the system. The primordial crust (igneous rocks) is chemically attacked by the ocean consisting of water and the excess volatiles. We impose the condition that chemical equilibrium be maintained within the aqueous and gas phases, between them, and between the aqueous phase and the sediments—the products of the reaction. Very little is known about the total mass, the physical configuration or circulation of the early atmosphere. To make the

computation possible, we had to let the oceans perform the whole weathering reaction and to assign a purely ancillary role to the model atmosphere. Thus, variables such as the fugacity of CO_2 merely reflect the properties of the component CO_2 in the aqueous phase as a result of the equilibrium condition. Complete equilibrium is maintained at all times between the sediments and the aqueous phase, so that the compositions of the solid products and their assemblages adjust themselves to that of the ocean as the reaction proceeds. This approach corresponds to a relatively rapid rate of reaction between sea water (pore fluids) and sediments. We could have assumed, on the other hand, that sediments once produced are buried and no longer available for reaction with the fluids. The real system is probably best modeled by some compromise between these two extreme cases, but modeling of this situation would greatly increase the computational task and introduce a number of arbitrary assumptions regarding reaction rates. We believe the assumption of complete equilibrium between sea water and the early sediments is reasonable and gives a good approximation of the early ocean system as a whole.

The thermodynamic basis for the calculations reported has been discussed by Helgeson and his co-workers (Helgeson, 1968; Helgeson and others, 1969; Helgeson and others, 1970), and the reader is referred to these works for a detailed account of the approach. Briefly, we set up the equations expressing conservation of mass and chemical equilibrium in the system. Taking the logarithmic derivatives of the amounts of the chemical species with respect to ξ, degree of advancement of the reaction, we obtain a system of independent linear equations with a unique solution. Then, by consid-

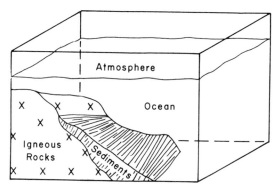

FIG. 2.—Schematic box model for the generalized reaction described in equation (1). See text for details.

ering very small increments of ξ, we are able to calculate the composition of the aqueous phase and the amounts of sediments produced at any given stage of the reaction, using standard methods of matrix algebra. The method is tantamount to taking a very small amount of igneous rock and distributing its components between the aqueous phase and the sedimentary minerals, then repeating this operation *ad infinitum*. Only chemical weathering is permitted by the computer program. This does not, however, seriously restrict the ability of our model to represent the generalized weathering reaction (which also includes mechanical weathering), for it is readily seen that dissolution followed by reprecipitation of a phase stable in the sedimentary environment is equivalent to mechanical transport.

We considered as potential products all sedimentary minerals for which thermochemical data are available (cf. Helgeson, 1969), except quartz. A given mineral appeared among the products when its ion activity product (IAP) exceeded its solubility product in the aqueous phase; if the IAP became less than the solubility product, the mineral was then allowed to dissolve. The concentration of dissolved silica was limited by the solubility of amorphous silica since it is well known that supersaturation relative to quartz can persist over geologic time. Because of lack of data, the kinetics of dissolution and precipitation were entirely disregarded and all relative dissolution rates were set equal to unity; thus the precipitation rates of solid products and reaction rates of dissolved species are solely controlled by the thermodynamic constraints built into the model.

Two factors determined our numerical choices of initial parameters for the model: the practical ease of computation and the scarcity of information regarding conditions during the early history of the earth. We decided to perform the calculations for a temperature of 25°C and a pressure of 1 atmosphere; those conditions simplify comparison with previous work (e.g. Rubey, 1951) and seem reasonable considering that the oldest dated rocks are metasedimentary, implying that liquid water was present at the time of their deposition. We adopted the composition of "average igneous rock" (Brotzen, 1966; Garrels and Mackenzie, 1971) to simulate that of the primordial crust, and recalculated it on an iron-free basis (table 1) because no reliable data on the stability of iron-bearing aluminosilicates are available at present. Thus, our calculations strictly apply only to the magnesium analog of the real system. The amounts of "excess volatiles" were

TABLE 1.—COMPOSITION OF THE AVERAGE IGNEOUS ROCK

Oxide	Weight Percent	
	After Brotzen 1966	Iron free Calculated from Brotzen, 1966
SiO_2	64.0	68.4
Al_2O_3	16.0	17.1
Fe_2O_3	3.0	
FeO	3.4	
MgO	3.0	3.2
CaO	5.0	5.3
Na_2O	3.3	3.5
K_2O	3.3	3.5

obtained from the compilation of Horn and Adams (1966) and are listed in table 2. We restricted our attention to the more abundant acids among the volatiles (that is, HCl, H_2CO_3 and H_2S) and considered only the lowest state of oxidation of sulfur. Even if the production of O_2 by photodissociation of water vapor is significant in the early history of the earth as suggested by Brinkmann (1969), the fugacity of oxygen would still be maintained at an extremely low level by equilibria such as sulfide-sulfate and ferrous-ferric iron until most of the reduced forms had been oxidized, a process which would probably consume hundreds of millions of years. Because the model system is iron-free and because most of the weathering is effected at a pH below 7, the role of H_2S is minor and its concentration can be held constant.

The remaining parameter, possibly the most important one, is the rate of degassing. We chose to consider the extreme case corresponding to instantaneous degassing to compare our results with those of Rubey (1951) who proposed a very similar model for the history of the oceans. In fact, degassing needs only be substantially faster than the rates of reactions between igneous rocks and volatiles for our

TABLE 2.—ESTIMATE OF THE MASS OF EXCESS VOLATILES*

Volatile	Units of 10^{20} g
H_2O	16,700
C as CO_2	1,110
S	31
N	39
Cl	560
H, B, Br, As, F . . .	16

* After Horn and Adams, 1966.

TABLE 3.—MODEL ACID OCEAN

Dissolved species	Concentration (moles/kg H₂O)
H_2CO_3	1.51
HCl	0.946
H_2S	0.058

assumption to be justified. This simplification allows us to calculate the composition of the primordial ocean before any reaction (table 3) directly from the estimates of "excess volatiles." The volatiles are considered to be entirely dissolved in the aqueous phase in accord with our previous assumption that all weathering is carried out by ocean waters. The only significant discrepancy between the model and what we know of the early earth is the distribution of CO_2 which would probably be more abundant in the gas phase than in the aqueous phase (Rubey, 1955). It is also clear,

however, that as the weathering reaction proceeds and the pH of the early ocean rises, more and more CO_2 must dissolve into the ocean until this component is distributed mostly between carbonate minerals and dissolved aqueous species as is the case today (Rubey, 1951). Assuming that the CO_2 of the "excess volatiles" is entirely dissolved before the reaction begins will tend to increase slightly the amounts of carbonate sediments produced at any given stage of reaction progress. This systematic error does not seriously affect our results, and because of lack of information about the physical characteristics of the early atmosphere, cannot be avoided.

Tables 1 and 3 summarize the initial parameters of our computer simulation.

RESULTS

The results of our computer simulation are presented in figures 3 and 4. We have plotted the compositions and abundances of the prod-

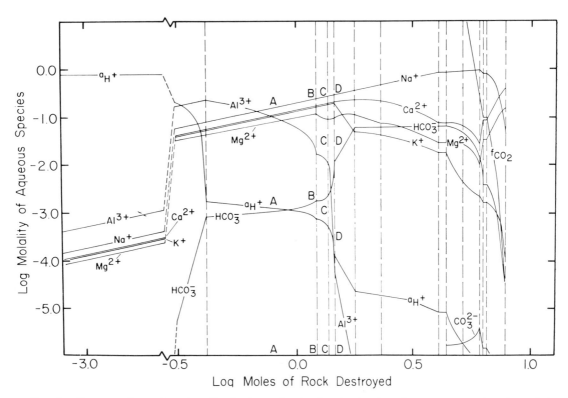

FIG. 3.—Concentrations of major dissolved species in the simulated early ocean as a function of the progress of the reaction (measured by the amount of igneous-rock minerals destroyed). The vertical dashed lines separate distinct phase assemblages of product minerals (see Fig. 4). The letters A, B, C and D correspond to the reaction path outlined in Fig. 5. The values of fco₂ are calculated by assuming equilibrium between the gas phase and the aqueous phase. All concentrations are relative to 1 kilogram of water. The logarithmic scales are used here for graphical convenience only. See text for a detailed discussion.

ucts relative to one kilogram of water against the degree of advancement of the reaction, represented by the amount of igneous rock destroyed. Figure 3 illustrates the predicted changes in composition of the early ocean as the reaction proceeds; for clarity, only the more abundant and geologically more important dissolved species are shown, although all complexes for which data are available were taken into account in the calculations. Figure 4 represents the abundances of the various sedimentary minerals produced by the reaction.

As dissolution of the igneous-rock minerals proceeds, the pH of the aqueous solution rises as a result of hydrolysis and neutralization accompanying the increase of the concentrations of cations. The latter grow linearly and proportionally to their abundances in the igneous rock until they are limited by precipitation of sedimentary minerals. The concentrations of bicarbonate and carbonate ions are determined by the pH, total dissolved carbon content, and the presence of carbonate minerals.

The first solid product to appear is amorphous silica, the presence of which at equilibrium fixes the concentration of H_4SiO_4 at $10^{-2.7}$ m (= moles per kilogram H_2O; for clarity, this parameter, being constant during most of the re-

action, has been omitted from figure 3). After dissolution of 63.7 g of igneous rock for each kilogram of H_2O involved in the weathering reaction, the solubility product of kaolinite is attained, and aluminum is removed from the solution as this mineral precipitates. The concentrations of sodium, calcium, magnesium and potassium ions continue to increase linearly. The lowering of aluminum concentration slows down the rise in pH and bicarbonate concentration. Kaolinite is produced until the stability field of magnesium-montmorillonite is reached after dissolution of 183.3 g of igneous rock (the latter figure is always relative to 1 kilogram of H_2O; this specification will be omitted henceforth). Kaolinite then becomes unstable and dissolves rapidly while the amount of Mg-montmorillonite increases sharply.

Figure 5 is a partial projection of the corresponding reaction path (Helgeson, 1967) on a logarithmic activity diagram in which log a_{K^+}/a_{H^+} and log $a_{Mg^{++}}/a^2_{H^+}$ are used as variables.*

---

* The use of such variables and their relation to fundamental thermodynamic parameters has been discussed at length by Garrels and Christ (1965) and by Helgeson (1967). The interested reader is referred to these works for a detailed exposition of the properties of logarithmic activity diagrams.

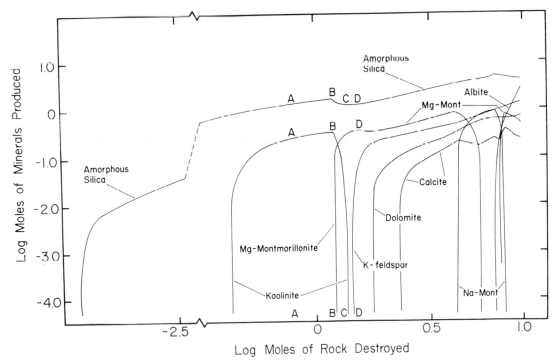

FIG. 4.—Amounts of sedimentary minerals produced (in moles) as a function of the progress of the reaction (abscissa as in Fig. 3). The letters A, B, C and D have the same meaning as in Fig. 3 and 5. Logarithmic scales are used for graphical convenience only. See text for a detailed discussion.

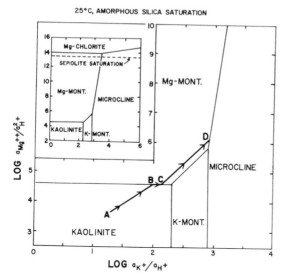

FIG. 5.—Logarithmic activity diagram illustrating part of the reaction path followed by our model system as the weathering reaction (equation 1) proceeds. This fig. is a two-dimensional projection of the more complex system; it involves the activities of Mg^{++}, K^+ and H^+ explicitly, and those of the other dissolved species implicitly. The activity of silicic acid is fixed by saturation with amorphous silica. See text for a detailed discussion.

The diagram is drawn for amorphous silica saturation. As the reaction proceeds from A to B, kaolinite is being produced; at B, Mg-montmorillonite becomes stable and is produced at a constant value of $a_{Mg^{++}}/a^2_{H^+}$ while kaolinite is destroyed. At point C, kaolinite has been entirely consumed and the reaction path follows line CD while Mg-montmorillonite is produced. At point D, corresponding to the destruction of 220.1 g of igneous rock, K-feldspar (microcline) becomes stable and the reaction path follows the boundary between the stability fields of Mg-montmorillonite and microcline toward increasing values of $a_{Mg^{++}}/a^2_{H^+}$ and a_{K^+}/a_{H^+}; montmorillonite and feldspar are produced simultaneously along this boundary. Increase of the amounts of these minerals is accompanied by stabilization of the concentration of Mg^{++} in the aqueous solution and decrease of that of K^+. The concentrations of Al^{+++} and of the other dissolved aluminum species drop more sharply, reaching a level low enough to justify the assumption of conservation of Al_2O_3 among the solid phases. The pH has a value of 3.92 at point D and continues rising rapidly along with the concentration of HCO_3^-.

After dissolution of 275.7 g and 376.25 g of igneous rock, respectively, dolomite, and then, calcite become stable. Their precipitation in-duces a slow decrease of the concentrations of Ca^{++} and Mg^{++} and stabilizes that of HCO_3^- at a level of about 0.06 m while the pH reaches a value of 5. The concentration of Na^+, which has increased linearly since the beginning of the reaction, is finally limited by precipitation of Na-montmorillonite after destruction of 689.05 g of igneous rock. At this point, Mg-montmorillonite begins to dissolve, while amorphous silica, K-feldspar, dolomite and calcite continue to be produced by the weathering reaction. The amounts of carbonate minerals reach a level such that the fugacity of CO_2 at equilibrium with the aqueous phase become roughly comparable to its present value in the atmosphere ($10^{-3.5}$ atm.). As the reaction proceeds still further, the pH reaches near-neutrality and the aqueous solution becomes saturated with (low) albite which precipitates as a product. The production of albite abstracts Na^+ from the solution and Mg-montmorillonite becomes again more stable than Na-montmorillonite. To maintain electrical neutrality as the concentration of Na^+ decreases those of Ca^{++} and Mg^{++} must increase, and those of HCO_3^- and CO_3^{--} decrease because carbonate minerals are at equilibrium with the solution. After destruction of 1362.25 g of igneous rock, the stability field of magnesium chlorite is reached.

We terminated our computer simulation at this stage for several reasons. First, it is obvious that the overall composition of "average igneous rock" can never reach complete equilibrium with an aqueous solution at 25°C and 1 atmosphere (cf. thermodynamic data in Helgeson, 1969). A steady-state may be attained, however, in which the composition of the aqueous solution is fixed by partial equilibrium with the sedimentary products only, while igneous rock is continuously weathered and dissolved. Thus, the very nature of the minerals produced is an essential control of the final oceanic composition. Although it is commonly found as a product of early diagenesis (Kastner, 1971), albite is not a primary constituent of modern or ancient marine sediments and its production may indicate that the equilibrium model is no longer a good approximation of actual long term processes. Secondly, the composition of the aqueous solution at the onset of chlorite stability cannot be very different from that of a steady-state. Precipitation of Mg-chlorite as the pH reaches a value of 7.66 reduces the number of degrees of freedom available in our model system (see figure 5), and the shape of the stability field of chlorite (cf. figures 1 and 5) severely restricts further variations of the pH with respect to those of

TABLE 4.—CALCULATED COMPOSITION OF SEA WATER AT TERMINATION OF THE COMPUTER RUN AND AT THE ONSET OF ALBITE STABILITY COMPARED WITH THE COMPOSITION OF PRESENT-DAY SEA WATER

Dissolved species	Calculated sea water (end of run = chlorite stability) (moles/kg H_2O)	Calculated sea water (albite stability) (moles/kg H_2O)	Present-day sea water	
			Constituent	Concentration (moles/kg H_2O)
Na^+	0.053	0.993	Na	0.4733
K^+	0.00012	0.002	K	0.0101
Ca^{++}	0.344	0.027	Ca	0.0103
Mg^{++}	0.130	0.010	Mg	0.0575
Cl^-	1.002	1.002	Cl	0.5553
HCO_3^-	0.000039	0.014	C (as carbonate species)	0.0024
(H_2S+HS^-)	0.058	0.058	S (as $SO_4^=$)	0.0286
	pH = 7.66 f_{CO_2} = 0.000038	pH = 6.17 f_{CO_2} = 0.427	pH = 7.5–8.5 f_{CO_2} = 0.00032 (surface water)	

the other variables Finally, investigation by computer calculations of the alternative choices of possible steady-states (e.g. not allowing dolomite, or albite, to be a sedimentary product, or removing sedimentary minerals from contact with the aqueous phase) is costly and out of proportion with the returns to be expected from this model, owing to the very simple and general character of our initial assumptions.

The compositions of the aqueous solution at the onset of albite stability, then of chlorite stability, exemplify what variability may be expected from the equilibrium model at an advanced stage of the weathering reaction, depending on what minerals constitute the sedimentary products. This range of compositions may be representative of what actual variations are possible over long periods of time in the natural system. In the light of all these critical factors, we shall focus our attention mainly on the conditions obtaining at the onset of albite stability.

Our final results, though intimately linked together by Equation (1), pertain to two distinct geological "spheres," the oceans and the sedimentary rock record. Table 4 lists the major parameters characteristic of the aqueous phase at the onset of albite stability and at the end of the computer simulation, as well as their corresponding values in present-day sea water. Table 5 gives the total mass transfer at the end of albite stability; the values for the grams of minerals produced are recast into a simulated sediment composition (table 6) calculated on the basis of individual product-mineral compositions and relative percentages at the onset of albite stability. For comparison, the composition of "average sedimentary rock" is also provided in table 6.

In general, good agreement is observed between the composition of the early ocean and that of present-day sea water. The major discrepancies are as follows. Owing to our initial choice of the abundances of "excess volatiles" the computed salinity is about twice that of today. The dissolved sulfur species are not

TABLE 5.—MASS TRANSFER AT THE ONSET OF ALBITE STABILITY (PER KG H_2O)

Item	Amount destroyed		Amount produced	
	Moles	Grams	Moles	Grams
Reactants	6.016	1035.15		
Products				
Amorphous SiO_2			4.750	285.37
Kaolinite	0.316	81.58	0.316	81.58
Mg-montmorillonite	0.794	289.01	0.794	289.01
Na-montmorillonite			0.856	314.67
K-feldspar			0.876	243.77
Na-feldspar			0.0	0.0
Calcite			0.237	23.76
Dolomite			0.622	114.74
			Total produced	982.31

TABLE 6.—CHEMICAL AND MINERALOGICAL COMPOSITION OF SIMULATED SEDIMENT AT ONSET OF ALBITE STABILITY COMPARED WITH THE COMPOSITION OF "AVERAGE SEDIMENTARY ROCK"*

Constituents	Simulated sediment (wt %)	Average sedimentary rock* (wt %)	Oxide	Simulated sediment (wt %)	Average sedimentary rock* (wt %)
Chert	29	37	SiO_2	65.1	66.0
Clays	32	39	Al_2O_3	15.0	16.1
Feldspars	25	13	MgO	2.6	2.9
Carbonates	14	11	CaO	5.0	5.3
			Na_2O	0.9	1.0
			K_2O	4.2	3.5
			CO_2	7.2	5.2

* After Garrels and Mackenzie, 1971.

present as sulfate but are in the reduced state. "Sea water" is saturated with amorphous silica, and thus contains $10^{-2.7}$ m or about 120 ppm of dissolved silica as compared to < 1–12 ppm at the present time. These differences are easily explained by invoking mechanisms which could not be incorporated in our model, and are discussed in detail below. They do not detract from the good similarity between our final results and sea water.

The total mass of $13,300 \times 10^{20}$ g of sediment produced by the weathering reaction at the onset of albite stability is in reasonable agreement with the limits of estimates of the present mass of sedimentary rocks (e.g. Horn and Adams, 1966; Garrels and Mackenzie, 1971). Also the composition of the computed sediment is in good agreement with that of the "average sedimentary rock." These compositions are listed in terms of modal and chemical analyses rather than lithological proportions because the latter are often poorly defined. The good correspondence between the chemical composition of the simulated sediment and that of "average sedimentary rock" is not surprising *a posteriori,* but vividly illustrates one of the more important results of this work. Although the actual weathering reactions are carried out by the aqueous phase, only a small fraction of the weathered material is ever present as dissolved species after the initial stages of the weathering process, as is shown by the overall mass transfer in table 5. Thus, the chemical composition of the solid products as a whole must be closely similar to that of the starting material. The latter has long been known to be similar to that of "average sedimentary rock" except for the "excess volatiles." Sodium is one element for which this argument fails because of its considerable abundance in the oceans. Excellent agreement between the sodium content of the simulated sediment and

that of "average sedimentary rock" further supports the validity of our model.

In conclusion, the appearance and succession of common sedimentary minerals during our simulated weathering reaction have been predicted solely on the basis of their relative stabilities and the initial choice of reactants. At the end of the computer run, considering the uncertainties and simplifications inherent to our model, the compositions of the early ocean and of the simulated sediment appear very similar to those of present sea water and average sedimentary rock, respectively. Furthermore, the amounts of sediment produced and of igneous rock weathered are in accord with the geologic record. The computer simulation alone provides support for the following conclusions: (1) evidence based on the geologic record cannot rule out a one-stage degassing process, (2) the generalized weathering reaction provides a useful reference frame for discussion of events on the early earth, (3) though past weathering environments may have departed greatly from present conditions, it is unlikely that the results of weathering and sedimentation have been much different from what they are today, and (4) the oceans at any given time contain but a small fraction of the previously weathered material.

DISCUSSION

The numerical results of a simulation of the generalized reaction (Equation 1) leading to the formation of the oceans and sedimentary lithosphere have been presented. The calculations were based on a number of simplifying assumptions. We shall now examine the implications of these original choices and the possible changes which would be effected in our final results by consideration of other sets of initial assumptions. Much of the following discussion must remain largely qualitative owing to lack of sufficient data. Nevertheless, the characteristics of our model, as illustrated in figures 3 and 4, provide the necessary framework for estimating and comparing the effects of particular modifications and for evaluating some important factors in the early history of the earth.

Three topics are discussed below at some length: (1) the degassing of the "excess volatiles," commonly assumed to have been a slow and gradual process; (2) the likely effects on our results of common geological processes that were ignored in our model; and (3) the extension of this work to systems containing iron.

Rate of Degassing of the "Excess Volatiles"

Rubey (1951) developed a degassing model for the history of the oceans and concluded that production of the "excess volatiles" must have been a slow and gradual process. His calculations were based on Equation (1) and a set of assumptions similar to those presented above. He concluded that "with a primitive ocean and atmosphere made up of all the "excess" volatiles . . . the amount of rock that would have to be decomposed . . . would be very large—considerably larger . . . than seems . . . to have been decomposed in all of geologic time"; "the total amount of Na dissolved in sea water would have to be much greater . . . than the amount which . . . appears to have been dissolved in all earth history", "the quantity of carbonate deposits required means that the Precambrian should have been a time of abnormally great carbonate deposition throughout the world." These factors appeared to Rubey distinctly unfavorable to a model in which degassing was a rapid process, whereas they could be avoided by a slow, progressive degassing proceeding at a more or less constant rate.

Our results strongly support the contention that a one-stage early degassing process cannot be ruled out. This possible discrepancy with Rubey's conclusions appears to be due to several different causes. Firstly, the use of expressions such as "considerably greater" and "much larger" can be misleading, inasmuch as no confidence intervals are available for the quantities being compared. Rubey, comparing the amount of igneous rock decomposed in his calculation (17,000 × 10²⁰ g) with his estimate of the total amount of igneous rock actually weathered (11,000 × 10²⁰ g), saw a considerable discrepancy. Present estimates of the total amount of sedimentary rocks preserved range from about 17,000 × 10²⁰ to 50,000 × 10²⁰ g, the "best" value being perhaps 32,000 × 10²⁰ g (Garrels and Mackenzie, 1971). Accuracy of

the various estimates as well as that of the weathering calculations may then perhaps be little better than a factor of two. Moreover, Rubey's predicted salinity (at P$_{CO_2}$ = 1 atm.) is quite comparable to our result, but does not necessarily mean that excessive amounts of Na have been dissolved in sea water. The same argument applies equally well to the amounts of carbonate rock produced.

Secondly, results from Rubey's calculations, or ours, should not be compared with the present amount and lithological composition of Precambrian rocks as a whole. Sedimentary recycling (Garrels and Mackenzie, 1969, 1971) may have altered these parameters to a considerable extent, increasing the relative proportions of shales and sandstones at the expense of those of carbonates and evaporites. Most of the sedimentary material produced in the early history of the earth probably has been incorporated in later depositional episodes and is no longer identifiable. It is clear that the composition of "average sedimentary rock" should serve as the standard for evaluation of our calculations, as well as those of Rubey. Good agreement between this standard and our results is encouraging; the main difference is largely due to our disregarding organic carbon in the simulation.

Thirdly, perhaps the most important cause of the differences between Rubey's conclusions and ours lies in the actual method of performing the calculations. Rubey let all dissolved metals accumulate in his early ocean until saturation with calcite was reached. No other mechanism was provided to control the composition of the aqueous phase. In contrast, we allowed for precipitation of all stable solid phases for which data were available, thus showing that the amounts dissolved in the ocean represent but a small difference between large quantities of igneous rock decomposed and sedimentary rock produced. The oceans cannot serve as a final repository for the dissolved load from chemical weathering; rather, they represent a chemical reactor, the composition of which is held constant owing to equilibrium with the solid products.

The arguments presented above are not intended to imply that degassing was necessarily a one-stage process. Data based on the composition of the oceans and sedimentary rocks are not sufficient for this question to be decided at the present time. The sequence of events illustrated in figures 3 and 4 could also be accomplished by a slow and progressive degassing process, maintaining the relative proportions of the acid volatiles constant. Because the weathering reaction would proceed faster than the generation of acid volatiles, the composition of the solution would rapidly follow the paths in figure 3, producing minerals as in figure 4, until a steady-state was attained. Further additions of volatiles would only result in additional production of sediments without markedly affecting the composition of the ocean, a situation very much akin to what we see today. Determination of the rate of escape of the "excess volatiles" and the growth of the ocean with time must await further independent evidence. At the present time, investigations on the isotopic compositions of sedimentary rocks and their changes with time appear to be among the most promising prospects.

Alterations and Additions to the Model

Many of the slight differences between the results from our simulation and the composition of present-day sea water or that of "average sedimentary rock" can be eliminated if we take into account important geological processes that could not be included in the computer simulation. For example, formation of evaporite deposits would be expected to take place during the early history of the earth if the early solar flux was comparable to that of today and areas of restricted oceanic circulation were present at the surface of the earth. By adjusting the total mass of evaporites, we could remove enough NaCl from the aqueous phase to obtain an ocean of normal salinity. Evaporite formation would also decrease somewhat the concentration of Ca, because of gypsum or anhydrite precipitation, if some of the sulfur was oxidized by reaction with the oxygen produced by photodissociation. Because of differential sedimentary recycling, the absence of evaporites among very ancient sedimentary rocks is not evidence that these chemical deposits were not present early in the history of the earth.

The reduction of the concentration of Na in the oceans by formation of rock salt would also make albite unstable and avoid large-scale production of this feldspar. Conversely, in an ocean saturated with amorphous silica at a pH close to neutrality, sodium concentrations of about 1 m would lead to deposition of large quantities of albite. Analcime, the other common authigenic sodium silicate, is not stable at a near-neutral pH and is unstable with respect to albite at high concentrations of dissolved silica. Petrologic studies of well-preserved and very ancient sedimentary rocks may help determine whether such a concentration of dissolved Na was in fact attained. Consideration of albite as a possible sedimentary product under particular conditions may also provide a supplementary sink for sodium and help resolve the geochemical cycle of sodium (Gregor, 1967).

Our decision to consider dolomite as a sedimentary product at equilibrium with the ocean also introduced some discrepancies between our results and the composition of present-day sea water, which is supersaturated with respect to this mineral. The concentrations of Mg^{++} obtained in this way were systematically lower than the corresponding values for Ca^{++}; the reverse is observed today. Disregarding formation of dolomite, on the other hand, would have seriously hampered comparison of the sediment produced in our simulation with the geologic record since carbonates in ancient rocks are mostly dolomitic. We can reason that although dolomite does not appear to form at equilibrium with the oceans, its production over long periods of time must abstract Mg^{++} from sea water, pore waters or sedimentary minerals. If we look at the overall mass balance, the equilibrium assumption offers a first approximation of the real processes. Introduction of a supplementary variable, e.g. the mass ratio of calcite to dolomite at any given time, would help to refine our model and make it more realistic. It would also, unfortunately, greatly complicate all numerical treatments of the general problem.

The assumption that all carbon is present as CO_2 in the aqueous phase led to slightly excessive amounts of carbonate minerals in our results. This discrepancy is magnified in table 6 in which only carbonate carbon is reported in the analysis of "average sedimentary rock."

In summary, a number of plausible geologic mechanisms allow us to adjust the results of our simulated weathering reaction so that it better corresponds to present earth conditions. Use of these mechanisms, however, means introducing a number of arbitrary parameters and complicating our basic model to a considerable extent. We shall simply note that our results, which are already in good agreement with the geologic record, can be further improved.

Extension to Iron-containing Systems

Introduction of iron in our model raises additional difficulties because of the possibility of redox reactions. Although it is generally agreed that conditions must have been reducing at the beginning of earth's history, we have no direct evidence concerning the time scale of oxygen development in the atmosphere and at the surface of the earth. Considering the sulfide-sulfate and the ferrous-ferric iron equilibria, we can, however, state that the fugacity of O_2 must have remained extremely low (about 10^{-70} atm.) until oxidation was more or less complete. Thus, Fe^{++} was probably the dominant dissolved iron species at that time.

The "average igneous rock" contains roughly as much iron as magnesium on a mole basis. We would expect the concentration of iron in the aqueous phase to vary sympathetically with that of Mg^{++}, except for reactions involving OH^- and sulfide species. The total amount of iron to be released during the weathering reaction is much larger than the total amount of sulfur available. Thus, we would have precipitation of all the sulfide sulfur with iron as pyrite and various ferrous sulfides, then accumulation of Fe^{++} in the ocean with simultaneous formation of siderite and ankerite. As the concentration of iron reached a level of 10^{-2} to 10^{-1} m and the pH approached neutrality, ferrous hydroxide and a ferrous silicate gel (Lafon, unpublished results) or minerals such as greenalite and minnesotaite would precipitate out of the solution and stabilize the pH at a value below 7. The main differences between iron-containing and iron-free systems are the following: (1) part of the sulfur is incorporated in solid phases, (2) ferrous hydroxide and ferrous silicates probably would accumulate as iron formations owing to their very rapid precipitation from the aqueous phase and (3) the carbonate sediments would be more abundant and contain considerable quantities of siderite and ankerite. These predictions are supported to some degree by recent mass balance calculations on the submarine weathering of basalts (Garrels and Mackenzie, 1971, and this volume).

If the early crust were closer to an oceanic basalt than to "average igneous rock" in composition, and thus contained more iron, little change in the evolution and steady-state composition of the ocean would result. The sediments, adjusting to the different primitive composition of the crust, would probably contain a little less chert and more carbonates and clay minerals.

ACKNOWLEDGMENTS

An earlier version of this work was critically read by Robert M. Garrels, Blair F. Jones, Harold C. Helgeson and Owen P. Bricker. We would like to thank them for their comments and suggestions, which led to improvements in the final manuscript.

The research was supported by the Petroleum Research Fund of the American Chemical Society and National Science Foundation Grant GA-11285.

REFERENCES

ABELSON, P. H., 1966, Chemical events on the primitive earth: Nat. Acad. Sci. Proc., v. 55, p. 1365–1372.
BECKER, R. H., AND CLAYTON, R. N., 1970, C^{13}/C^{12} ratios in a Precambrian banded iron formation and their implications: Am. Geophys. Union, EOS Trans., v. 51, p. 452.
BERGER, H., 1967, Foraminiferal ooze: solution at depth: Science, v. 156, p. 383–385.
BERKNER, L. V., AND MARSHALL, L. C., 1964, The history of oxygenic concentrations in the earth's atmosphere: Faraday Soc. Disc. Proc., v. 37, p. 122–141.
———, 1965, History of major atmospheric components: Nat. Acad. Sci. Proc., v. 53, p. 1169–1226.
———, 1966, Limitation on oxygen concentration in a primitive planetary atmosphere: Jour. Atmos. Sci. v. 23, p. 133–143.
BERNER, R. A., 1965, Activity coefficients of bicarbonate, carbonate and calcium ions in sea water: Geochimica et Cosmochimica Acta, v. 29, p. 947–965.
BRINKMANN, R. T., 1969, Dissociation of water vapor and evolution of oxygen in the terrestrial atmosphere: Jour. Geophys. Research, v. 74, p. 5355–5368.
BROECKER, W. S., 1971, A kinetic model for the chemical composition of sea water: Quaternary Research, v. 1, p. 188–207.
BROTZEN, O., 1966, The average igneous rock and the geochemical balance: Geochimica et Cosmochimica Acta, v. 30, p. 863–868.
CLARKE, F. W., 1924, The data of geochemistry: U.S. Geol. Survey Bull. 770, 841 p.
CULBERSON, C., AND PYTKOWICZ, R. M., 1968, Effect of pressure on carbonic acid, boric acid, and the pH in sea water: Limnology and Oceanography, v. 13, p. 403–417.
CULKIN, F., 1965, The major constituents of sea water, in RILEY, J. P., AND SKIRROW, G. (eds), Chemical oceanography, London, Academic Press, v. 1, p. 121–161.
FRENCH, B., 1966, Some geological implications of equilibrium between graphite and a C-H-O gas phase at high temperatures and pressures: Rev. Geophysics, v. 4, p. 223–253.
GARRELS, R. M., AND CHRIST, C. L., 1965, Minerals, solutions and equilibria: New York, Harper and Row, Publishers, xiii + 450 p.
———, AND MACKENZIE, F. T., 1969, Evolution of sedimentary rock-types, relative proportions as a function of geological time: Science, v. 163, p. 570–571.
———, AND ———, 1971, Evolution of sedimentary rocks: New York, W. W. Norton and Co., 397 p.
GOLDSCHMIDT, V. M., 1933, Grundlagen der quantitativen Geochemie: Mineral. Krist. Petrogr. Fortsch., v. 17, p. 112–156.

GREGOR, C. B., 1967, The geochemical behavior of sodium: Nederl. Akad. Wetensch., Afd. Natuurkunde, Verh., v. 24, no. 2, 66 p.

HELGESON, H. C., 1967, Solution chemistry and metamorphism, *in* ABELSON, P. H., Researches in geochemistry: New York, John Wiley and Sons, v. 2, p. 362–404.

———, 1968, Evaluation of irreversible reactions in geochemical processes involving minerals and aqueous solutions, I. Thermodynamic relations: Geochimica et Cosmochimica Acta, v. 32, p. 853–877.

———, 1969, Thermodynamics of hydrothermal systems at elevated temperatures and pressures: Am. Jour. Sci., v. 267, p. 729–804.

———, BROWN, T. H., NIGRINI, A., AND JONES, T. A., 1970, Calculation of mass transfer in geochemical processes involving aqueous solutions: Geochimica et Cosmochimica Acta., v. 34, p. 569–592.

———, AND MacKENZIE, F. T., 1970, Silicate-sea water equilibria in the ocean system: Deep-Sea Research, v. 17, p. 877–892.

———, GARRELS, R. M., AND MacKENZIE, F. T., 1969, Evaluation of irreversible reactions in geochemical processes involving minerals and aqueous solutions, II. Applications: Geochimica et Cosmochimica Acta, v. 33, p. 455–481.

HOLLAND, H. D., 1962, Model for the evolution of the earth's atmosphere, *in* ENGEL, A. E. J., JAMES, H. L. AND LEONARD, B. F. (eds.), Petrologic studies, a volume to honor A. F. Buddington: Geol. Soc. America, p. 447–477

———, 1964, On the chemical evolution of the terrestrial and cytherean atmospheres, *In* BRANCAZIO, J., AND CAMERON, A. G. W. (eds.), The origin and evolution of atmospheres and oceans: New York, John Wiley and Sons, p. 86–101.

———, 1965, The history of ocean water and its effect on the chemistry of the atmosphere: Natl. Acad. Sci. Proc., v. 53, p. 1173–1183.

HOLSER, W. T., AND KAPLAN, I. R., 1966, Isotope geochemistry of sedimentary sulfates: Chem. Geol., v. 1, p. 93–135.

HORN, M. K., AND ADAMS, J. A. S., 1966, Computer-derived geochemical balances and element abundances: Geochimica et Cosmochimica Acta, v. 30, p. 279–297.

KASTNER, M., 1971, Authigenic feldspars in carbonate rocks: Am. Mineralogist, v. 56, p. 1403–1442.

KOCZY, F. T., 1956, The specific alkalinity: Deep Sea Research, v. 3, p. 279–288.

KRAMER, JAMES R., 1965, History of sea water, Constant temperature-pressure equilibrium models compared to liquid inclusion analyses: Geochimica et Cosmochimica Acta, v. 29, p. 921–945.

———, 1967, Equilibrium models and composition of the Great Lakes, *in* GOULD, R. F. (ed.), Equilibrium concepts in natural water systems: Washington, D.C., Am. Chem. Soc., Advances in Chemistry, v. 67, p. 243–254.

KUENEN, P. H., 1946, Rate and mass of deep-sea sedimentation: Am. Jour. Sci., v. 244, p. 563–572.

LAFON, G. M., 1969, Some quantitative aspects of the chemical evolution of the oceans (Ph.D. thesis): Evanston, Illinois, Northwestern Univ.

LI, YUAN-HUI, TAKAHASHI, T., AND BROECKER, W. S., 1969, Degree of saturation of $CaCO_3$ in the oceans: Jour. Geophys. Research, v. 74, p. 5507–5525.

MACKENZIE, F. T., AND GARRELS, R. M., 1966, Chemical mass balance between rivers and oceans: Am. Jour. Sci., v. 264, p. 507–525.

MASON, B., 1966, Principles of geochemistry: New York, John Wiley and Sons, 3rd ed., 329 p.

PERRY, E. A., JR., 1972, Diagenesis and the validity of the boron paleosalinity technique: Am. Jour. Sci., v. 272, p. 150–160.

PETERSON, M. N. A., 1966, Calcite: Rates of dissolution in a vertical profile in the central Pacific: Science, v. 154, p. 1542–1544.

PYTKOWICZ, R. M., 1967, Carbonate cycle and the buffer mechanisms of recent oceans: Geochimica et Cosmochimica Acta, v. 31, p. 63–73.

———, 1971, The chemical stability of the oceans: Oregon St. Univ. Tech. Rept. 214, 24 p.

REYNOLDS, R. C., JR., 1965, The concentration of boron in Precambrian seas: Geochimica et Cosmochimica Acta, v. 29, p. 1–16.

RUBEY, W. W., 1951, Geologic history of sea water, an attempt to state the problem: Geol. Soc. America Bull., v. 62, p. 1111–1147.

———, 1955, Development of the hydrosphere and the atmosphere, with special reference to probable composition of the early atmosphere, *in* POLDERVAART, A. (ed.), Crust of the earth: Geol. Soc. America Special Paper 62, p. 631–650.

RUTTEN, M. G., 1962, The geological aspects of origin of life on earth: Amsterdam, Elsevier Publishing Co., 146 p.

SILLÉN, L. G., 1961, The physical chemistry of sea water, *in* SEARS, M. (ed.), Oceanography: Am. Assoc. Adv. Sci. Pub. 67, p. 549–581.

———, 1967, The ocean as a chemical system: Science, v. 156, p. 1189–1197.

STUMM, W., 1964, U.S. Public Health Service Pub. 999-WP-15, p. 299–323.

———, AND MORGAN, J. J., 1970, Aquatic chemistry: New York, Wiley-Interscience, 583 p.

TUREKIAN, K., 1965, Some aspects of the geochemistry of marine sediments *in* RILEY, J. P., AND SKIRROW, G. (eds.), Chemical oceanography: London, Academic Press, v. 2, p. 81–126.